BIRD
OF
PARADISE.

WOLF.

GREATER KUDU.

SERVAL.

COATIMUNDI.

THE WONDER WORLD OF NATURE

Uniform with this volume:

    A PAGEANT OF HISTORY
    THE WONDERS OF SCIENCE
    THE NEW WONDER WORLD ENCYCLOPEDIA

High in the Scottish mountains the golden eagle builds its eyrie. Here the adult bird is seen with one of the young chicks, still in its first white down.

The wild ponies of the New Forest wander over the roads and into the villages at will They are beautiful animals, and great favourites with all visitors.

THE WONDER WORLD
OF NATURE

COLLINS

LONDON   GLASGOW

FIRST PRINTED	1959
REPRINTED	1959
,,	1960
,,	1961
,,	1962

CONTENTS

v

CONTENTS

CONTENTS

ACKNOWLEDGEMENTS

The Publishers are indebted to the undernoted for permission to reproduce the photographs in this book.

Aerofilms Ltd.: p. 118. *Hugh Aldred*: p. 87. *Alasdair A. MacGregor*: p. 313. *Maurice F. Allward*: pp. 105, 142, 143. *Australian News and Information Bureau*: pp. 243, 308, 309, 310, 311, 312, 313, 314, 315. *Lt.-Col. A. E. Bagwell-Purefoy*: pp. 230, 231, 232. *Black Star*: pp 149, 222, 224. *P. W. Blandford*: p. 82. *British Travel and Holiday Association*: p. 148. *Canadian Government Travel Bureau*: pp. 217, 219, 220. *Central Press Photos Ltd.*: p. 162. *Chawbrook Riding School, Eastbourne*: pp. 202, 203, 204. *Roy Church*: pp. 83, 88. *High Commissioner for New Zealand*: pp. 316, 317, 318, 319, 320, 321. *Daily Mail*: pp. 201, 205. *Gabor Denes*: p. 164. *J. Dias*: p. 295. *J. R. Edward (Barmouth)*: p. 93. *E. N. A.*: pp. 256, 259, 269, 275, 276, 277, 279, 282, 284, 285, 288, 292, 293. *Evening Citizen*: pp. 56, 57, 58. *Fairchild Aerial Surveys Inc.*: pp. 255, 257, 303. *Fox Photos Ltd.*: pp. 161, 163, 165, 166, 223, 225, 261, 268, 271, 274, 276, 281. *Eric Guy*: p. 145. *Harris's Picture Agency*: pp. 248, 249, 250, 252, 253. *260, 262, 264, 265, 266, 267, 273, 274, 278, 280, 283.* *Controller H. M. Stationery Office (Crown Copyright)*: pp. 139, 140, 141, 147. *E. O. Hoppé*: pp. 294, 295, 298, 299, 300. *Eric Hosking*: pp. 10 (top), 11 (bottom), 14 (bottom), 15, 16, 24, 29, 33, 37, 39, 40, 62, 63. *Information Service of India*: p. 296. *Ley Kenyon from his book " Collins Pocket Guide to the Undersea World " published by Collins*: pp. 175, 177 (top and left). *R. G. Lewis Ltd.*: p. 177 (bottom). *John Markham*: p. 22. *Noel McNaught*: pp. 84, 85. *Mondiale*: pp. 60, 61, 124, 239 (top), 306, 307. *Moss Bros.*: p. 154. *Mount Palomar Observatory*: pp. 99, 101, 102. *Natural History Museum*: p. 138. *Photoflights Ltd.*: p. 19. *The People's Dispensary for Sick Animals*: pp. 72, 73, 74, 75, 78, 79, 80. *Pictorial Press*: p. 81. *Paul Popper Ltd.*: pp. 44, 216-21, 284, 286, 287, 289, 292, 297. *Radio Times Hulton Picture Library*: pp. 59, 68, 69, 71. *Royal Society for the Prevention of Cruelty to Animals*: p. 77. *The Royal Zoological Society of Scotland*: pp. 323, 324, 325, 330. *Paul Shillaber*: p. 331. *David Stephen*: pp. 9, 10 (bottom), 11 (top), 12, 13, 14 (top), 17, 20, 21, 23, 25-28, 30, 32, 34, 35, 36, 38, 39, 41, 43, 45, 47-49, 109-111, 332, 333, 334, 335, 336, 337, 338, 339, 341, 343, 344. *Satour*: p. 254. *The Director of the Science Museum South Kensington*: pp. 236, 238, 241, 242. *Sport and General Press Agency Ltd.*: pp. 132, 157-60. *United States Information Service*: pp. 217, 219. *Tom Weir*: pp. 94, 95, 96, 97. *Douglas P. Wilson*: p. 176. *Reece Winstone*: pp. 150, 167-8, 170, 172, 173. *Dick Wolff*: pp. 246, 248, 270.

ILLUSTRATIONS IN COLOUR

The swallow is possibly the best known of our migrants, being found nesting at farms throughout the country and in the remotest places. The bird winters in South Africa, arriving in Britain in March and April. It leaves again from September onwards.

BIRD MIGRATION

THE ONLY certain thing known about migration is that birds migrate; as to why birds migrate, or how they find their way, we are not much better informed than the one-time Bishop Godwin of Hereford who thought they migrated to the moon.

Gilbert White, the English country parson who has been rightly styled the father of modern ornithology, was aware that birds migrated, but he thought also that some of them hibernated. He was convinced this was so in the case of swallows. Every modern schoolboy knows differently; yet in the past few years birds of the swallow family have been found in a torpid state in America. The extent of this habit is not known.

Many theories have been put forward to explain the migratory urge in birds. One such theory, for long a favourite, was called the glacial theory. This held that birds were driven south by the creeping ice cap, then returned north as it retreated. For a number of reasons, this theory has been rejected.

Food supply available in winter may be an important factor, but it cannot explain the whole mystery. It seems reasonable to argue that birds whose food supply is cut off should move south to where it becomes available again. Yet the fact remains that individuals of certain species migrate, while others of the same species stay where they were born all the year round. Even individual swallows have been known to stay in the south of England through the winter.

TRUE MIGRATION

Migration in the strict sense must not be confused with " dispersal " or " irruption." Birds which merely disperse over a wide area of the country after the breeding season are not true migrants. Similarly when bands of birds like crossbills appear suddenly in this

The whitethroat, a large warbler, is an early arrival, and nests low down in bushes, on commons and among nettles.

The willow warbler, or willow wren, is one of the commonest migrants. It nests on the ground making a domed, feather-lined nest.

The sand-martin, a member of the swallow family, nests in burrows, in sand pits and river banks, made by using feet and bill.

The wheatear, a bird of the mountains and waste ground, arrives in March and nests in rabbit burrows, among rocks and in holes.

country, driven either by bad weather or failure of their food supply, it is still not true migration.

True migration is a regular movement; a predictable movement. It involves the entire population of a species. It means that the species moves out *en masse* to another part of the world; that the breeding, and wintering, quarters are entirely, and annually, different.

Migration in this strict sense can truly be described as spectacular. Birds cross continents and vast stretches of water when making their two-way journeys. Our own swallow flies from the remote north of Scotland to the south of the African continent. Certain terns travel from the Arctic to the Antarctic. The corn-crake, which looks but an indifferent flier, travels from the far Hebrides to North Africa and Palestine.

The corncrake is now an uncommon bird, although it used to be familiar from one end of the country to the other. Its rasping cry of *crake-crake* was one of the best-known sounds of the June dusk. The bird nests in deep grass and lays up to ten eggs.

UNDERLYING CAUSES

Many experiments have been conducted in recent years in an attempt to explain why birds migrate and how they find their way. It has been found that increased light, and much activity, affect the breeding condition of birds, and it is known that breeding condition has something to do with the migratory urge. But, in fact, neither comes near explaining the problem and we are still left with it.

Some day, perhaps, man will at last understand the meaning of this " inherent rhythm." In the meantime he knows certain things connected with the actual migration movements.

THE HOMING INSTINCT

Firstly, there is no high-speed move from one part to another. Birds travel steadily at so many miles per day, and may take weeks to reach their destination. Temperature and food supply affect the rate of advance, and birds of the same species will advance more rapidly along one route than on another. But, just as the initial urge has not been explained, so the ability to find a destination accurately is not understood.

This " homing instinct " is a wonderful thing, and does not have to be taught. Birds don't have to travel in the company of others who have done the trip before in order to find their way. So there can be no question of birds " learning the way " as homing pigeons have

to do to a very great extent before they are flown in races.

At one time it was thought that this homing instinct, or ability to orientate, was in some way connected with the earth's magnetic field. But

The redwing is a Scandinavian thrush which comes to this country in the autumn.

The golden plover is the plover of the high ground. It is a partial migrant, moving varying
distances from its breeding haunts at the end of the nesting season.

this was disproved by attaching magnetic bars
to the heads of certain birds. These bars were
powerful enough to kill any effect of earth
magnetism. The birds found their way just as
easily as others of the same species which were
fitted with non-magnetic bars of the same
weight.

So we are left with the twin mysteries—the
Why of migration, and the *How* of finding the
place.

For it is true that the swallow born in an
English or Scottish barn will return there, or
close-by, the following year, if it survives the
double journey. It is also true that the swallow
which nested in my barn in 1951 returned in
1952 and built a new nest right on the same
point on the same rafter in the same barn that
held its nest of 1951.

RINGING BIRDS

This kind of thing can be proved by ringing
the birds with numbered aluminium rings.
Individual birds can be watched, and identified,
by placing coloured rings on their legs as well.
Bird ringing, indeed, has shed much light on
the distance travelled by migrants, the route
they take, how long they live, and so on.

The little willow-warbler, so familiar in
woods and gardens all over Britain, spends the
winter in South Africa, Egypt and Asia Minor.

The sand-martin, a member of the swallow
family, winters in South Africa as far as the
Cape. The whitethroat winters in South Africa.
The nightingale goes to North Africa, Egypt
and Syria. The wheatear, a bird of the moorlands, spends the winter in tropical Africa,
India and Persia.

MIGRATION IS WORLD-WIDE

But not all migration is from Britain. Many
birds come to us from other countries farther
north. So we get wild geese from the Arctic
tundra, redwings and fieldfares from Scandinavia, and a variety of waders from all round
the Arctic circle. We have often, too, birds on
passage, that is birds passing through this
country on their way to, or from, their actual
destinations.

Many revealing experiments have been
carried out to test the homing abilities of birds
in the middle of the actual breeding season.
Thus swallows brought over to this country
from Germany and released were shown to
return to their German territory in a few days.
A great deal has been done with sea-birds in
this respect, in this country notably by R. M.
Lockley. However you approach the mystery
of migration, and homing, you will have a
subject to occupy your mind for the rest of
your life.

The giant capercaillie is found only in Scotland. It used to inhabit most of Britain. It became extinct in Scotland in 1760, but was successfully reintroduced from Sweden in 1837 and later. The bird nests mostly in coniferous woods and usually near the base of a tree.

GAME BIRDS

GAME birds are a special class, and have long been preserved by man for his sport. A vast literature has grown up round about them; their natural history has been intensively studied. And special laws have been passed concerning them.

Our true game birds are: the red grouse, black grouse, ptarmigan, pheasant, partridge, quail. The giant capercaillie, which is a grouse, was extinct in this country when the Game Act was passed in 1831, so it was not included in that Act. However, it was reintroduced from Sweden in 1837, and we have it once more in many parts of Scotland. It was given normal game bird status in the Protection of Birds Act, 1954.

THE CAPERCAILLIE

The capercaillie is the biggest bird you'll meet in any Scottish pinewood. It looks like a turkey, and the cock bird might be mistaken for an eagle by the inexperienced. It has the typical game bird flight, quick wing beats followed by glides on down-curved wings.

Capercaillies prefer coniferous woods at all times, and are closely tied to them. The hen nests usually within a few feet of the base of a tree. She undertakes the entire work of incubating and rearing the chicks.

The cock bird is all black and grey and beetle-green, with brilliant wattles. The hen is smaller, about the same size as the blackcock, mottled brown with a chestnut patch on her breast. Her voice is like the pheasant's " kook-kook-kook," but the cock's cry is raucous and rattling, and he can make sounds like the popping of a cork.

Capercaillies feed on the leading shoots of spruce and pine trees, so they are never short of food in the wildest weather.

The blackcock is the male of the black grouse, the female being called the greyhen. The blackcock has a special display ground, called a lek, which he uses in the spring. There he crows, croons and postures, and there the greyhens come to be mated.

The red grouse, unlike the black grouse and the capercaillie, is monogamous; that is to say he has one mate and lives with her as the cock partridge does. Red grouse are devoted parents and both tend the chicks after they leave the nest.

THE BLACK GROUSE

In the black grouse, the cock is called the blackcock and the hen the greyhen. They are completely dissimilar in appearance. The cock has a lyre tail and plumage of shot ebony, with a brilliant wattle. The hen is like a smaller edition of the hen capercaillie, but she has a slightly forked tail.

Like the hen capercaillie, the greyhen is left entirely on her own with the duty of incubating the eggs and rearing the chicks. She meets her mate only in the spring, and does not have any dealings with him afterwards.

The black grouse has a wonderful display ritual in the spring. The display ground is called the lek, and is a piece of ground, usually with small hillocks, where the male birds gather in the early morning to posture and challenge. The hens visit them on the lek. There is little real fighting among the males but they perform a kind of figure dance, with tails spread and wings down. Their calls are like the ruckety-cooing of dovecot pigeons.

Black grouse are birds of the tree fringe. They are usually found on moorland with scattered birches and pines, or in pinewoods.

THE RED GROUSE

The red grouse is the true bird of the heather. It lives among the heather, lives on the heather, and nests in the heather. This species is the élite among game birds. Kings have left their kingdoms to come and shoot it. And many fine birds have died to make the world safe for the red grouse.

Cock and hen red grouse are devoted to each other, and feed and guard the chicks together. The cock is, indeed, bold in his defence of his nest. The eggs are laid usually in deep heather, and may number from five to nine.

Red grouse, when overcrowded on a moor, are periodically thinned down by disease. The disease is caused by a parasitic worm and is called strongylosis.

THE PTARMIGAN

The ptarmigan is the grouse of the high tops, and is found mostly above the 3,000 feet contour. When the blizzards blow, the ptarmigan is the last to come down to the lower

The ptarmigan likes mountain tops about 3,000 feet, and the hen lays her eggs on stony ground, often near a boulder. Ptarmigan live high most of the year, and it takes severe snowstorms to drive them down from the tops. Ptarmigan turn white in winter.

Partridges are birds of the farmlands, but you will also find them in the glens of Scotland nesting beside the red grouse. Like the red grouse the patridge is monogamous, and both adults tend the chicks after they leave the nest, which is usually within twenty-four hours.

The red-legged partridge is a local species, confined to certain parts of England. It is a distinctive bird. The hen is reputed to lay two clutches of eggs, on one of which the cock bird broods. This partridge is also known as the French partridge.

The pheasant is popularly supposed to have come to this country with the Romans. The cock is a handsome bird, and polygamous. Pheasants are popular sporting birds, and many are reared each year under domestic fowls for restocking the coverts. The cock is a great fighter.

slopes. The ptarmigan changes to white in winter, but many birds retain a fleck of black here and there. In summer the plumage is brown and grey, laced with white, with white belly and wing tips.

A ptarmigan on the nest is difficult to see, because she matches the heather and stones and lichens among which she nests. Both sexes are devoted parents. Ptarmigan tend to pack in the autumn.

THE PHEASANT

The pheasant is not a true native, and is supposed to have arrived with the Romans.

Most British cock pheasants to-day have a white ring, or part of a white ring, on their necks. The older type, called " Old English," had a green neck. Many varieties of pheasant have been turned down in Britain from time to time, but the ring-necked cock has stamped his mark on them all. Hen pheasants of all varieties are sober-hued birds, with brown in varying shades predominating.

The cock pheasant, like the blackcock and the capercaillie, has many mates. But sometimes, when he has only one hen, he will take a share in the incubating of the eggs. In the nesting season, at dusk and dawn, he crows and drums a great deal, flapping his wings while standing on tiptoe with puffed-out chest.

THE PARTRIDGE

Partridges are birds of the arable farmlands, and are widely distributed. It has been said that good farming and partridges go hand-in-hand, and this is largely true.

The cock partridge is a model father, and though he does not sit on the eggs, he takes a share of the family as soon as they hatch, feeding and tending them as well as the hen can do. If his mate is killed he will rear as many chicks as he can himself.

His interest in the family begins as soon as they hatch. When the eggs are chipping the hen goes off the nest, seeks him out, and brings him back with her. And beside her he waits till he has been given his quota of chicks.

The cock partridge has a distinct chestnut horseshoe on his breast, but as this is also found on many hens the mark is not an infallible guide to sex. Young partridges have no horseshoe mark at all.

The red-legged partridge, called French partridge, was introduced in the 18th century, and is common in east and south-east England, becoming rarer towards the north. Elsewhere it is seen only occasionally. It likes wasteland of stones and sand, shingle and chalk downs, and arable fields.

THE QUAIL

The quail is like a bantam partridge, no bigger than a starling. It nests infrequently in the south of England, and rarely in the south of Scotland. It is a shy bird with a call which has been rendered "Wet-my-lips; wet-my-lips."

ANIMALS AND MEN

IN the zoological sense, all living things which are not plants are animals, so, strictly speaking, the fly, the fish, the snake and the sparrow are animals every bit as much as the horse or the cow. In popular language, the word animal has come to be used more and more for those creatures with four legs and warm blood which are more properly known as mammals. But mammals are, in fact, merely a group of animals.

In his everyday life man affects animals in a thousand ways, and is affected by them in a thousand ways. And, in the first instance, his attitude to them is determined by purely practical considerations. Ethical, or moral, considerations come afterwards.

Everyone can understand why man should wage war on the rat. Nobody questions the ethics of rat-killing. Why? Because the rat spreads diseases that afflict both animals and human beings, it destroys man's food supplies, and it contaminates food in warehouses and shops.

In the same way, everyone can understand why the lapwing should be held in such high esteem in the countryside. It is one of the best friends the farmer has, it is entirely useful, and harms no one. That is why it has been protected by succeeding Acts of Parliament.

However, in the cases of the rat and lapwing we are dealing with two creatures that are as near Black and White as we're ever likely to get. Most cases are not so simple.

ANIMALS DOOMED TO EXTINCTION

Looked at in this way, the disappearance of such animals as the wolf and the wild boar can be more easily understood.

With the spread of civilisation, and the entry of man's flocks and herds into the remotest Highlands of Scotland, the extermination of the wolf became a certainty, and a necessity. In a shrinking countryside there was no room for it, and man could not afford such a predator battening on his livestock. So the wolf disappeared.

The wild boar lingered on during the forest period as a beast of the chase. Then it had to go, firstly because there were no longer any vast, wild areas where it could live in seclusion,

and secondly, because it would be a menace to man's cultivated crops.

From this you will gather that man's first attitude to animals is the result of their effect on his own survival, or what he considers to be their effect on his survival.

His secondary attitude arises from his pursuit of amusement, or sport. The animals he sets aside for this purpose are given special protection, and war is waged unceasingly against any other creatures that may be in the slightest degree dangerous to them. This creates many problems, as you'll see.

Lastly, there is the fact that practically every action of man affects some animals in some way, often without the results being intended or even foreseen.

THE EXTERMINATION OF PESTS

Let us take the first attitude first, where man attempts to control or destroy those animals that imperil his crops or forests or stores. I have instanced the rat.

If you were a fruit grower, you would be engaged in a form of large-scale food production of prime importance. You would, naturally, take every possible step to protect your fruit trees and fruit from the ravages of all sorts of pests. You would kill them by fumigants, poison sprays and so on. And, as a result, you would kill vast numbers of insects at all stages of their growth. Your sole concern would be the growing of good, sound marketable fruit.

But besides looking around for man-made ways of killing pests you would encourage every kind of natural ally. Naturalists would show that the ladybird beetle is a great killer of aphids. So you would cherish the ladybird. In the same way, you would give your protection to all insect-eating birds that preyed upon the pests attacking your fruit. You would, in fact, sort out your own affairs into two watertight compartments—the good and the bad.

The farmer approaches his work in the same way, and makes the same kind of distinctions.

The arable farmer, who grows crops for food, knows that such animals as voles attack his growing corn, so he looks with a friendly eye

18

When man builds he also destroys: as he creates towns and factories for himself he also destroys the habitats of many species of birds, mammals and insects. The drainage of marshes means the destruction of habitats suitable to such birds as ducks and waders.

on all things that attack voles—owls and kestrels for example.

He knows that the rodents generally—voles, mice and rats—are a menace to his crops, growing or in stack, so he encourages most of their enemies, and keeps cats at the farm to help in the war.

He wages war on foxes because they will kill hens or lambs from time to time. The modern farmer is not so inclined to kill weasels, because he knows they are killers of rats. He does kill wood-pigeons because they are devourers of his grain. And so on.

As the result of experience he has come to

Red deer calves are born usually in early June, and do not follow their mothers for some days. Out of season calves are not rare, but seldom survive the winter.

The brown rat is an alien species which came to this country from the East. It is a carrier of many diseases.

The carrion crow is the southern kinsman of the Highland hoodie. Both have the same bad reputation and are black-listed by law.

realise that most birds are useful, and that only a few are harmful or, at worst, neutral. Into the first category fall all the so-called songbirds, of which we are all so fond. We take songbirds completely for granted, and would be furious at the thought of any man killing them.

We can perhaps, understand the farmer killing crows or magpies, which kill his chicks and attack his corn stacks in winter, even although the actual destruction may be very slight. But songbirds we look upon as "special." And, of course, we're right in thinking so.

ETHICS GOVERNED BY LIVING STANDARDS

Yet, if you consider the status of songbirds in certain other countries you soon realise that the outlook is not the same everywhere. We frown when we hear of peasants in certain

The jay is the most beautiful of the crow family, but is very local in its distribution. It is more plentiful in England than in Scotland. It is aptly named the Watchdog of the Woods, for its scolding cries alarm the neighbourhood at the approach of an intruder. Gamekeepers wage war on this species because it sucks the eggs of game birds.

European countries eating singing birds. We think it is simply a question of ethics. It isn't. We don't need to eat singing birds nowadays; we have a standard of living that makes it unnecessary. But the Mediterranean peasant, living in a mud hut, and half-starved for most of his life, eats what he can get. We, on the other hand, can afford to be ethical about songbirds, because our ethics are based on a higher standard of living.

We tend, in this country, to see the songbirds as a class apart. That is why, for so long, we were quite passive about the destruction of birds and beasts of prey by the game preserver. The things which he killed were killers of songbirds, so they were bad. But that attitude is quite wrong. The birds of prey which eat songbirds do not make any difference to the number of songbirds and are simply killing their food.

The sheep farmer in the Scottish Highlands and the English Fells wages war on foxes because they kill lambs; the Highland shepherd used to persecute the golden eagle for the same reason. But eagles are not molested to the same extent now; research has shown that only a minority ever touch a live lamb. And, in fact, the eagle is now protected by law.

The Forestry Commission wages war on squirrels and rabbits, and to a lesser extent on roe deer. Squirrels and rabbits do great damage

to trees, and are costly to control. But the problem of control has not been solved.

Broadly speaking, man wages war against the creatures which he considers harmful, even if his warfare makes little or no difference to the numbers of his enemies. And he encourages those creatures that are useful, even if their attacks on pests make little difference to the numbers of those pests.

It would be true to say, therefore, that our attitude to songbirds, to most birds of prey, and to a number of our hunting mammals, arises in the first instance from the fact that they have been proved either useful or of no importance either way. From there we have developed the idea of conservation, which means preserving what we have left and even finding room for rarities which may do a little damage on the side.

SPORTING INTERESTS

Sport, which determines man's second attitude to wild life, has had a profound effect on the number and distribution of many animals. The main efforts of the game preserver were directed against those animals which could, by any stretch of imagination, be considered harmful to his sport, even although they might be useful to agriculture or forestry. Let us examine this.

Until recent years, all hawks and falcons were destroyed by game preservers. This meant the destruction of kestrels which were useful to the farmer. It meant the destruction of owls, which were also useful. So here you had sport acting against the interests of food production.

In the same way the foxhunter used to preserve foxes for his sport. The foxes destroyed poultry, and the poultryman was compensated for his losses by the foxhunter. There is less of this nowadays, because foxes have to be controlled at all times. We can't afford the luxury of preserving them. The trouble is that we still do not know the secret of control, so we still have as many foxes as ever, despite the expenditure of much time and money in their destruction.

The game preserver exterminated, or nearly exterminated, the pine marten, which is a weasel of the trees. The pine marten was a killer of squirrels. It also killed game birds. But the pine marten has now been given a sanctuary because anything that kills squirrels in large numbers is an asset in this new age. We also realise that the pine marten, now extremely rare, must be conserved for it's own sake, for posterity. And that is where ethics come into the picture again.

The game preserver was responsible for a very long time for keeping large numbers of

Contrary to popular belief, squirrels do not hibernate in this country. They hide nuts in the ground, but do not always remember where they put them.

The fox survives over most of Britain despite the constant war waged on him by man. Fox cubs play at the den mouth a great deal from the age of six weeks.

rabbits for sport. This acted most adversely on farming and forestry. To-day, we look upon the rabbit as vermin, and there is a campaign afoot for its total destruction. But the strongest objection to the extermination of the rabbit still comes from the sporting section of the community who have no real stake in the land.

Thus you will see that man's attitude to wild life is, in most cases, determined by his own private needs and preferences. But, nowadays, the attitude is changing considerably, and we look upon wild life from the point of view of the greatest number, that is the population as a whole. And one of the guiding factors is food production. Which is as it should be. For man has to compete for his living along with all other animals.

Lastly, there is the unavoidable effect on wild life of man's actions outside the realms of food and sport, effects which are not intended and often unforeseen.

CHANGING CONDITIONS

When a farmer takes a piece of rough ground, where curlews and redshanks nested, and cultivates it, he makes it unsuitable for these birds, so they vanish from that neighbourhood. But, in changing the nature of the ground, man has made it suitable for other species, lapwings for instance, or partridges, and a variety of songbirds. Every new act in land-use causes just such changes as

these and they are, of course, unavoidable.

The change is even more marked when man drives a new road through an area, or drains a marsh, or builds a new town.

A new town means the virtual destruction of vast areas of farmland, or woodland. Bricks and concrete and tarmac take the place of grass and ploughland and trees and hedgerows, and every form of life to which such things were necessary disappears from the scene. In this case you have the destruction of entire habitats. And such destruction is inevitable because man must have new towns to house the increasing population.

The same applies in varying scale with the draining of marshes or the building of aerodromes. In the first case, new types of wild life take over because of the change in habitat. In the second, practically everything disappears because tarmac is no kind of habitat for anything.

It follows, therefore, that every new form of human activity upsets or changes the wild life complex unceasingly and unavoidably. Where man is culpable, is when he destroys certain forms of life deliberately for no reasonable purpose, or where a small section of the community destroys something of general interest and use for narrow, selfish ends. And man will only assume his real relationship with animals when our attitude is determined on the basis of the greatest good for the greatest number.

The nightingale has been famous throughout recorded history for its song. Though its singing is most striking at night, when most other birds are silent, it sings also by day. It is a migrant, which has recently nested in Scotland.

SONGBIRDS

WE TEND to class as songbirds only those whose singing pleases our ears, so when we use the term we have in our minds a very definite idea of the kind of birds we mean. Yet the harsh cawing of the crow, or the bubbling hoot of the tawny owl, is as much a song as the wild whistling of the mistle-thrush in a February gale or the melody of the skylark as he mounts skyward in the cloudy daybreak.

To me, the haunting pibroch of the curlew is one of the finest of all bird songs, yet how many of us look upon this long-beaked, long-legged bird as a songster? Few I should think. The same is true of many others—birds like the wood-pigeon, or the greenshank. Their voices delight us in season, but we do not look upon them as songs. Songster for us means the nightingale, or the blackcap, or the thrush, or others of that ilk.

A WEALTH OF BIRD SONG

Britain is rich in birds, and richer in bird song. We do not have the gaudy birds of the tropics, or many of the lordly ones of the northern wilds, but we do have a wealth of bird song which is surpassed nowhere in Europe. Certain families are better singers than others, by which I mean that their voices please

The thrush is another famous songster, for long a favourite with the poets. It builds a strong nest, finished with a lining of plaster and lays sky-blue eggs spotted with black. In Scotland the song-thrush is called the mavis.

us more. Let us look at some of our more famous performers.

Most people acclaim the nightingale, which comes to England in the spring, and is almost unknown in Scotland, as the greatest singer of them all. It is, certainly, a wonderful performer, with a wide range of notes; but it has many harsh notes, and I remain stubbornly devoted to the blackbird. I often wonder just how much the timing has to do with our opinion of the nightingale. He sings at night, almost alone, and that is magic enough to make us forget the day-time singers who have so much competition.

THRUSHES

We have the thrushes all the year round— the mistle-thrush, the blackbird and the song-thrush; in spring we get the ring-ouzel, or mountain blackbird, and in winter the fieldfare and the redwing. They all have voices of note.

The mistle-thrush has power, and his voice is wild and free, almost a challenge to the elements on a gusty spring morning. The blackbird is a fluter; he speaks his golden song without bravado. The voice of the song-thrush, or mavis, is sweet and stirring and is always in favour.

WARBLERS

One of the largest groups of songsters is the family of the warblers, which are migrants like the nightingale. Best known, perhaps, in all this galaxy is the little willow-warbler, often called willow-wren, which is erroneous. This bird is found all over the country in spring and summer, and builds its domed nest lined with feathers even on mountain-sides in the north of Scotland.

The wood-warbler is a similar bird, but it does not line its nest with feathers. The sedge-warbler is a brilliant performer, and often sings

The blackbird is a thrush. It builds a nest similar to that of the song thrush, but without the plaster lining.

at night, so that it is mistaken in many places for the nightingale. The sedge-warbler nests, as its name suggests, in the rushes of loch and pond, and is widely distributed. The reed-warbler, on the other hand, is confined to the southern half of England. The marsh-warbler is more local still, and is found only in the extreme south.

The blackcap, which is a bird of woodland and garden is a fine songster which often sings at night. The grasshopper-warbler also sings in the late evening, and has a curious voice which resembles the sound made by a fishing reel. The whitethroat is a biggish bird, like the nightingale, and has a soft churring note which is unmistakable.

FINCHES

The finches have long been favourites, which is why, like the linnets, they were once kept so much in cages. Many of them are common and widely distributed, like the chaffinch, greenfinch, and bullfinch. The goldfinch is more local and the hawfinch uncommon. The chaffinch is probably the greatest favourite; it is also notable for its nest, which is a neat, well-finished structure of moss and lichens and hair. The nest of the greenfinch, on the other hand, is untidy and always looks as if it had been built in great haste.

The siskin, always a favourite and still kept as a cagebird, is the finch of the Scottish pine-woods. In the same way, the brown linnet is the lintie of the moors and gorse brakes, while the twite, or mountain linnet, is the lintie of the high places.

BUNTINGS

Among the buntings, the yellow-hammer is probably the best known; in Scotland it is sometimes called the Scotch Canary. Its song has been aptly rendered as *A Little Bit of Bread and no Cheese*. The reed-bunting is also common, but is a bird of the marsh and riverside and loch margin, building its nest among the thick rushes. Least common is the cirl-bunting, which is found only in the English counties south of the Thames. Lastly, there is the corn-bunting, a larger bird, which frequents arable land and rough ground near the sea.

Perhaps I should mention the snow-bunting, for a few of these handsome birds now nest on the high tops in Scotland. The song of this species is loud and clear, and is usually delivered from a rock.

SOME OF THE FINEST SINGERS

Many of our commonest birds are among the finest singers. Everyone knows the robin, which, in spring, has a strong, clear, musical song, and which can always deliver a ghost trill in the bleak winter days. The dunnock,

The robin nests in banks and under hedgerows, where there is plenty of cover. The sexes are alike; the young freckled.

or hedge-sparrow, is a quiet, secretive little bird with a pleasant song. It builds a neat nest in thorn bushes, and such places, and lays a sky-blue egg without any kind of markings. The redstart, which loves old lichened woods, where it nests in holes in trees, has a squeaky little song and is something of a mimic.

PIPITS AND LARKS

The meadow pipit and tree pipit are birds of similar tastes, and their songs and song-flight are also similar. The meadow pipit is perhaps the most frequent victim of the cuckoo in this country, and one of our most widely distributed birds.

Both the skylark and the wood-lark are in the front rank as songsters, but while the first is known throughout Britain, the second is a local bird which breeds in certain parts of southern England and in Wales.

The skylark, of course, draws attention to itself by its habit of soaring as it sings. By day it is easy to watch the bird mounting, singing strongly as it rises, then circling lower and finally dropping earthwards. No singer is better known, yet the skylark has a habit which is not so well known as it might be.

When the hen lark is sitting on her eggs the cock has a habit of alighting on a fence post, or dry-stone dyke, near at hand, and singing to her. I have photographed a skylark singing in this fashion, while I was in a hide beside the nest taking pictures of his mate. The cock does not sing so much after his chicks hatch, for he is kept busy helping to feed them. Incidentally, young skylarks start running to meet their parents long before they are able to fly.

The song of the wood-lark is, in many ways, like that of the skylark, but is perhaps more mellow and less rhythmic. The bird sings either in flight or from a perch, and, because it sometimes does so at night, it is another one of the many often mistaken for the nightingale.

Everyone knows the skylark because of its habit of singing as it soars skywards. The nest is built on the ground, in grass fields or hayfields, and the chicks start running about before they can fly. Both parents feed the young.

The curlew is the bird of the wild moorlands, to which it returns in spring. The nest is a hollow in the ground, lined with bents. The eggs are large and pear-shaped. The chicks run from the nest within twenty-four hours of hatching. They have long thick legs, and short straight beaks. In Scotland curlews are called whaups.

SONGBIRDS OF LESS NOTE

Songbirds of less note, though they all have pleasant voices, are the wagtails, the wren, the chats, and the members of the swallow family. The starling is a bird of many parts, and a born mimic, and, when he likes, can sing very sweetly, especially from a chimney pot on a soft spring morning. The tits, too, have pleasant belling voices, and the wild calling of the great tit can make the woods ring.

All the birds I have mentioned are songbirds of varying accomplishment, but it would be a great mistake to imagine that they exhaust the list even of those in the class which we usually consider " songsters." I should like now to mention a few with " songs " of another quality.

THE OWL, CURLEW AND WOOD-PIGEON

In the April dusk, when the stars are bright and the air is crisp with frost, the long-drawn-out hoot of the tawny owl is the very voice of the night and the solitude. It has an eerie quality, but it also has power and music and a special kind of appeal.

I have already mentioned the curlew, known in Scotland as the whaup. There is nothing sweeter than the wild, haunting trill of the whaup when it rises in song-flight in the gloaming, and even in its cry of alarm there is stirring music. To my way of thinking, the curlew has a voice that is far ahead of those of many more famous songsters.

In the hot noonday, when the grass is sheened with silver in the sun and the clegs are biting, the drowsy crooning of the wood-pigeon is the only song to fit time and mood. Like the call of the cuckoo, the crooning of the wood-pigeon can become monotonous in the extreme, but on a hot, hot day it breathes coolness and contentment. It can almost put one to sleep.

BRITISH BIRDS OF PREY

AMONG birds, here are the lordly ones—the bold and the mighty—the hunters—the highwaymen of the air. And they are beautiful, the lordly ones—some of them aristocratic, and not one of them ignoble. They kill to live—bird, mammal, frog, or insect, according to their needs and powers—and who are we to say that they are no better than "cut-throats" or "vermin"?

Vermin! It has been said for a hundred years. It is still said. It will always be said—by some people. Why? Because certain birds of prey kill songbirds; because others kill birds and beasts which man cherishes for his own private sport of killing; because some men believe they would have more sporting birds for themselves if all the birds of prey were killed. This is not true. It was never true, though many people believed it to be so.

The truth is that birds of prey exercise little, if any, effect on the numbers of the creatures which they kill as food. They do not determine the numbers of their prey; it is really the other way round. And, if you think about it for a moment, you'll see it could not be otherwise. Surely the amount of food available to any species determines the number of mouths that can be fed?

A PERIOD OF PERSECUTION

In Britain, the extermination and killing down of many species of prey birds has been due entirely to the actions of game preservers. In this respect we have the worst record in Europe. Yet, at one time, most British birds of prey had an honoured place in sport. For centuries they were the pride of kings, nobles and prelates. But that was in the age of falconry, before the days of gunpowder. Then the peregrine falcon sat on the wrist of kings; in the nineteenth and twentieth centuries its place was the gamekeeper's vermin board, hanging by the neck—dead.

So birds of prey fell on evil days. The osprey and the sea eagle vanished altogether; the golden eagle and the harrier became thinned down to danger level; the peregrine and the merlin disappeared from long-familiar places.

The goshawk became extinct during the era of intensive game preservation, but has nested again in recent years.

But a new spirit is abroad in Britain now, if belatedly. All British birds of prey are now heavily protected by law—all except the dashing sparrow-hawk. And why the sparrow-hawk should have been excluded I do not know.

Here is the list of birds of prey that breed in Britain.

GOLDEN EAGLE

Our largest predator, now specially protected. Nests mainly in the Scottish Highlands, but a few pairs now breed in the Southern Uplands of Scotland as well. So far, has not been able to re-colonise the north of England.

Nest of the golden eagle is called its eyrie. Most eyries are under 2,000 feet, and many under 1,000. In the Outer Hebrides nests are common at 500 feet. The breeding season is from late March, when the eggs are laid, until mid-July when the young birds fly. Two eggs are usual, but often there is only one, and occasionally there are three. Where twin eaglets hatch out, the stronger chick, usually a female, sometimes kills her nest-mate. Eaglets fly at between 11 and 12 weeks of age, but are supported by their parents for some three months

When the golden eagle leaves her nest she does so with a mighty thrust of her feet, then flaps slowly away. At close range one can hear the swoosh of her wings.

Eagles are much given to decorating their eyrie with branches during the period when the chicks are in the nest. Illustration shows the cock eagle bringing nest " decorations."

afterwards. Young eagles have a great deal of white in their tails.

Their food is mainly mountain hares, grouse and rabbits. But they also take crows, fox cubs, ptarmigan and plover regularly. In some parts of the country rats are a frequent item. In addition, you may find in eyries wood-pigeons, gulls, curlew, raven, blackcock, red deer calves, roe deer fawns and carrion. Lambs are rarely taken by eagles, and are usually dead before the eagle touches them. You will hear much talk of lamb-killing, but most of it is talk and no more. Eagles do not attack human beings at their eyries.

Most eagles have two or more nesting sites, on which they ring the changes, but sometimes you'll find the same eyrie occupied year after year. The species is now holding its own, due largely to the bounty, offered by the Royal Society for the Protection of Birds, which is paid to anyone who ensures that young eagles fly safely from the nest. The golden eagle is protected, and there is a special penalty for destruction of the bird or its eggs.

SEA EAGLE

This species, more vulture-like than the golden eagle, does not now nest in Britain. The adult has a white tail, which gives it its other name of White-Tailed Eagle.

Most nests in this country were on sea cliffs. Visiting birds still turn up on our coasts but no sea eagle has nested in Britain since 1908. The second bird of this pair disappeared in 1918, after sitting each year in an empty nest. The place was Shetland.

This species preyed on much the same food as the golden eagle, but also took a great deal of fish and offal, and many sea-birds. It was reputed to be a great killer of lambs, and as a matter of fact its destruction was due largely to sheep interests. There is every likelihood

The sea eagle is seen regularly in Scotland, but has not nested for a great many years.

The peregrine falcon is the king of all the British falcons much persecuted by game preservers, but now given total protection by law. Peregrines feed on grouse, blackcock, wood-pigeons and sea-birds. During the nesting season the peregrine is noisy and demonstrative in defence of its young. It is, however, easily trapped at the nest, but since it prefers to kill its own food can rarely be trapped to a bait.

that the sea eagle will now return to breed with us. Like the golden eagle, it has been given special protection.

PEREGRINE FALCON

This is the king of British falcons, now specially protected by law. Though not rare, it is by no means common. It is a bird of the wild sea coasts and inland crags, and nests year after year in the same rock or cliff. The male is the tiercel; the female is the falcon and is considerably bigger than her mate.

The peregrine is a fine, bold falcon who hunts high and fast and does all his killing in the air, up in the open where everyone can see him. He kills by dropping on his prey from above in a breath-taking stoop, and sometimes the impact can be heard a quarter of a mile away. Grouse, duck and pigeons are common prey, but the peregrine will take almost any kind of bird big enough to interest him, and sometimes very small ones as well.

The nest is a simple, unlined scrape on a rock shelf. Nesting time is April to May—roughly April in England and May in the north of Scotland. Eggs usually number 3 or 4. Chicks hatch in just over 4 weeks, and leave the nest at between five and six weeks of age. They are fed for some time afterwards by the parents, and sometimes the prey is passed to them in the air.

Much of the persecution suffered by the peregrine was due to its predation on grouse. It is still killed on certain grouse moors, but the penalty is heavy now and the bird may see better days.

MERLIN

This is the smallest British falcon, the little male being scarcely larger than a mistle-thrush.

The merlin is a very small falcon, little bigger than a mistle-thrush. It nests mainly in deep heather.

He may measure no more than 10½ inches from beak to tail-tip.

The merlin is not plentiful to-day, and for that reason has been given the same special protection as the eagles and the peregrine. It haunts heather moors, sea cliffs and coastal sand dunes. On moors it is not liked by grouse preservers, and there it is incessantly harried. Yet, in fact, it seldom takes young grouse! Its main prey is small birds, with insects and small mammals from time to time. All observers of the nesting merlin know that it preys hardly at all on grouse. And, even if it did, its death would not put one extra grouse over the guns in August. Grouse numbers rise and fall for reasons far removed from the appetite of the merlin, or any other falcon.

Most merlin nests are on the ground, but some nest in cliffs and some in the old nests of hoodie or carrion crows. In Scotland, the great majority of nests are in deep heather, in a scrape lined with some heather twigs and wisps of moss. Four or five eggs are usual, and the chicks leave the nest before they are a month old.

HOBBY

This is a pocket peregrine, of the same royal blood as, and little bigger than, the merlin. It is a summer visitor, and winters in Africa.

The hobby is a tiny falcon for all the world like a pocket peregrine. It is a summer visitor to this country and is still very rare. It preys on very small creatures including beetles, dragonflies and butterflies.

The hobby is a rare falcon, and nests in England. There is only one record of it nesting in Scotland; there are several from Wales. But England usually has all the nesting hobbies. In the northern isles of Scotland hobbies on passage have been seen.

Like our other falcons, the hobby builds no nest. In England it uses the old nest of crow, magpie, wood-pigeon or sparrow-hawk. Three eggs are usual, and the chicks fly in something over a month from hatching. The hobby is specially protected.

KESTREL

The commonest falcon in Britain, and a killer of mice, voles, young rats, shrews, and frogs, the kestrel has been protected for many years in most parts of Britain because of its usefulness as a killer of small rodents. It is protected under the new laws, but does not carry the special penalty imposed in the other cases.

Nesting kestrels use the old nests of carrion crows or magpies. Eggs number five or six, and the chicks fly in just over a month.

This is the falcon you see hovering above fields and commons as if suspended from an invisible wire. In this way it seeks mice in the grass; when it sees one it plunges vertically to

The kestrel is the commonest of British falcons and can always be recognised by its habit of hovering in the air spying the ground for mice, voles, shrews or baby rabbits.

earth, opening its wings at the last moment and clutching with its feet.

HARRIERS

There are three species of harrier nesting in Britain, the rarest being the marsh harrier, which is confined almost entirely to Norfolk.

Harriers are long-winged, long-legged hawks which nest on the ground. None of the three

Montagu's harrier bred in Scotland for the first time after the Second World War. It nests on the ground on heather moors and preys mainly on small birds and mammals. It is given complete protection by law.

species is common, and all are specially protected. The commonest of this rare trio is the hen harrier, which nests right up to the northern isles of Scotland. The Montagu's harrier, which has been nesting for some time in the south of England, has bred in Scotland for the past 2 or 3 years, in Perthshire. A photograph of the male bird is shown opposite.

The food of all the harriers is mainly small birds and mammals, frogs, lizards, and, in the case of the marsh harrier, fish.

BUZZARD

The buzzard is a large, ponderous bird of prey, which is frequently mistaken for the golden eagle. It is widely distributed in Britain, and common in the Highlands of Scotland.

The main food is rabbits, but all kinds of small mammals are taken. Game birds are rarely touched. In some parts of the country carrion is a frequent item of food, especially dead sheep or lambs.

Several buzzards can often be seen flying together. This is often reported as " many eagles." You have to be careful that your eagle isn't a buzzard. The buzzard has clean,

Buzzards became much more plentiful between the two world wars. They feed mainly on young rabbits and are, as a rule, harmless to game. Here is a young buzzard.

yellow legs; the legs of the eagle are feathered right down to the feet.

KITE

As a British breeding bird the kite is confined entirely to the mountains of Wales. Only a few pairs breed now, and they are constantly protected during the breeding season against egg collectors. They are given special protection by law. But the kite in Wales fails to multiply. And that is the danger once a species sinks to a low ebb; it is difficult to build up again. There is never any fresh blood to give a fillip to the stock. And there is always the danger from collectors, whose business it is to send a rare thing to extinction.

OSPREY

Now extinct as a breeding species in Britain. Used to be common on all Scottish lochs, but no ospreys have bred in this country since 1908. We still have visiting birds from time to time. The osprey is the fish hawk of North America. It is now specially protected in this country.

GOSHAWK

This powerful, dashing hawk is like a huge sparrow-hawk. It became extinct as a breeding bird in Britain, largely because of game interests. A pair nested in Yorkshire in 1893.

The kite in Britain is now confined to Wales where a few pairs breed each year.

The sparrow-hawk is the one bird of prey which is given no protection in Britain. It is a fine dashing hawk which feeds on small song birds and young game birds.

The osprey has long been extinct in Britain, but it is hoped that it will become re-established as a breeding species.

It has bred again in recent years, and is specially protected.

SPARROW-HAWK

The only black-listed British bird of prey, presumably because it takes game chicks and is a killer of songbirds, though just what the sparrow-hawk is supposed to do about it I do not know.

The sparrow-hawk is fairly common, and is a woodland hawk. It builds its own nest of twigs and branches, usually high up in a tree, against the main stem. The nesting season is May. Four or five eggs are usual and the chicks leave the nest at any time between three and four weeks. The male, who is very small compared with his mate, kills all the food in the early stages, bringing it to the nest or a plucking place where he gives it to his mate.

Sparrow-hawks are bold, active hawks whose favourite method of attack is to fly low and swiftly over a hedge or wall right into the midst of a group of feeding birds. The main food is small birds, but female sparrow-hawks kill many wood-pigeons which are a pest to the farmer.

The short-eared owl nests on the ground. During vole plagues it rears large families.

BRITISH OWLS

THERE is a widespread belief that owls can't see in daylight; but of course they can, and better than you or I can see in the dark. The truth is that they are specially equipped for hunting at night, and that is another thing altogether.

Owls have big eyes—extraordinarily large for the size of the bird—and as the light fades the pupils become larger, just like yours or mine. In the same way, a photographer opens the lens of his camera wider and wider as the light becomes poorer.

THE SHORT-EARED OWL

But not all owls hunt at night. There is one British species in particular, the short-eared owl, which makes a habit of hunting in daylight and on the edge of dusk. And because it is such a notable exception to the general rule I shall deal with it first.

The short-eared owl nests on the ground among heather or deep grass, and its chicks start running about, or rather wandering about, before they can fly. This is the species which flocks to whatever locality has plenty of voles. Voles are subject to spectacular increases in numbers in certain years, and whenever there is a plague the short-eared owls appear. At such times you'll find large numbers nesting close together, feeding their young almost entirely on voles.

You must understand what is meant by the name short-eared. The owl has no ears showing as yours do. What it has are short feather tufts on its head, and these are raised when the bird is at rest. Since they look like ears, and are short, the bird is called the short-eared owl.

THE OWL WITH " HORNS "

Our other breeding species with ear tufts of this kind is the long-eared owl, and as the name suggests its tufts are very much longer. As a matter of fact, when the long-eared owl is at rest, with its tufts erect, they look more like horns. These ear tufts are never erect when the bird is in flight.

The long-eared owl is a woodland species, and is especially fond of pinewoods or thick, dusty larch woods. By day it prefers to rest, roosting in some dark tree. It is strictly a night hunter, and you'll seldom see one flying by day unless it has been disturbed.

My own experience has been that the long-eared owl hunts on the darkest nights, when many tawny owls go to roost to wait for a little more light. The long-eared owl has orange eyes with small black pupils, but when the night is dark the pupils dilate so much that you can't see the orange at all!

While the food of the short-eared owl is largely voles, that of the long-eared is made up of voles, mice, rats, shrews and songbirds. In many nights of watching at nests of this species I noted that about one kill in ten was a small bird. The rest was made up of rats, mice, voles and shrews.

Long-eared owls nest in March and April, but in most years the eggs are all laid before the end of March. The bird builds no nest, but uses the old one of carrion crow or magpie. Some long-eared owls lay their eggs on the ground, or in rabbit burrows. In such places, as with the short-eared owl, the chicks sometimes fall a prey to prowling foxes.

The tawny owl is also a woodland species. It is the bird with the familiar hoot, which Shakespeare put into words as " Tu-whit tu-whoo." In fact, this rendering of Shakespeare's seems to be made up of two things, the bird's call note which is " Kee-wick," and its hoot which is a long, bubbling " Hoo-oo-oo-oo! "

THE TAWNY OWL

Tawny owls hunt usually from sunset till sunrise, but after a night of constant rain, when no hunting is done, the bird will often fly by day when the weather clears. I've watched a bird bring prey to its chicks at two o'clock in the afternoon, following such a wet night.

Like the long-eared, the tawny owl is an early nester, and most of them have eggs in March. Again, no nest is built, but the old one of crow or magpie used. This owl is bold in defence of its nest, and will attack even

The long-eared owl can hunt on the darkest nights. The " ear " tufts are depressed in flight and erected when the bird is roosting or on the nest.

Tawny owls are noisy and demonstrative when nesting, attacking any intruder.

human beings after dusk. And, make no mistake about it, the tawny owl can be dangerous. I never climb to a nest after dusk without eye shields.

Food is much the same as that of the long-eared, but in my experience the tawny takes fewer birds, about one in twelve. The other food is rats, mice, voles, shrews, baby rabbits, moles and an occasional weasel.

In some parts of the country, this owl favours hollow trees for nesting in.

The chicks are very noisy when they start to fly, and have dark eyes, quite unlike the orange and black of the young long-eared owl.

THE SCREECH OWL

The barn owl is the species most closely associated with human habitations. It is the owl of the church belfry and the farm loft, and has a terrifying screech, which gives it one of its other names—screech owl.

This bird likes to nest between rafters in loft or belfry, and often the nest is composed of nothing but rat bones. It lays more eggs than the woodland owls, and sometimes nests

Barn owls nest in farm buildings, ruins or holes in trees and may have young of all ages in the nest. These owls kill a great many rats.

twice in one year. The chicks hatch at all times, and you'll find a variety of ages in the nest.

Food is rats, mice and voles. This species hunts quite a lot during the late part of the day, just before dusk, and you'll see it hunting wherever there are rats for the killing.

A BANTAM OWL

The little owl is a bantam among British owls. It is an alien, which is to say it is not a true British owl but an import. But it has spread widely over England since its introduction and is common in many parts of the country.

Much has been said, and written, about the

The little owl is an alien species about which there is still a great deal of controversy. It has not colonised Scotland.

Little owl with violet ground beetle.

little owl's depredations on songbirds and game chicks. But, as a matter of fact, all investigations into its food show that it kills mainly worms, beetles and moths, mice and voles.

This species nests in holes in trees and walls, and under the tiles of old roofs. Many people would have liked to see it black-listed by law, but, like the other owls, it is completely protected.

Certain other species of owl turn up in Britain from time to time, but they are rare, and do not nest. The most imposing of these are the eagle owl and the snowy owl, both much bigger birds than the biggest of our natives.

Red deer calves are spotted at birth. The hinds leave the herd at this time, returning when the calves are able to follow at foot. Before they are up on their legs, calves have two main enemies—foxes and, to a lesser extent, eagles.

BRITISH DEER

THERE are many species of deer to be found in Britain to-day, but only three can be called truly British. They are the red deer, the roe, and the fallow. It is, however, doubtful whether the fallow should be included. Once plentiful, it disappeared from most of Britain after the Ice Age. It may never have become quite extinct in the south of England, but so many foreign strains have been imported that there is probably no such thing to-day as a true British fallow deer bred in unbroken line from the old parent stock.

Deer are cloven-hoofed mammals with the same complex stomach as cattle, and like cattle they chew the cud. Because of this, deer and cattle are known as *Ruminants*. But they are quite different in the matter of horns and antlers. In deer, the antlers are made of bone; they are shed, and re-grown, each year. In cattle, the horns are really made of horn, and they are permanent.

Generally speaking, only male deer wear antlers. A notable exception is the reindeer, which in Canada is called the *Caribou*. In this species both sexes are antlered. Horned

females are rare in most other species of deer but occur rather more frequently among roe.

Antlers grow yearly from knobs on the skull called *Pedicles*. New antlers are complete about 4 or 5 months after the casting of the old and, during the growing stage, before the bone has hardened, are covered with skin and hair which is nourished by a network of blood vessels. This covering is called *Velvet*. When the antlers are fully grown the blood vessels shrivel up; the velvet rots and is rubbed off by the deer. When the velvet has stripped completely the antlers are said to be *Clean*. Up till then the stag was *in Velvet*.

There are various names for male and female deer, but there is also a correct one for each species, which does not vary. For male deer, the names *Stag*, *Buck* or *Bull* are used; for females they are *Hind*, *Doe* and *Cow*. But each species has its own particular title, which I shall indicate later on. Similarly, the young of deer have their particular names—*Calf*, *Fawn* or *Kid*. We speak of a *Bull Moose* when we refer to the moose male; but the male red deer is a *Stag*. A young reindeer is a *Calf*; a young roe is a *Fawn* or *Kid*. And so on. . . .

Each species has its particular breeding season, which is called the *Rut*, and when the males start challenging or fighting they are said to *Take the Rut*. Some species take many mates at this time and are said to be *polygamous*; others take only one mate (usually) and are said to be *monogamous*. The red deer comes into the first class; the roe into the second.

Now let us examine briefly the deer themselves—those that you can see in this country either running wild or in Parks. A *Deer Park*, by the way, is a piece of ground, usually wooded, where deer are kept enclosed for ornamental purposes.

RED DEER (*Cervus elaphus scoticus*)

First on the British list, and our largest land mammal, is the red deer. It is found mainly in the Scottish Highlands, but also on Exmoor (where it is hunted by the Devon and Somerset Staghounds) and in Westmorland.

The male is the Stag, female the Hind, and young the Calf. Stags stand about 4 feet at the shoulder; hinds 3 feet 6 inches. The red deer stag is polygamous. He takes the rut in September/October and gathers as many hinds as he can. But for most of the year the sexes live apart. The calves are born in early June of the following year and are spotted with white at birth.

The red deer society is a *Matriarchy*; that is to say it is founded on the *female*. In other words, the red deer hind is the real leader of the herd. The stag may lord it over the hinds at the rut; he may bellow and make the hills rumble with his thunder; but he does not lead. He is not the monarch of the glen. In the society of the red deer he is of no account outside the breeding season.

Wild red deer are among the most wary of animals. They have keen sight and hearing, and a sense of smell which is extraordinary. They rely almost entirely on this sense, so their lives are largely governed by the wind which carries the scent of their enemies. Red deer shift ground regularly and readily. During heavy snow they come down to the low ground; during hot weather they go high for the fine grazing and to escape the flies. Their summering and wintering grounds may be many miles apart.

A *Master Stag* is a stag in possession of hinds. Master stags are often hornless beasts called *Hummels*. These, because they do not have to use up strength growing antlers, are usually heavy and powerful, more than a match for the most handsome antlered stag.

In Scotland the red deer is important in the sport of *Deer Stalking*, and stags have been classified according to the number of *Tines*, or points, on their antlers. The antlers are divided into the *Burr* or *Coronet*, at the base, the *Beam*, or main shaft, and the *Tines*. First, second and third points from the base are called *Brow*, *Bez* and *Trez*; points higher up are called *Points on Top*. A *Royal Stag* is a stag with Brow, Bez and Trez, and 3-point top —6 points on each antler. Other stags are referred to by the actual number of points they carry—8-pointer, 9-pointer, and so on.

Antlers are cast in March/April and full grown again by August/September.

ROE DEER (*Capreolus capreolus thotti*)

This is a woodland deer, widely distributed, but commonest in Scotland, and found also on most ground used by red deer.

The male is the Buck, female the Doe, and young the Fawn or Kid. Bucks stand from 25 to 29 inches at the shoulder. Does are smaller and lighter. The roebuck is, for the most part, monogamous. He takes the rut in July/August, when he barks a great deal; fights fiercely with his rivals, and drives the does in circular tracks. These rings become well worn with use and are often referred to as the *Fairy Rings of the Roe*. Fawns are born in late May or early June of the following year. They are spotted at birth, but the spots disappear in the autumn when the little beasts are growing their winter coats.

The roebuck, unlike the red stag, is devoted to his family. Except for a short period after the rut, when he retires to live by himself, he runs with his doe and fawns right through to the following May. He is a powerful and fearless fighter and will face dog or fox in defence of his family. Roebucks have short, sharp horns and are dangerous opponents. There are records of human beings being killed by roe.

Roe come out to feed at dusk, and do so on and off during the night. They feed heavily

Roebuck in first " Velvet." The roe sheds his antlers each year in November and the new ones start to grow at once. During the growing period they are covered with skin and hair which is called " Velvet." The bucks rub this off against trees.

at daybreak then retire to lie up for the day. In quiet places they will move about during the day, but roe are secretive and not often seen.

Bucks, when mature, usually carry three points on each antler. The antlers rarely exceed 9 inches in length, and are usually full grown and clean by April. They are shed in November. Horned does occur from time to time. The so-called *Peruke* head on bucks is the result of injury. White roe are not uncommon.

Roe eat a variety of food, from grass to fungi. They browse a great deal on twigs and leaves of trees, and are very fond of mushrooms.

FALLOW DEER (*Dama dama*)

Fallow deer are seen mostly in Parks, but there are many living wild in England, for example in the New Forest and Epping Forest. There are also several herds in Scotland, notably in the Dunkeld area and in Ross-shire. But the fallow is mainly an ornamental deer. Our present stocks are of foreign origin, and popular belief credits their introduction originally to the Romans.

The male is the Buck, female is Hind or Doe, young is the Fawn. Bucks stand about 3 feet 2 inches at the shoulder. Does are smaller and lighter. The fallow deer is polygamous. He takes the rut in late October, gathering as many does as he can, and fighting off rivals. Fawns are born in the following May or June. The call of the buck is half grunt half bark, accompanied by much jerking of the head.

The fallow deer is a great roamer, and is up and down much more than either the red or the roe. The bucks live with their small herd from the time of the rut till the end of the winter when the sexes separate. Then the does play a great deal with their fawns of the previous year. The fallow buck is not so dangerous to humans as the roe.

Antlers of the fallow deer are *Palmated*; that is to say they flatten out at the top, like the palm of your hand, and are serrated along the back edge. There is usually no bez tine. The buck casts his antlers in May and the new ones are clean by August.

Fallow deer, though gregarious, are rarely seen in big herds, and certainly never in herds approaching the size common in the red deer.

Fallow deer are now mainly seen in Parks, but there are several wild herds in Britain.

NON-NATIVE DEER

All other deer found in Britain have been imported. Most are in Parks, but many run wild, and some species have become common in certain areas. Let us consider them briefly.

JAPANESE or SIKA DEER (*Cervus nippon*)

This species has strayed over much of the

country, and is common in certain parts of the West Highlands.

A small relative of the native red deer, the Sika buck, stands about 2 feet 9 inches at the shoulder. Does are smaller, lighter, and hornless. The rut is a little earlier than in the case of the red deer. The buck is polygamous, but seldom collects more than 6 or 8 wives. During the rut, the bucks whistle and scream.

Both sexes are tailed, like the fallow deer. They have a white rump patch edged with black.

Reindeer are now to be seen in Rothiemurchus, where they have been experimentally reintroduced.

The antlers of the Sika are of red deer type, but thinner and poorer. There are no bez tines. Points rarely exceed eight.

Two types of Sika have been introduced The second, which is larger than the Japanese, is the Manchurian (*Cervus nippon mantchuricus*).

SIBERIAN ROE (*Capreolus pygargus*)

This species of roe, originating from the famous Deer Park at Woburn, is now running wild in certain parts of the English midlands. It is not unlike our own roe deer, but it is altogether a bigger beast. Our own roe has no tail that you can see; this one has just a little more. It has also bigger antlers.

CHINESE MUNTJAC (*Muntiacus reevesi*)

This little deer, which stands only eighteen inches high, is sometimes called the barking deer because of its characteristic call. It has antlers only a few inches long. The few running wild in England are the offspring of escapes.

There is always the possibility of escapes from any deer park, and if the escaping animals survive and breed their offspring will run wild. As it happens most deer seem to do well in this country, and there are records of at least three other species now known to be running free in certain parts of England. They are the Chinese water deer (*Hydropotes inermis*), the Indian Muntjac (*Muntiacus muntjak*) and the North American black-tailed deer (*Odocoileus columbianus*).

You can see there are many types of deer. But, apart from the red, roe and fallow, the species you are most likely to see is the Sika, which breeds freely, is very hardy, and quite common.

Red stags shed their antlers from March to April, and the new ones are fully grown by September.

THE HUNTING MAMMALS OF BRITAIN

THOUGH we have lost many of our greatest hunters with the spread of civilisation, the cry of the wolf is still a fading echo in the mountains of Scotland. We still had the Caledonian bear when the proud Legions of Imperial Rome were trying in vain to conquer Scotland; but we had the wolf in the mountain fastnesses of Scotland until the 18th Century.

SCOTTISH WILD-CATS

What have we to-day among the hunters? The great tuft-eared, big-fisted lynx has gone, with its moon face and eviscerating claws, and, perhaps, in our shrinking countryside, there is no longer any place for it. But we still have the great cat of the wilds, our British tiger, the Scottish wild-cat, powerful beyond the powers of any domestic tabby and completely untameable. It is true that the wild-cat will interbreed with the domestic variety; it is true that there are many wild-cats roaming the mountains of Scotland to-day that have domestic blood in their veins. But the true wild-cat is still with us, and there is no mistaking him.

The Scottish wild-cat is now confined mainly to the wildest mountain country although, in recent years, it has been extending its range southwards. Increasing afforestation will almost certainly help our tiger, for although it lives on the mountains it does so because it has been forced there; it will gladly live in forests if it is allowed to do so.

HOW THEY LIVE

Wild-cats breed once or twice in the year. Those breeding twice probably do so because of some admixture of domestic blood. The female hides her kits in some remote cairn, and hunts for them alone. As with many cats the male is not welcomed at this time; he is just as likely to savage his kits as to fend for them. Wild kits are beautiful little creatures when they first start playing about at the den mouth, but they are spitfires from the day of their birth and remain aloof and unalterably savage to the end of their lives.

Once out of the kitten stage the wild-cat has little to fear from anything except man with his traps, dogs and guns. Wild-cats are notoriously easy to trap. But no terrier is fit to tackle a wild-cat. A pack of terriers will bay one, and hold it, till men arrive, but they will not close with it. Even the big hill fox will not readily seek a quarrel with an adult wild-cat. He will, however, kill kits at any time, for the dog and cat feud is never relaxed. I once saw a fox that had been ripped apart by a wild-cat. The cat died first, but the fox was beyond help at the end and died shortly afterwards.

The wild-cat's hunting style is the careful cat-stalk, with a final rush on the victim. Then the armed forepaws and the great tusks come into play. When fighting, the wild-cat likes to be underneath. Then he grips with his forepaws and treads with his hind feet, tread-mill style, ripping at his opponent's belly with his terrible claws.

THE HARDY HILL FOX

The hill fox belongs to the same species as the foxes of the Shires; yet he is different in many ways because he leads a different kind of life. Hill foxes generally come bigger and harder, for they lead a hard, strenuous life in a country where every man's hand is against them.

In the Highlands foxes kill lambs; in the lowlands they kill poultry. But it would be a great mistake to think that they do nothing else. Their prey is extremely varied. Rabbits are the main item in this country, but rats, mice, voles, hares, and birds of all kinds are taken. Rats, in fact, form a much bigger part of the fox's diet than is generally realised. In addition, many foxes will take meal from pig troughs, and all kinds of scraps from farm middens. Recently, with rabbits scarce, they have been eating vegetables like brussels sprouts.

The fox breeds once a year—in the spring. Mating takes place in December and January in the south, in January and February in the north. Cubs are born in March and April, and may number anything from four to nine. Five or six is a good average. Both sexes care for the cubs, and when they are very small the dog fox does all the hunting. Foxes are good parents and will die in defence of their cubs.

The family begins to break up in the late

Foxes live mainly on rabbits, voles and rats, but will kill anything they can catch and hold, including game birds, poultry and ducks.

summer and early autumn. The cubs wander off in twos, or singly, and are self-supporting at the final break. Many cubs take with them their favourite plaything when they leave home. Dog and vixen do not run together again till the winter, and it is probable that the same pair join up if both have survived. During winter Highland foxes will frequently hunt in couples, co-operating as few animals are known to do, and in very savage winters three or four foxes may join together to form a temporary pack. I suspect that when this happens the company is made up either of cubs from the same litter, or the two parents and members of the family.

THE BADGER

Foxes and badgers favour the same kind of country, and this is particularly true in the mountains where they seek the same cairns. It is not at all unusual to find a fox in a badger den, and it is something of a mystery why the badger puts up with the fox, for Reynard is a dirty housekeeper. Yet Brock not only puts up with the fox; when the den is raided by terriers he will go to the front and take all the punishment himself.

The badger is, indeed, a wonderful fighting machine, who fears nothing that walks or flies. Though he is a member of the great weasel family, you might be forgiven for thinking he was a bear because of his squat shape, bulk, and great clawed feet. But he is, in fact, a true weasel.

Badgers mate in the late summer, July and August, but the cubs are not born until the following March. In a big set, or cairn, there may be several families, but there is no fighting, for Brock is sociable with his own kind, and there is much coming and going among families.

Brock is a cleanly beast, who changes his bedding and makes sanitary arrangements that no Medical Officer would fault. The great spring-cleaning is, indeed, a badger ritual, and immense masses of old bedding are trundled out and hidden in odd corners before the new bedding is trundled in. By the presence of such bedding it is possible to tell at a glance whether badgers are using a cairn.

Badgers are far more strictly nocturnal than foxes, and their daily life really begins with the going down of the sun. It is not often that badgers are caught away from home in daylight, but in many parts of the Highlands young badgers do come out in the sunshine, and sometimes they wander quite a way from home.

Though a true weasel, Brock is not even mainly an eater of flesh. He takes it when he can get it, but he is not fit to catch much on foot; what he gets is mainly young, or injured, creatures, or rabbits caught in traps. He can, of course, dig out nests of young rabbits with ease, and when he does so he digs right down on them from above—not from the entrance to the nesting burrow.

His main food, however, is vegetable. He eats many kinds of roots and tubers, and is fond of bluebell bulbs, chestnuts and dog-hips. He also eats grass in quantity, and there is hardly a fruit that he will not take.

OTHER MEMBERS OF THE WEASEL FAMILY

The remaining British weasels—the stoat, weasel, polecat and pine-marten—are all flesh eaters, and the last two are extremely rare.

Most members of the family smell of musk to a greater or lesser degree, but the pine-marten is almost odourless and is often referred to as the sweet-marten for that reason. For the same reason, at the other extreme, the polecat is referred to as the foumart, or foul-marten.

The pine-marten, now confined to a restricted area in north-west Scotland, is the weasel of the trees, agile as a squirrel and a killer of squirrels throughout its life. With the grey squirrel a present-day menace to forestry, the pine-marten will probably be allowed to come back in strength. It was killed off by game-keepers in the nineteenth century. Both pine-marten and polecat will kill anything they can catch and hold, and, in fact, that is true of all the weasels.

The common weasel is the smallest member of the tribe, but by no means the least fierce. For his size he is perhaps the most courageous and savage animal we have. A weasel weighing less than four ounces will seek out and attack big rats up to 6 times his own weight. I have actually watched a weasel kill three such rats in ten minutes.

There is a tradition that we have, in this country, two sorts of weasel, one of them being a smaller beast called the mouse-weasel or kine. In fact, there is only one species. The belief arose because male and female weasels differ markedly in size, the large ones being the dog weasels. This kind of difference between sexes is called sexual dimorphism.

THE STOAT

The stoat is a larger version of the weasel. In addition he has a bushy, squirrel tail, tipped with black. He turns white in winter, which the weasel never does. In the south of England stoats do not always change in winter; in the north of Scotland they almost invariably do. At this time stoats sometimes run in packs, and such a gathering is formidable. The pack will not turn aside for dog or fox, and even a man interfering is liable to be attacked. In this I speak from experience, because I once had a pack all over me, and was badly bitten.

In the matter of food, the stoat is like the others; he will take anything he can catch and hold. But rabbits are a favourite item, and when a stoat is running a rabbit's trail he sticks to it—turning aside for no other. A stoated rabbit runs a little way, then squats down, frozen with terror. The stoat moves in quickly and death is swift and clean.

THE OTTER

The handsome otter is a weasel of another kind; he is the water-weasel, with webbed feet, designed to hunt for his living in river and loch, and in the sea itself.

Otters breed mainly in the spring, but cubs

The stoat is a larger version of the weasel and has a bushy tail tipped with black. The black tip remains even after the change to white in winter. Stoats sometimes run in packs in winter, and such packs will attack anything interfering with them.

IN the shrinking countryside of Britain we still have a great variety of wild life. Birds are more readily seen by the casual wayfarer; but the wild animals are there too if you know where, and how, to look for them.

The bigger the animal the more likely you are to catch a glimpse of it, and a glimpse is usually the most you'll get. In any given place you are more likely to see a deer than a fox, and a fox is more likely than a stoat. But all are shy and wary and none will thrust itself on your notice if it can avoid doing so.

Naturally it helps if you know whereabouts to look, and it helps, of course, still more if you learn to read tracks, for these are the signatures of the animals of the wild.

The fox is one of the most cunning of all animals, and an expert at using every blade of cover.

The fawn of the roe is spotted at birth. The spots disappear during the late autumn.

The stoat is a member of the weasel family, distinguished from the common weasel by his larger size and his bushy, black-tipped tail. In Scotland stoats turn white in winter, and sometimes run in packs.

The kestrel is a falcon, killing mice, voles, shrews and young rats. He is the farmer's friend.

Hedgehogs are insectivores like moles and shrews, but will take any kind of flesh food they can get. When alarmed, the hedgehog rolls itself into a ball, and this "hedgehog defence" is proof against its enemies, except perhaps the badger and man himself. Hedgehogs sleep through most of the winter.

can be born in any month of the year. I have seen a bitch with cubs in January, when the snow lay deep and frozen. Baby otters do not enter the water willingly; they have to be coaxed or pushed. But, once they are in, they swim well and instinctively. Before they leave their nursery they are tended by the bitch otter; after they are in the water they meet their father for the first time. At least, that is the way it has always seemed to me.

No British mammal wanders more than the otter. They make trips up and down the rivers, settling down only to rear their families. Many otter routes become well known, and there are holts, or dens, and crossing places which have a tradition of otters, and there you can always expect to find them.

Though the otter is a water hunter, that does not mean to say he cannot do so on land. In winter, especially, during a freeze-up, otters will hunt on land for rabbits and birds, and when severely hit by famine will sometimes raid a hen-house. One of the most remarkable sights I ever witnessed was an otter on a frozen loch with a duck, fighting two foxes in order to keep it. He lost it, for he was no match for two foxes. He would not have lost it to a single fox, for the otter is a terrible fighter, but he was no match for two of them.

Many other animals could be classed as hunters—the hedgehog who hunts almost anything, the little shrews who are as savage as tigers, and the moles who hunt worms; but they are the lesser ones, and not to be classed with the real hunters.

The otter is the weasel of the water, and has webbed feet. Although living mainly on fish (mostly eels) and frogs, he will take rabbits and birds at times.

A grey Atlantic seal bull basking in the grass beside his breeding wallow. Seal cows, weighing about half a ton each, join him in his wallow.

THE SEALS ROUND BRITAIN'S COASTS

TWO species of seal commonly frequent the British coasts: one is the Atlantic or grey seal, and the other is the common seal, which is smaller and more numerous. Apart from size and colour—the Atlantic seal is larger and lighter in colour than the common seal—the two species differ in breeding behaviour and in their choice of a place in which to give birth to the calves. Of the breeding habits of the common seal little is known. It is fond of estuaries and the calves are usually born on a tidal sand spit, swimming away with the mother on the flood tide a few hours after birth. Not so with the Atlantic seal, which comes ashore to breed, the calves being born well above high-tide level.

While ashore the animals are particularly vulnerable, since they are not equipped for movement on land, and before giving birth to the calves, the cows are sorely hampered. In the past great destruction was wrought by sealers surprising the helpless beasts while " hauled up," and clubbing them to death. So great was the slaughter that a special Act of Parliament has been passed to protect the Atlantic seal. In earlier times, sealing was a winter occupation in the Hebrides, where the great seal or " ron mor " is a part of the folklore; but to-day they are left much to themselves.

The Atlantic seal is found breeding only on remote islands and on the west coast well out of reach of the common run of men. Small colonies exist in Cornwall and South Wales, and some are found on the Farne Islands off the coast of Northumberland. The greatest numbers are to be found, however, in the Western Isles of Scotland and particularly in the tiny isles of North Rona, Gasker, Hasker and Shillay. In North Rona there are thought to be over 1,000 calves born every year, and in the others several hundred annually. Other breeding-grounds of lesser importance are to be found in the Inner Hebrides.

THE BABY SEAL'S FUR COAT

At the beginning of September the bulls come ashore and take up territories. In mid-September the cows arrive, haul up and give birth to the calves, which possess a thick coat of white fur which they keep for three weeks and then cast before taking to the sea. The milk of the cows is particularly rich in fat, and a calf weighing 30 lb. at birth will probably weigh nearly 100 lb. when it takes to the sea in three weeks' time. They become " inflated," as it were, at the rate of about 4 lb. per day.

The cows soon find their way to the breeding wallows of the bulls, which fight savagely to defend their territory and harem of cows against other interfering bulls. Since no food is taken during the time the animals are ashore, the old bulls fall out of condition quickly, and are replaced by younger and fitter males which have been awaiting their chance in the sea.

The older bulls usually hold the territories at the beginning of the season and the younger ones towards the end of the period. Mating takes place in the breeding wallows or on the edge of the surf, and the whole process—taking the case of one individual cow—from emerging from the sea to give birth to the calf, suckle it, mate, and return to the sea takes about three weeks. After this period the calf is weaned, has lost its baby coat and is ready to follow its mother into the sea. During the summer the seals disperse over a wide area along the British, Scandinavian and Baltic coasts. They rove the coastal seas in packs and can often be seen basking on the shore rocks.

At the end of September of 1953 I went to watch the Atlantic seal colony on the island of Shillay at the western end of the Sound of Harris. Shillay has never been permanently inhabited by man, although it has been, and still is, used as a winter grazing for sheep. The island has an area of about 113 acres, most of which is taken up by rough hill pasture, which rises to a height of 265 feet above sea-level. In the south the ground flattens out to form a low promontory, called Àrd an Laoigh, which extends to about thirty acres, and here a surf-stricken strait separates the main island from its rocky neighbour, Little Shillay.

Àrd an Laoigh is the seal area, and on all except its eastern shore it is girdled with rocks. In the east, however, there is a small beach of sand formed from the finely-ground particles of sea-shells. This beach is the gateway to the breeding-ground, and it is around it that this action takes place. Above the sand there is a storm beach with large smooth boulders which is topped by a two-foot dune escarpment. A low sand-dune about twenty yards broad gives way to a green island pasture strewn with large storm-thrown rocks, and scarred by deep rank pools and water-courses.

Immediately to the north of this area the ground rises in a rough hillside with boulders which provide good cover from which to watch the seals.

WHISKERED FACES IN THE SEA

There were three of us in the expedition, which lasted for ten days. The only safe landing-place is on the small beach, and when our boat approached, the entire seal population took to the water. In the sea around us were a multitude of curious whiskered faces, and the calm waters of the little bay were broken by thrashing bodies. Ashore we discovered some seventeen white, helpless, wide-eyed calves left behind by their mothers in their dash for the sea. The ages of the youngsters were, of course, different; some large plump ones were about ten days old, while other small thin ones were only a few hours old. To begin with we were able to stroke the calves, but later this proved impossible, even with those one day old. Invariably they threw up their heads and hissed with anger.

The calves, with their pathetic crying, the bewildered expression on their faces, their helplessness, and their beautiful coats, are quick to win the affection of the human intruder. It is difficult to believe that at one time men could have been so brutal as to club the poor animals to death as they lay crying for their mothers, whose fate would have been similar had they waited behind to defend their offspring.

While we were on Shillay one of the calves was swept from the rocks into the mountainous surf, and when we discovered this tragedy, with its mother by its side, it was fighting in vain to keep its head above the tumult of breakers. Nothing more was seen of it.

Sometimes the calves are born in the bull's territory, but he takes no interest in the babies, and will often crawl over them, his great hulking body weighing about ten hundredweight. The cows, on the other hand, lavish attention on their babies, suckling and licking them, and defending them from the attentions of other jealous females.

To make up for the shock of our arrival on the colony, we decided to watch the seals for a couple of days from long-range behind the boulders on the hillside. After that time, however, they appeared to have recovered sufficiently, and we began to move closer. First of all, I began to reconnoitre the approaches to the shore over the dunes. This I did at low tide when the animals were gathered far down the beach. The escarpment of the dune formed a low balcony overlooking the storm beach, and from there one's view of the colony was unimpeded. My plan succeeded, and I returned to the hillside without disturbance. From that time onwards, we were able to reach the dune scarp—carefully avoiding wallows occupied by bulls—with comparative ease at any state of the tide, without causing alarm.

Movement within the seal area was slow, and restricted to the " cat crawl," where the body is never raised from the ground. While moving, a constant watch was kept on the colony, and should the attention of a seal be attracted, the stalker remained motionless, sometimes for minutes, until the beast lost interest, turned away, or closed its eyes. As time advanced, our knees, elbows and muscles became accustomed to the constant crawling, and we moved smoothly and ever more boldly towards closer contact with the colony on the beach.

THE SEAL-LADY

The first reconnaissance of the beach was carried out by the second member of our party, a young lady. I watched her progress from behind some tall irises growing beside the dunes, where I was awaiting the arrival of a cow to suckle a hungry calf. I saw my companion move inch by inch over the dune scarp in full view of the seals, and take up a new position behind a large spar of drift-wood on the crest of the storm beach. Presently the nearby calf began to cry, and a cow came through the surf. My attention was diverted for about thirty minutes, and after it was all over I glanced again at the spar on the storm beach. She had gone! I glanced at the beach colony. To my astonishment I saw the recumbent figure of the young lady on the open sand midway between the storm beach and the slumbering colony—at that time about thirty strong.

Photographing a bull seal in his wallow, near the sea, which is the breeding place.

An Atlantic seal calf. About 30 lbs. in weight at birth, he gains about 4 lbs. per day for the first two or three months when he is fed on his mother's milk, which is rich in fat. His creamy coat soon turns to dark grey.

Slowly I withdrew from the iris flags and made my way in a hurry to the dune scarp. Over I went into her tracks, but so much care had to be exercised not to cause alarm, that by the time I had cleared the storm beach my companion was literally lying among the seals. I watched her " shooting " with her ciné-camera at a range of about ten feet, and then slowly withdraw. I met her half-way down the beach, and lying flat and motionless, she whispered something about running out of film. Cautiously, we both withdrew over the dune scarp, leaving the seals in undisturbed reverie.

To the south of the beach lay a stretch of rocky shore on to which the seals hauled in good numbers at low tide. This area was first explored by the third member of the party. From time to time I watched his progress through binoculars from a range of about 100 yards. I was busy setting up a camera tripod at that point when I saw him move in, and approach close to a group basking in the autumn sunshine. Presently, my photograph taken, I moved along the dune scarp. Suddenly my colleague caused a stir in the colony and

came hastily up the storm beach to where I lay. He had come suddenly upon a great bull. Instead of withdrawing—as he expected—the beast closed with him. Holding his fire to the last minute, he had raised his camera when the animal was almost upon him. Instantly it slewed and dashed for the sea.

ADVENTURE WITH A BULL

Towards the end of our stay on Shillay I visited those rocks at low tide and also made another approach to the beach colony over the open sand. There I was challenged by a huge bull which came lumbering up from his harem. With a camera in each hand—one with colour film, and the other with black and white—I held my ground. On he came until, about fifteen feet from me, he stopped and showed me the pink interior of his spacious mouth. In a few minutes he returned to his cows, and I was now troubled by a hungry calf which, thinking me to be its mother, came hurrying towards me from the rocks. To avoid his attention I moved away up the beach.

In the wallows behind the shore we had to

be careful lest we disturbed resident bulls. One morning while we were in the locality, a large black bull suddenly got out of a wallow about 100 yards from the beach and rolled over on the grass. We watched him dumb-founded. Back into the wallow he slid, and we approached cautiously. He had disappeared! For a moment we were puzzled, and then his head broke the surface. In a half-interested way he looked up at us, took a deep breath, and sounded again. He was gone for about ten minutes, and after repeating the per-formance several times he got out and flopped back to the sea.

By the time of our departure there were about 200 seals in and around Shillay, and on the shore were about forty calves. The first-born calves of the season were now about three weeks old, were casting their coats, and were preparing to take to the sea. During our stay we found two dead calves only a few days old, and these were eaten by the great black-backed gulls which frequented the island. The arrival of the launch to take us away sent panic through the populace, and the sea was thronged with their glistening shapes. By this time, however, some of the old bulls had become accustomed to our presence and watched the proceedings from the shore like wise old men.

THE RIVER

Clear and cool, clear and cool,
By laughing shallow, and dreaming pool;
Cool and clear, cool and clear,
By shining shingle and foaming weir;
Under the crag where the ouzel sings,
And the ivied wall where the church-bell rings,
Undefiled, for the undefiled;
Play by me, bathe in me, mother and child.

Dank and foul, dank and foul,
By the smoky town in its murky cowl;
Foul and dank, foul and dank,
By wharf and sewer and slimy bank;
Darker and darker the farther I go,
Baser and baser the richer I grow;
Who dare sport with the sin-defiled?
Shrink from me, turn from me, mother and child.

Strong and free, strong and free,
The flood-gates are open, away to the sea,
Free and strong, free and strong,
Cleansing my streams as I hurry along
To the golden sands, and the leaping bar,
And the taintless tide that awaits me afar,
As I lose myself in the infinite main,
Like a soul that has sinned and is pardoned again.
Undefiled, for the undefiled;
Play by me, bathe in me, mother and child.
Charles Kingsley

DOGS WHO WORK FOR A LIVING
The Story of Sheepdog Trials

SHEEPDOG Trials are now a common feature of our country life, but in fact the very first Trial was held just over eighty years ago. It was organised by a man named Lloyd Price, and was held at Bala, in Wales. The first attendance was quite small, but since that day, the popularity of these Trials has grown to such an extent that hundreds are now held every year, not only in Great Britain, but all over the world.

The purpose of these Trials is twofold—firstly, to improve the breed of the dog, and secondly, to encourage farmers and shepherds to train their animals to a high pitch of perfection.

In order to understand how these Trials are conducted, have a look first of all at the sketch. You will notice a post and the figure of a man, towards the base of the picture. This is where the handler stands. Handler is the name given to the shepherd or farmer who is running his dogs. The course is set out on a large field, and the arrows show the way the dog must run. At the far end an unseen man releases the sheep.

The number of sheep varies. It is usually five for one dog, six for two, and ten or even twenty sheep at an International Championship.

Facing the course is a small stand for the judges, who allot so many points for the way the dog runs, and how well he does his job. A stop-watch is used, too, because the run is timed—usually about 10 minutes—and if the dog has not completed his job by then, he is disqualified.

ALL DONE BY WHISTLES

When the signal is given to start, the handler whistles directions to his dog. He is not allowed to touch the animal, or the sheep. A different whistle is used for each command—for instance, one indicates " go left," another " go right," another " lie down " and so on. The whole purpose of the commands is to instruct the dog to go out and gather the sheep at the top of the field. He then drives the sheep from the top of the field, down to the

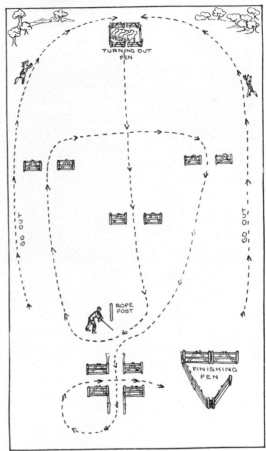

The layout for a sheepdog trial, showing how the dogs are sent out to collect the sheep and bring them to the shepherd.

first two-gate obstacle, and then on until they are finally penned.

The *way* the dog runs is taken into consideration when the judge allots his marks, and this is something that cannot be taught. It is entirely a matter of breeding.

Nowadays, practically the only dog used for this work is the Border Collie. He should be bought from a reliable breeder, and both parents must be registered with the International Sheepdog Society, and the puppy itself must be registered, too. Otherwise he will not be eligible to run in National or International Trials.

Some of the shepherds with their dogs watch a fellow competitor at work whilst they wait their turn. Competition is very keen at International Trials such as this.

THE CANINE FAMILY TREE

This business of parents and grandparents is very important, because certain qualities are born, not made, and without these qualities, no sheepdog can ever hope to reach Trial standard. He should move with a stalking, crouching style, and from the moment he sees his sheep, the collie fixes them with his eye and never takes it off them. This style of working is known to breeders as " eye," and can only be seen perfectly in pedigree dogs.

When the judge is awarding his points, for gathering, driving, shedding—that is, dividing the flock—penning and finally, style, it is the above qualities he is looking for.

And these Trials have, indeed, done a great deal to improve the breeding of the Border Collie so that, to-day, his sons and daughters can be found on farms wherever you may travel. They work the flocks, just as you see them at Sheepdog Trials, in such distant lands

as the ranches of America, the veldts of South Africa, the Highlands of Japan, or the vast plains of Canada. Wherever there are sheep, in fact, there you will find the Border Collie.

He is so called because he came originally from the English-Scottish border.

Not long ago, one of our best-known British handlers went on tour in America and Canada, where he gave exhibitions, using six dogs at once. In order to do this, each dog has to be taught a completely different set of commands. Once he has learned these, he never forgets them. What is more, he will never act on any other command. And it is a fascinating sight to watch one dog penning perhaps three sheep, while the others crouch on the ground, waiting for their own instructions.

Nowadays, in order to encourage young boys to take up this hobby of sheep-dog training, most country districts hold special

Sheepdog trials have been held occasionally in Hyde Park, London. Here the shepherd with his dog, Tam, is shedding two sheep, that is separating two from the others.

The moment of triumph at a sheepdog trial, when the sheep are finally penned.

" novice classes." At these, boys can run their dogs for the first time, with small prizes to encourage them. Experienced shepherds attend these small local Trials to give helpful advice and encouragement.

PURCHASING A PUPPY

Before buying a puppy, it is a good idea to take an experienced farmer into your confidence. He will be able to tell you where one can be bought. The next step is to find it a temporary home in a shepherd's or a farmer's house. Here it will be taught both behaviour and obedience from its earliest days.

When the puppy is about twelve weeks old, he will be allowed to follow his master about the farm or hill where sheep or cattle are being tended. It is now that he begins to show " eye " with the hens and ducks, and he will even try to pen them in the farmyard. This trait will be encouraged by the farmer, who will persuade him very gently to bring his master the objects of his interest.

It is, however, essential that the puppy should not *touch* the animals. Always he must keep a reasonable distance away, otherwise he will frighten them. You will notice this if you watch a dog working the flocks, he never gets too near the sheep. If he does make this mistake, they scatter, and his work has to begin all over again.

Another important point. You must never, never make a dog afraid of you. Sometimes, if a puppy is rough, he may need a sharp smack, but this should be given very seldom. Puppies will do anything for a person they love, and this perfect confidence between a dog and his master, is one of the most essential features of training.

TRAINING A YOUNG COLLIE

When the actual training begins, the owner must take his dog out *every* day, no matter what the weather. And he must be taught only one command at a time. This command must be thoroughly learned, before attempting to teach a second one. The young collie, however, is eager and keen to learn, and it does not take him very long. The whistle must, of course, be a very clear and distinctive one, as often the animal has to hear it from a distance of half a mile away. And there must be no possibility of the dog mistaking one whistle for another. For these reasons, only one dog

Two collies at work trying to pen the sheep, guided only by their master's whistle and voice. The relative positions and stealthy method of working ensures that the sheep do not panic.

The shepherd is driving his flock over the Downs, and his dog is constantly on the alert to round up any stragglers and keep the flock together.

should be trained at a time, as he needs the undivided attention of his master.

These days, big business is involved in the breeding of really first-class Border Collies. Two hundred pounds is quite a normal sum to give for a dog which has reached International Trials standard. And in addition his stud fees are worth a good deal, while a bitch's puppies will be snapped up by farmers in no time. Most farmers like to breed and train their own dogs, but they *can* be bought ready-trained. Where this is the case, the words or whistles of command are part of the price, and will not be taught to another dog.

Some of our best-known handlers started with novice classes, when they were only fifteen years old, gradually progressing from local to National and from there to International Trials.

THE REWARD OF A GOOD HANDLER

Most country districts, where sheep are reared, run their own local Trials, and men come from all over the British Isles to run their dogs. Every Trial is " experience " and a dog that does well here, may then compete in the National Trials. The peak of them all

is the International Trials, which are held every year in turn, in Scotland, Wales, and England. It is the ambition of every handler to run his dogs at an International, because this brings him, as well as his Border Collies, immense prestige.

It brings a good monetary reward, too. A first-class dog can win as much as one hundred pounds in a day, and many of these shepherds go all over the country, competing at Trials practically every week. Both they, and their dogs, rapidly earn a reputation in farming circles, or wherever men meet who are interested in the Border Collie.

But as in all competitions, the beginner is given a fair chance, and in the novice class he will only compete with others of the same experience as himself. So that there is nothing to stop the young boy who wishes to embark on this fascinating—and usually lifetime—hobby. Not only is it one of the most satisfying of country occupations, but these Sheepdog Trials do good in quite another way. Spectators are charged an entrance fee, and charity has benefited by many thousands of pounds, as well as by the endowment of hospital beds all over the country.

The violet has become the symbol for modesty, for its delicate flowers tend to shelter among its leaves and the plant is usually found in semi-shaded places.

WILD FLOWER NAMES
Their History and Meaning

THE popular names of our common wild flowers become unexpectedly interesting when we make the discovery that they have a hidden history and meaning. Indeed, they open up a new and inviting path for rambling exploration. Why is a violet called a violet? We know that the personal name Violet is borrowed from the flower. But where did the flower's name come from? And what does it mean? Evidently there is a story somewhere.

Such questions launch us on an expedition that carries us backwards in time for thousands of years and leads our footsteps all across Europe and sometimes even beyond. For wild flower names are little signposts pointing the way to some of the notable characters and events, the beliefs and superstitions, of earlier days. They are likewise lamps that cast a revealing gleam on forgotten customs of the past.

FOREIGN NAMES FOR WILD FLOWERS

One of the first surprises we encounter on our journey is that the majority of the names of our more familiar wild flowers are not English—or not wholly English—in origin. If we were to stroll down a country lane and recite the names of the flowers blooming there, we should be using words, or expressing ideas, drawn from half a dozen different languages. We do not find this disproportion of alien terms in the names of our native birds and beasts. Why, then, have we allowed foreigners to supply so many of our wild flower names?

The answer lies across the Channel. But, before we go in search of it, it seems proper to explore our own country and track down some of the names that *are* English. We can begin with the daisy. The name is one of a group of plant names that were often on the lips of our half-barbaric Anglo-Saxon ancestors. Many of the group were brought over from the Continent when the invaders' keels grounded on Britain's shores during the fifth and sixth centuries. " Daisy " means " day's eye," or " the eye of day." In other words, the golden-centred, white-rayed blooms are likened to that true eye of day, the sun. Another of the group —garlic—is less poetic and more in keeping with the rougher side of the sea-rovers' character. The syllable " lic " means simply a leek; but a " gar " was a spear or javelin. The shape of the leaves doubtless suggested the weapon that was as familiar to the warriors as the umbrella is to us. The meadow-sweet gives a glimpse of the Saxon in their hours of ease. Their name for the plant was meadwort. And the mead they had in mind was not a meadow, in allusion to the plant's home. It was the heady national drink made of honey and water. Apparently then, the Saxons flavoured the beverage with the richly-scented blooms of the herb.

There are many more of these ancient English plant names—clover, flax, foxglove, strawberry, etc. But the three cited will sufficiently show how the names, still surviving after centuries of use, cast their fitful little sidelights on the past.

FRENCH NAMES

Now we can cross the Channel. France has given us quite a number of wild flower names, amongst them pansy. The word comes from *pensée*, thought. Maybe the French applied it to the plant as the flower of remembrance for friends and lovers.

Many of the " French " names, however, were not actually French inventions. Our cross-channel neighbours had done some borrowing too. The queer name fumitory is an instance. We imported it from France. But it is not really a French creation, for the French evidently received the underlying idea of it from the Latin of the ancient Romans. But it is not a Latin creation either, because the Romans copied their name from the Greeks. So, after travelling a couple of thousand years or more into the past, we arrive in Greece.

GREEK AND LATIN NAMES

The Greeks and Romans used the fumitory as an eye-salve and, as its juices made the eyes water like smoke, they called it the smoke-plant. In the Middle Ages the people of western Europe, who were not strong on botany, conceived a bright idea. They decided that the herb was produced from a sort of smoke rising from the earth. So they called it —in the Latin that was then the universal

The celandine is the swallow-plant, said to flower throughout the swallow season.

language of the educated—*fumus terrae*, smoke of the earth. In England, the rough popular usage of the term changed it gradually to fumitory.

The mysterious name basil has a somewhat similar life-history. The plant was supposed to be an antidote to the venom of a fearsome and wholly imaginary reptile, called the basilisk, which could kill a man merely by looking at him.

Greece and Rome are the principal sources, direct or indirect, of our alien wild flower names. They cover many of the most familiar blooms of the countryside and they are packed with legend and myth and folklore. From Greek, celandine, centaury, and hawkweed (which is Greek in idea), and from Latin plantain, vervain and violet come this numerous company.

Celandine means the swallow-plant and there were two ways of interpreting it. The first was that the flowers remained in bloom throughout the season of the swallows. The other is rather more sensational. The swallows, it was soberly declared, used the plants to restore the sight of their young—even when their eyes had been plucked out! The centaury

Meadow-sweet, which was once used to flavour mead, the Saxon wine.

Hera. Then, in order to provide her with delicate and wholesome nourishment, he created violets and called them after her.

GREEK LEARNING

The reason for the adoption of so many of these foreign or foreign-inspired names is that, in the main, they have been borne to us over countless years on the tide of historical events. The ancient Greeks, who have bequeathed to us so many attractive plant names, were a highly-cultured people. They were far in advance of the rest of Europe in their knowledge of the arts and sciences, including botany and medicine. The Romans who conquered them in the second century B.C. eagerly absorbed their superior learning. Thus numbers of the Greek plant names passed into Latin.

In the fifth century A.D. the Roman Empire in the west (of which Britain was an outlying province) was overrun by German tribes. The classical Greek and Latin learning became almost submerged. In time, however, the barbarian kingdoms (Anglo-Saxon England was one of them) which had been established within the bounds of the fallen empire came to a full appreciation of the value of the ancient literature. Much of it was recovered, principally from the fourteenth to the sixteenth

is named after Chiron the centaur. According to the old fable, the centaurs were monstrous hybrids with the body and legs of a horse and the trunk, arms and head of a man. Chiron was a great " medicine-man " and it was believed that he was the first to reveal to mankind the healing powers of the plants named in his honour. The hawkweed was so called because the Greeks believed that the knowing hawks, after which they named this plant, used the sap to strengthen their failing sight.

The shape of the leaves of the greater plantain seems to give the clue to the meaning of the name. Evidently it comes from the Latin *planta*, the sole of the foot. The inconspicuous vervain has a prouder history. It is thought to have been the most sacred of the sacred herbs, called the *verbenae*, which were used by the Romans in solemn affairs of state and in various religious ceremonies in their homes and temples. The Latin name of the violet was *viola*. We do not know much about its origin, but it may be related to the Greek name, *ion*, about which quite a lot could be said. One of the ancient legends which explain the word describes how Zeus, the principal god of the Greeks, changed a maiden named Io into a heifer, because of the jealousy of the goddess

St. John's wort, which flowers at the same same time as the saint's festival.

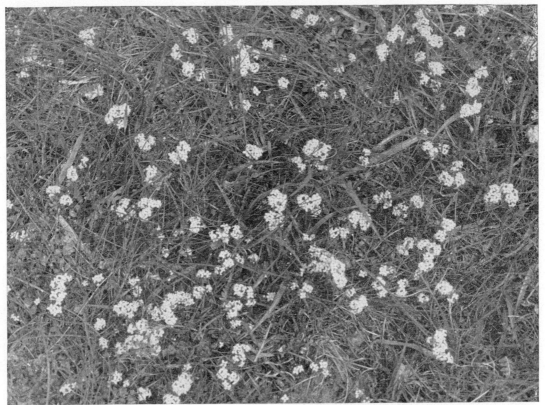

Lady's bedstraw, dedicated to the Virgin Mary. The dried leaves were once used for bedding when straw was a usual bedding material.

centuries; and one result was the revival throughout western Europe, including England, of Greek and Roman botany and medicine, with, of course, the plant names. These two sciences were closely geared to each other. Until modern times plants were the principal source of medicine. Hence there was a particular reason why the herbs, whose supposed healing qualities had been described by the ancients, should be sought out and studied. It was as a result of these events that the old plant names continued their great westward trek.

THE INFLUENCE OF THE CHURCH

After the fall of Rome, the Catholic Church played the leading part in " nursing " the barbarians and the new states they founded and teaching them the A.B.C. of settled and orderly life. A minor outcome of the influence of the Church was the creation, in England and on the Continent, of many new plant names of a sacred character. Several plants, of which the St. John's wort is one, were given the name of the saints whose festival coincided with their flowering time. Others, such as the Lady's bedstraw and Lady's smock, were dedicated to the Virgin Mary. Sacred legends, associating the familiar herbs of the field with the teachings of religion, were piously circulated. One of the most dramatic of these has left its mark to-day in the name of the Devil's-bit scabious. The root-stock of this plant looks as if the end had been chopped off and it was this peculiarity that gave rise to the tale. The herb had a tremendous reputation as a cure for plague and pestilence and a host of other common evils. Such a universal blessing was evidently more than the Devil could endure. In his consuming hatred for mankind he savagely bit off the root so as to destroy it.

THE MEDICINAL USES OF HERBS

There is, or was, a whole catalogue of names,

An illustration from a thirteenth century manuscript by Roger of Salerno (the famous medical school of the Middle Ages) showing the herbs being selected, pounded and boiled.

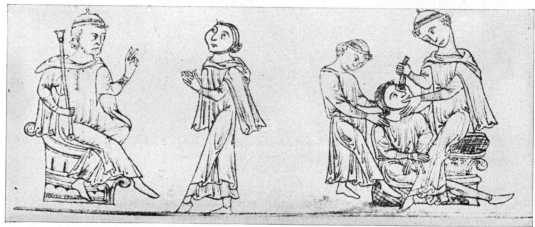

From the same manuscript this second illustration shows the patient consulting the doctor, and then the application by the latter of herbs to relieve pain in the eye.

besides those already mentioned, that indicate the extent to which our forefathers relied on herbs for medical purposes. This brings us back to the close connection which existed between botany and medicine. During the Middle Ages country people habitually sought out healing herbs in the neighbouring fields and woods and also cultivated them, along with kitchen herbs, in their gardens. Thus the humble cottager would stock his little plot and richer folk set up their more formal and extensive herb gardens. For a long time the principal gardens were attached to the monasteries. The monks were foremost in the study and cultivation of medicinal herbs. The medicines they compounded from them were needed for the treatment of the monastery inmates; but the monks also made it their particular duty to minister to the poor of the surrounding countryside.

THE WORK OF THE APOTHECARIES

From the latter part of the period onwards, the professional preparation of drugs and medicines was carried out mainly by the apothecaries. In London most of the needful herbs were brought to the markets in basketfuls by countrywomen. In the early seventeenth century the Society of Apothecaries organised regular botanical excursions to enable apprentices to gain a practical knowledge of herbs and their properties. Later in the century the Society laid out the Physic Garden at Chelsea which is still flourishing. Similar gardens had already been established elsewhere, one of

The doctor visits his patient and gives him an infusion of herbs to drink, whilst he holds a pomander in his hand. Medical science was primitive in the sixteenth century consisting mainly of herbal remedies and bleeding. A razor for this latter purpose is in the doctor's hand.

them being that which John Gerard cultivated in the then rural village of Holborn. In 1596 Gerard could boast of over a thousand different kinds of plants, native and foreign, growing under his care. His *Herball, or Generall Historie of Plants*, as enlarged in 1633, described nearly three thousand. This immense work is a veritable treasure house of facts and fancies concerning the names and medical virtues of the wild, cultivated and foreign plants then known in England.

In the times we have been considering, almost every plant was believed to possess some particular healing quality and many of them were named accordingly. Some plants, indeed, were credited with such a variety of virtues as to become a positive panacea or cure-all. Thus the betony, a common herb of abundant growth, was recommended for sore eyes, throat and nose, toothache, fever, the bites of adders and mad dogs and a host of other ills, including nightmare. To-day, the chemist's preparations have mostly taken the place of the old herbal remedies. None the less, physicians still look to a number of herbs for certain useful drugs. Among our native plants, the foxglove affords digitalin, the henbane hyoscyamine, the deadly nightshade atropine, and so on.

REAL AND IMAGINED USES OF HERBS

Most of the old " medical " plant names have gone the way of the remedies themselves. Amongst those which have survived are eye-bright, woundwort, self-heal, lungwort and stitchwort. Concerning some of these plants the most extravagant beliefs existed. Eye-bright would actually restore sight to the blind. Woundwort would heal the goriest gashes in record time. Self-heal, in addition to its many other virtues, was a wonder-worker in healing cuts received from edged tools.

Another class of names bears witness to the former household uses of herbs. The soft herbage of the bedstraws was found highly acceptable when straw formed a common bedding material. The soapwort was used for washing clothes and wool from very early times. Before the days when soap as we know it came into general supply, the lather which could be worked up from the leaves of the plant was a real aid to cleanliness. The name rest-harrow is of another character. The "rest" means "arrest" and refers to the stubborn obstruction which the tough and solid roots of the plant offered to the progress of the ox-drawn harrow.

One peculiar feature of wild flower names is the considerable number that bear the prefix " fool's," "dog," " horse" and the like. These words are very commonly used as a term of contempt. They are labels that expose the coarseness of the plants that bear them or their inferiority to some similar species. The fool's, or dog's, parsley is a telling instance. It resembles the garden parsley but is a worthless, and indeed a poisonous, herb. Sometimes, however, the " animal " names indicate the particular creature's liking for the plant. Pigs devour the underground tubers of the pig-nut with gusto.

Only a small selection of names has been examined here. A large proportion of the remainder are equally rich in entertaining tit-bits of out-of-the-way knowledge and old-world lore.

THE HUNTER

Merrily winds the hunter's horn,
    And loud the bay of dogs replying,
When before the shout of the fleet-foot morn,
    The shadows of the night are flying.

Sullen the boar in the deep green wood,
    And proud the stag that roams the forest,
And noble the steed with his warlike blood,
    That exults when the toil is sorest.

Fair is the land of hill and plain,
    And lonesome dells in misty mountains;
And the crags where eagles in tempest reign,
    And swan-loved lakes and fountains.

These are the joys that hunters find,
    Whate'er the sky that's bending o'er them,
When they leave their cares on their beds behind,
    And earth is all fresh before them.

Day ever chases away the night,
    And wind pursues the waves of ocean,
And the stars are brother-like hunters bright,
    And all is in ceaseless motion.

Life is a chase, and so 'tis joy,
    And hope foretells the hunter's morrow;
'Tis the skill of man and the bliss of boy
    To gallop away from sorrow.
                    John Sterling

BEEKEEPING IS A SPLENDID HOBBY

BEEKEEPING is a fascinating hobby and one which has much to recommend it, for it not only offers a natural history study of great interest, but serves the double purpose of honey production and pollination. It is a mistake to go in for beekeeping thinking there are great profits to be made, but it can become a self-supporting hobby, providing honey supplies for the household and, in good years, a generous surplus for gifts or sale.

Another great advantage to the craft is that with one or two colonies or hives of bees it does not make a heavy demand on time. Bees can be thoroughly and carefully tended in a few hours every week, provided knowledge and skill are employed.

The first task, therefore, of the intending beekeeper is to learn about the hive and its occupants.

INSIDE THE HIVE

Modern hives, of which there are many types obtainable, are designed to give complete protection to the bees and yet at the same time facilitate the working of the bees for the owner, so that the colonies may be kept scrupulously clean, and at the appropriate time the honey removed with the greatest ease and the least disturbance.

The hives are divided into lifts, the bottom one being the brood chamber, consisting of 10 movable frames in which the queen bee, a large number of the worker bees and all the eggs, larvæ and young bees are housed. On to this can be placed further shallow lifts, each of which contains 12 frames, into which the bees build their combs, which they fill with honey. It is not an unusual sight to see a hive with 3, 4 or even 5 lifts, which a strong bee colony at the height of the season will fill with honey.

On top of the lifts a cover is placed to keep the bees from crawling into the outer framework, and a hive lid, usually designed like the roof of a house, to permit the rain to drain away.

STARTING A COLONY

There are two ways of starting a colony of bees. You can either buy a swarm of bees, which consists of an army of worker bees and a queen,

and house them in a brood chamber, the frames of which should, if possible, consist of built-up comb, or else you can purchase what is called a nucleus. This is a small colony of bees housed on 4 or 5 frames of built-up comb with stores and brood or young bees and a queen. Opinion differs as to which of these methods is the better. A good deal depends on the age of the queen. If the queen is old she may not be very fertile and the stock will in consequence be weak and may produce only a small quantity of honey, and find it difficult to survive a hard winter. If possible expert advice should be taken on this point; consultations with the local Beekeepers' Association will save much valuable time and money.

THE OCCUPANTS OF THE HIVE

The bees themselves are divided into three distinct types, the queen, the drones and the workers. The queen is the mother of the colony. She is the biggest of the bees with a long tapering body and, although easily recognisable, is rarely seen unless sought for. Her function is to produce eggs and this she does at the rate of about four thousand a day. These eggs may be either male or female. If male they will develop into drones whose sole purpose is to fertilise the queen when she puts out on her maiden flight. For the rest they make short exercise flights and eat the forage brought into the hive by the workers, for their tongues are too short to allow them to gather nectar from flowers. The drones are larger than worker bees but not so large as the queen, and have blunted ends to their bodies.

It is upon the workers that the survival of the hive depends. They are in fact undeveloped females and their strenuous lives may only be of six to eight weeks' duration, during the height of the summer, for they work themselves to death.

The workers, developed in the late summer, live through the winter to the following spring, so maintaining the life of the hive. The worker bees have many tasks to perform, but perhaps the most important is foraging. On forage flights which may be as long as 2 or 3 miles, the bees collect pollen, nectar, water

The handling of the frame must be done with the greatest possible care, using slow, deliberate movements. When handled in this way the bees will not be in any way disturbed, but if the beekeeper hurries or is awkward in movement, the bees will probably sting.

and a gluey substance taken from trees such as the horse chestnut, called propolis. This is used for sealing in the hive so that no wind or draughts get inside. Each of the substances taken into the hive is treated either to make honey, intended, of course, for the winter food store of the bees, or different kinds of food which is given to the larvæ or converted into wax to build up the combs within the hive.

FEEDING THE BEES IN WINTER

Life in the hive is regulated by the turn of the seasons. In winter activity is at its lowest ebb. It is usual at this time for the beekeeper to confine the colony to the brood chamber alone, or to the brood chamber and one lift of the hive if it is a strong one. The worker bees who have survived the strenuous work of the summer look after the queen and make quite sure that any draught holes are kept tightly sealed. They also carry food down to the brood chamber from the upper lift. The drones have been killed off at the end of the summer and the queen will not start to lay eggs until the spring, so there are no larvæ to tend.

It is not necessary for the beekeeper to do anything for his hive at this time of the year, except to make sure that the bees have enough food. This is done by placing a feeder bottle,

of sugar and water or surplus low grade honey, which is devised to drip at a regulated pace into the hive. If the bees are hungry, which happens if the weather is very cold and a great deal of honey has been taken from the hive in late summer, then their feeder bottle is emptied regularly. If they are not in great need of food the bees will take away the food slowly and the bottle will not empty. Experience guides the beekeeper in these matters, but the great thing at this time of the year is to open the hive as little as possible, in order that the temperature may be maintained at a high level.

On warm winter days a few of the worker bees take short exploratory flights or they can be seen sunning themselves on the landing-board, enjoying the warmth and fresh air, but apart from a subdued hum which comes from inside the hive there is scarcely any movement at this time of the year.

With the return of spring the activity increases, more bees swarm away on forage flights and even in February or March workers return laden with pollen from the catkins, and inside the queen starts to lay her eggs. By May, depending of course on the weather, activity is considerable. The workers build queen cells, bigger and longer than ordinary cells, and feed the larvæ from the female eggs which have been deposited in them with a

A swarm has been collected and the bees have been " unloaded " on to the ramp leading up to their new hive. Bees become very rapidly accustomed to their new environment, and set out to collect nectar almost at once.

special food which turns a worker larva into a queen. If the beekeeper does not want his bees to swarm and divide into two colonies, when going through the hive he can take out the queen cells and this helps to keep swarming down to a minimum.

THE WEDDING FLIGHT OF THE QUEEN

A swarm is really the wedding flight of a new queen. Having been newly hatched out of her cell, part of the hive splits off from the main body and decides to give allegiance to her. A tremendous buzzing and commotion predicts the activity which is to follow. A large number of workers and drones pour out of the hive and somewhere in their midst is the new queen. With a mighty buzzing, and flying close together in a dense mass, they soar upwards. Sometimes they settle quickly on a bush or tree. At other times, particularly if the weather is hot, they will fly a considerable distance. But eventually they come to rest

and then the beekeeper comes along and shakes them into his basket and carries them back to the apiary. If they refuse to settle a little spray of water may help. In fact, with knowledge and skill the whole business of swarming can be handled very easily.

It is usual to let the swarm stay quietly in the covered basket until sundown, then it can be shaken on to a white cloth spread out to lead up to the entrance of the new hive and with a little coaxing the bees soon march inside and will not be long before they start filling up the combs with honey. The new queen will lay her eggs and set up a thriving brood chamber.

If the swarm happens early in the year it may be possible to take honey from the upper lifts later that season. If the swarm occurs in late July or August then there will be no opportunity to take honey and the bees may well have to be fed constantly through the winter, as they will have had no time to build up a store of their own food. Hence the old saying

" a swarm of bees in May is worth a load of hay."

HOW DIFFERENT TYPES OF HONEY ARE PRODUCED

As the year advances and fruit blossom gives way to cultivated or meadow flowers and finally to heather and autumn blossoms, the honey collecting goes on apace. In accordance with the way the beekeeper arranges his hive, different types of honey are produced. Usually above the brood chamber at the bottom of the hive the beekeeper places a queen excluder. This is a piece of thin metal perforated with elongated holes which are big enough to allow the worker bees to go all over the hive but small enough to confine the queen to her brood chamber where she must lay all her eggs. In this way the top lifts are kept for honey only.

If bottled honey is required lifts containing 12 frames are put in. These frames can be bought with a sheet of wax wired into place. Using this as a partition the bees build up a honeycomb of wax with untiring energy and then they fill each hexagonal receptacle with honey and then seal it neatly with a little wax cap. When a number of frames has been filled they can be removed, the little wax caps cut off the honeycomb with a sharp knife and the frames hung vertically in a honey extractor. This is a large tin receptacle not unlike a dust-bin. It is designed to hold the frames on a movable central spindle which can be rotated rapidly by a handle. The movement spills out the honey from the comb and gradually the golden liquid drains to the bottom of the extractor and after straining, sieving, etc., can be bottled. The frames of built up honeycomb can be replaced in the hives and the bees will at once start to fill this again. Due to the cleanliness of the bees themselves, the wax frames remain fresh and sweet almost indefinitely. No mould or rot attaches to honey or bees-wax unless disease has made the colony unhealthy.

The other type of honey produced is called section honey, where both the honey and the honeycomb is intended for consumption. This is a luscious way of eating honey but it is more expensive, for the honeycomb, which as already stated can be used repeatedly, is eaten as well as the honey itself.

With the best of the honey, which the colony can spare, removed, the hive is cleaned up and put down for the winter. The ends of the frames even in the brood chamber are scraped clean of any unnecessary wax or propolis, any dead bees brushed away and the whole hive tidied up.

HOW TO AVOID BEING STUNG

It is a source of amazement to beginners that the hive can be opened and the bees " worked." This is not as difficult as it seems. It is advisable for the beginner to equip himself or herself with a head veil and a pair of gloves which, while leaving the fingers mobile, do not permit stray bees to crawl up the sleeve. Then with the aid of a smoker, which is a pair of bellows enclosed in a box into which smouldering paper is placed, bees can be subdued. The hive is opened, the top jackets, old blankets or dry sacks taken off, and the coverlet to the top layer lifted up gently. A few puffs from the smoker will send the bees scurrying away into the interior of the hive, and examination of the frames can proceed. All movements of the hands should be deliberate and unhurried as bees react very quickly to people who are afraid of them, and, if there is any evidence of hurrying or uncertain behaviour, they will sting out of nervousness.

It is as well to remember that a bee has only one sting and that after using it he dies, so it is not likely that it will be used unless the bee feels considerable apprehension for the safety of the hive. Some people find the stings very troublesome but generally after two or three stings a certain immunity is set up. There is the claim, furthermore, that bee stings are valuable as a preventative and cure for rheumatism. Whether this is so has not yet been proved conclusively.

THE BEST POSITION FOR AN APIARY

The location of an apiary is a very important factor. It should be, if possible, in the lee of some shelter, a hedge or fence preferably, and the bees should face south or south-west. This position may be varied slightly in order to avoid exposure to a particular prevailing wind. This ensures that whatever sun is available keeps the bees warm in winter and free from draught. The bees should also be placed on dry ground, and, if a meadow site is selected, the grass should be cut to keep the damp in check. A brick under each of the four feet

In Cornwall there has been, of recent years, a revival of the ancient craft of mead-making. The honey-farmer stands amidst his hives with the mead-making buildings in the background.

of the hive is also a help in this connection.

Some people hesitate to keep bees in a small garden but this can be done provided that there are some open spaces within a mile and that the surrounding gardens are well cultivated, providing plenty of blossom from which honey may be taken. A garden with a high fence is also to be desired in this case for the bees then learn to fly off from the hive, high into the air to avoid the fence and cannot trouble neighbours. If near fences are low the bees will take off at a lower angle and the actual passage of the little creatures, to and fro all day long, can be an annoyance.

The need to keep the hive warm, dry and well ventilated and clean has already been mentioned. With this latter point in mind the whole of the outside of the hive should be scrubbed down at least once a year, and every two years a coat of paint applied. But as bees are very sensitive to smell every precaution must be taken to free the hive from the smell of paint before the bees can be put back into it again.

These and many other aspects of this really wonderful hobby will be fully appreciated as knowledge and experience of hive management are acquired. Beekeepers, if they are to become real experts, must be prepared to learn all the time and while neglect must never creep in, they must resist the temptation to interfere unduly with their hives, gaining both pleasure and knowledge by watching the bees, whose fascinating habits are a delight.

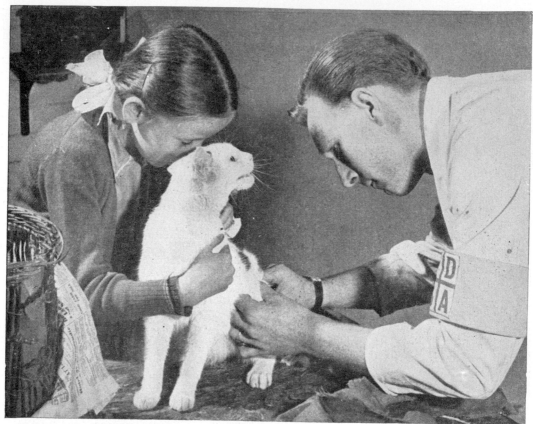

Children often bring their pets to the P.D.S.A. Dispensary in order to ensure for them expert treatment. This little girl comforts her cat whilst the treatment is carried out.

THE WORK OF THE P.D.S.A.

"All Animals Treated—All Treatment Free"

THE words of this title are familiar to millions in Britain and abroad. They are the slogan of the P.D.S.A.—The People's Dispensary for Sick Animals; a kind, courageous, patient body of men and women who bring help, comfort and treatment, free of charge, to the injured and suffering animals of the poor.

It must seem very cruel to us in these enlightened times, that anyone should try to cure sick and injured animals by giving them such dangerous " medicines " as turpentine and iron filings, and by fastening broken bones together with long nails. Yet this kind of " treatment " was common in Britain less than forty years ago. Ignorance, superstition and neglect on the part of animal owners caused unspeakable suffering among dumb creatures, which Professor Huxley aptly described when he said, " If our ears were sharp enough we should hear sighs and groans of pain from animals thousands of times a minute, like those heard by Dante at the gates of Hell."

Such conditions were accepted by simple-minded poor people as normal, and it was not until 1917 that the dark silent world of animal suffering was brought to the notice of the public.

A BENEFACTOR OF DUMB ANIMALS

In that year a woman working among the

The founder, Mrs. M. E. Dickin, C.B.E., has been responsible for saving many sick animals.

war-distressed families of London's slums was dismayed by the pitiful misery endured by great numbers of sick, starving and injured animals upon whom the poor depended for their living—the horses who day after day painfully hauled firewood, fish and vegetables through the narrow streets, the dogs who guarded homes and shops, the cats who kept down the rats and mice, the fowls, rabbits, goats and donkeys essential to thousands of families.

This woman, Mrs. M. E. Dickin, could not bear to see the heart-breaking way that these helpless, suffering, four-footed creatures struggled on faithfully until they dropped in their weary tracks. She decided that she must help them, and all suffering creatures whose owners were too poor to pay for treatment.

She had no money, and adverse criticism greeted her. People did not believe the conditions she described, nor that the poor would accept help if it were offered. Besides, it was war-time, and to give money to relieve suffering animals was considered outrageous waste.

Mrs. Dickin did not waver. She tramped in vain the streets of the East End looking for a

suitable room in which to begin work. A kind-hearted clergyman at last came to her aid. He loved animals and loaned her his cellar in Whitechapel where he himself had been trying in a small way to help animals. The cellar was thirteen feet square, stuffy and dingy; a dark flight of uneven steps led down to it from the dirty, narrow street. Within this unwholesome room was a broken chair, a wooden form, a rickety table, a paraffin lamp, lethal chamber and box of simple remedies.

Joyfully Mrs. Dickin accepted the premises. A well-known animal practitioner who had heard of her plan gave his services gladly, and with meagre basic equipment in readiness Mrs. Dickin hung out the first sign bearing the now famous slogan: "Bring Your Sick Animals—Do Not Let Them Suffer—All Animals Treated—All Treatment Free."

THE FIRST ANIMAL PATIENTS

The brave crusade of the People's Dispensary for Sick Animals had begun. That first grey November evening four patients were shyly brought for treatment: a cat with mange, a dog with canker of the ear, another dog with a broken leg, and a limping donkey.

The old man who owned the donkey suspiciously passed the cellar several times before summoning courage to ask for help. He could not believe there was nothing to pay. For three days he brought the little animal back for treatment. His delight at its recovery was boundless. He told all his friends, emphasising the most wonderful fact of all: there was nothing to pay!

From that day onwards cases began to flood in until there was no more room in the cellar and patients had to lie on the pavement outside. The need for larger premises was desperate, and Mrs. Dickin found four rooms opposite the People's Palace in Whitechapel. Here an average of 100 cases were treated daily, many of them so terrible that Mrs. Dickin vowed she would not rest until dispensaries were opened throughout London, and then Britain; and why not, her conscience demanded, throughout the world?

It was a tremendous plan for a woman with no money behind her save that given by a few sympathetic members of the public. Such donations came in slowly, and miraculously proved just sufficient to meet the increasing expenses of the work. There is no record of the weariness and anxiety which must often have oppressed this brave woman, only her detailed chronicle of the thousands of cases treated, the comfort brought to suffering creatures and their anxious owners.

By 1922 seven P.D.S.A. dispensaries were treating some 70,000 cases a year in London. Benefactors were stepping forward to help in the work which Mrs. Dickin had proved was desperately needed. One had only to read the records which were kept, of every case, to realise the shocking suffering among animals, the fringe of which the P.D.S.A. had only begun to touch.

Everywhere there was evidence of astonishing ignorance. One coster " wormed " his horse by tying its head back to a beam, then pouring a pint of linseed oil and turpentine down its throat. The state of the animal alarmed him and he sent for the P.D.S.A. They found that the " medicine " had gone down the windpipe into the animal's lungs.

THE FIRST CARAVAN DISPENSARY

Mrs. Dickin realised that the spreading of

knowledge was as important as treatment and kindness. In 1923 she bought an old gipsy horse-caravan, painted it and equipped it with drugs, bandages, splints, chloroform, surgical instruments, literature and a microscope and chart for lectures, as well as cooking utensils and a tent for the staff to sleep in at night. Thus began the first tour of the first P.D.S.A. caravan dispensary.

Again people's ignorant callousness towards the suffering of animals brought despair to Mrs. Dickin and her staff. At one country school they found that a little boy had taken all the baby birds from a nest and cut off their legs and wings. One man had filled his dog's cankerous ear with petrol, ready to set it alight, believing that this was the " cure." A boy whose dog's broken leg had been set was told how to tend it, but when he was handed the poor animal he threw it on the ground, expecting it to follow him home.

With patience and kindness, P.D.S.A. staffs in all centres continued their work to overcome such ignorance. The headquarters became too small, and once again the purchase of larger premises was made possible by a

The **P.D.S.A.** finds its way even to the most remote villages, where pet owners queue up outside the Mobile Dispensary to receive treatment for their sick animals.

timely donation. At the new headquarters, 542 Commercial Road, London, E., drugs and dressings were stored and issued daily to all the dispensaries, and here, too, all major operations were performed. There was hospital accommodation at last for in-patients, and living quarters on the premises for day and night staffs.

Gradually additional caravans for mobile dispensaries were donated. The first permanent provincial dispensary was opened at Salford, near Manchester, as a result of pleas to a visiting caravan staff—another step towards Mrs. Dickin's goal to increase the number of dispensaries until every sick and injured animal would be within range of P.D.S.A. help.

HEALING ANIMALS IN FOREIGN LANDS

Only seven years after the first case was treated in the dingy Whitechapel cellar, the first dispensary abroad was made possible by

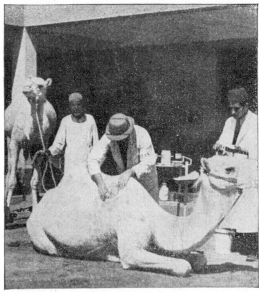

This is a scene at a P.D.S.A. hospital in the Middle East, where many camels, donkeys and other animals are treated daily.

The first-aid van is now hailed with joy in foreign countries where the natives formerly did not feel that animals were deserving of any special treatment. Here is a caravan on the outskirts of a Middle East town, where an assortment of animal patients await treatment.

a donation. It opened in 1924, at Tangier. In this crowded Moorish city with its blistering heat, filth and flies, the mass suffering of animals was more terrible than anything that had been seen in the worst slums of Britain. Apart from camels and domestic animals, there were donkeys by the thousand, and nearly all these poor patient beasts (the Moor's chief form of transport) were in the most pitiful condition. Hundreds upon hundreds were mere walking skeletons struggling along in the heat under twice the loads a healthy donkey should carry. The cruel weight pressed the harness into their bodies, causing festering wounds that doubled the suffering already endured from wounds caused by the Moors' habitual goading of their beasts with knives, needles, thorns and nails.

Such had been the conditions in the whole of North Africa for generations. Little wonder that the P.D.S.A.'s battle there was long and gruelling! As in all the foreign work, there were superstitious and religious beliefs to overcome; difficulties of language and climate. How well the P.D.S.A. did their work is evident to-day in the fact that horses, dogs, cats, camels, cows, sheep, goats, poultry, even tortoises are tended and guarded by the P.D.S.A. in Tangier and its barren outposts.

The Moors, who in 1924 were astonished to learn that each dumb creature has a heart, lungs and stomach, just like a human being, and suffers many of the same diseases, now travel miles to bring their ailing animals to the dispensary. Their gratitude is often touching. A handful of dates, a few tomatoes perhaps, are offered with a blessing for help received, the hands and feet of P.D.S.A. officers are kissed and vows made to pray for the success of the merciful work; vows which are earnestly kept.

The first foreign hospital was opened much later, at Abbassia, on Cairo's outskirts, and a year later a dispensary followed in a poor district of Old Cairo. It was also possible to buy a small first-aid van to tour villages and markets in the desert. Here more difficulties arose. The natives were afraid to bring their animals for treatment. With characteristic determination a member of the staff overcame the trouble in a courageous way. Knowing a little Arabic, he borrowed a camel, dressed himself as an Arab and mixed with the people,

squatting on the ground, chatting and drinking coffee with them. Slowly he completely gained their confidence. Thereafter the first-aid van was hailed with joy.

" LORD DOG DOCTOR "

Meanwhile, an animal-lover in the far-away island of Bali, Dutch East Indies, distressed at the crude wholesale slaughter of the thousands of starving, diseased pariah dogs overrunning the island, sent the P.D.S.A. a cheque which enabled them to begin work on the island. A caravan was bought and humane destruction of the animals begun, together with treatment and teaching.

People soon began to come on foot over the long chain of volcanic mountains and the rushing rivers to bring their animals to the caravan; and the experiences of the caravan officer answering calls for help in the roadless wilderness of the interior, where temperatures often reached 110 degrees in the shade, were frequently hair-raising. The " Lord Dog Doctor " in his " Caravan of Healing," as the Balinese called the P.D.S.A. officer and his caravan, came to be regarded as a worker of miracles, as well he might be considering the circumstances in which the work was successfully carried out.

Nearer home, steps were then taken to help the millions of unfortunate animals among the poor of Paris. A small dispensary was opened near Notre Dame. The story of suffering, want, callousness and ignorance found in Britain's teeming cities was repeated, but soon people were flocking to the dispensary in such great numbers that another centre became imperative.

The second French dispensary was opened at Les Lilas in 1931, and soon it, too, was overcrowded. But this time nothing more could be done, owing to lack of funds, and it was not until 1939 that money left to the P.D.S.A. by a generous American enabled ground to be bought and a splendid hospital to be built in Paris.

ANIMAL WELFARE IN ROMANIA

About this time news reached Mrs. Dickin of the great need for animal welfare work among the peasants of Romania. She was impatient to open a dispensary there, but funds were lacking. As so often happened

Among the P.D.S.A.'s many acts of mercy is the care of animals during quarantine periods. Here is a quarantine dog run.

stable and was tied with its foal to a tree in a temperature of nearly twenty degrees below zero. The animal was on the verge of death from exposure.

Such is the suffering that is being relieved in many parts of the world to-day, despite the fact that both the Romanian centres and Paris hospital were forced to close owing to war damage and international difficulties. The stop in the work is only temporary. When funds permit it will be resumed, for the P.D.S.A. is well accustomed to overcoming difficulties.

During disasters this splendid movement is much in evidence. In blitzed London alone, 7,241 terrified and injured animals were rescued in one week; during the Spanish Civil War, P.D.S.A. staff workers rescued many animals from the chaos of fighting and slaughter, although no P.D.S.A. centres exist in Spain; and thousands of helpless animals are saved and fed during floods and blizzards.

QUEUEING UP FOR TREATMENT

To-day London has twenty-seven permanent dispensaries, including the new Theatreland Dispensary in the cosmopolitan centre of Soho, for which our famous actors and actresses have made themselves personally responsible. Provincial dispensaries are found throughout England, Wales and Scotland, and centres have been opened in South Africa, Japan and Greece. In England there are five fully-equipped animal hospitals, six stray dogs' homes and twenty caravan dispensaries which regularly visit over 200 isolated villages and small towns, and travel up to 200,000 miles in one year.

During 1952, over 162,000 animals, large and small, were helped by the caravan dispensaries alone. Wherever these large cream and blue vans go, their motto " All Animals Treated—All Treatment Free " plain for all to see, queues of men, women and children are waiting with their sick animals in their arms.

Pensioners, whose pets often are their only companions in lonely old age, blind children to whom a dog or a kitten is the most beloved friend in the world, school children, trades-people, housewives—all wait with hope and gratitude for the arrival of the P.D.S.A.'s

when the need arose, a timely gift was received and the P.D.S.A. was able to set to work in yet another country whose language they did not understand.

A small dispensary and a caravan were acquired, and the work was so welcomed by both the people and the authorities that it became possible to open a hospital in Bucharest. High officials gave help and encouragement; King Carol consented to be President of the P.D.S.A. in Romania; and the work received the blessing of the Romanian Greek Church at the official opening of the first dispensary at Moreni, a heartening ceremony attended by the mayor, a police contingent in full uniform, representatives of the army, a number of wealthy residents of Moreni and a great crowd of bare-footed poor people.

The work in Romania was heart-breaking because of the dire poverty of the peasants. One among many thousands of similar cases shows the great need that existed in the country. The caravan, visiting a horse belonging to a peasant family, found the family nearly starving, with barely any clothing. The horse, their only means of support, had no

The P.D.S.A. did valuable work during the war, and many thousands of helpless animals were rescued by staff workers during the blitz. Here is an injured dog being removed on a stretcher from the ruins of a bombed building.

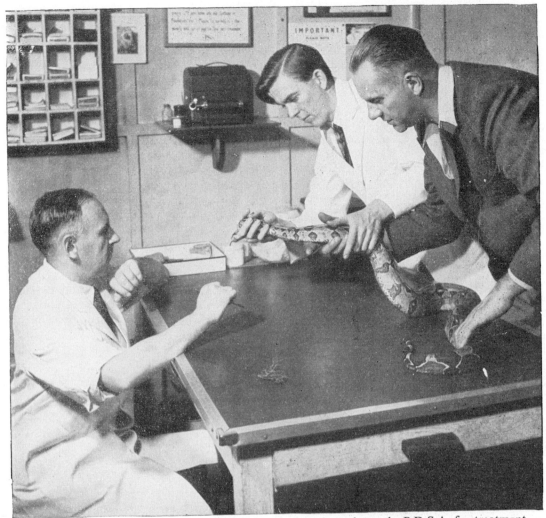

Not only animals but birds, fish, and even snakes, are brought to the P.D.S.A. for treatment. Experts on the staff are constantly extending their veterinary knowledge.

kindly staff and their up-to-date "clinic on wheels" with its medicines, dressings, operating table and other healing equipment. Pleas for more caravan dispensaries are constantly received. More than twice as many motor caravans as the P.D.S.A. owns at present would be needed to meet these urgent requests, so vast, still, is the need for practical help among our dumb friends in Britain alone.

With all these added activities, the second headquarters which Mrs. Dickin acquired in the East End became too small years ago. At that time it was a big step for the P.D.S.A. to buy property and erect buildings, but in 1927

so many cases, especially horses, had to be turned away from the East End premises owing to lack of space that Mrs. Dickin bought the farm near Ilford, Essex, on which the headquarters now stands.

A REST-HOME FOR ANIMALS

In the then quiet countryside, near a little stream, a new sanatorium and offices were built. To-day the roar of main road traffic is not far away, but the sanatorium itself is still like a farm, with its groups of buildings and soft green paddock where weary horses, ponies and donkeys find rest and, often for the first time in their hard-working city lives, crop growing grass. Close to the paddock is a sloping garden, bright with flowers and gleaming white stones. This is the animals' cemetery where many a cherished pet has been laid to rest in a little grave frequently visited and tended by the fond owners.

There is quietly efficient organisation within the homely-looking buildings that comprise headquarters. Here is accommodation for medical and food stores; a pharmacy, out-patients' waiting-room, a forge for making the special shoes needed by horses with hoof trouble; a fully equipped X-ray room; a research laboratory where constant work is carried on to find cures and extend veterinary knowledge, and an anatomical museum.

In the main building is the dressing-room and the small animals' ward, each " bed " having its own chart, like a human hospital. Next door is the splendid operating theatre, its equipment identical to that of modern human operating theatres, with thoughtful innovations such as a heat blanket which keeps the operating table at body temperature so that the patient will suffer less operational shock. Sterilising and anæsthetic rooms adjoin the operating theatre.

The adjacent horse ward is a long airy building divided into roomy stables, each with its clean water-trough and generous supply of sweet hay. And in the large entrance yard are the cream and blue caravans, the ambulances and horse ambulances, all of which have been presented by the generous members of the public.

It will thus be clearly seen that the P.D.S.A. recognises its responsibilities and forgets no detail that will help to make its work as proficient and as speedy as possible in this humane cause.

P.D.S.A. dispensaries and hospitals never close. Day, night, week-ends and holidays, every call for help is answered promptly. At headquarters, house surgeons sleep on the

Emergency treatment is given on the spot to injured animals, as in the case of this dog, which was hurt at the London Docks and received prompt medical attention.

A P.D.S.A. hospital. The dog wears a "ruff" to prevent him scratching his injured ear.

premises, ready for night emergency cases. Through darkness, snow, fog and rain, P.D.S.A. officers find their way to the side of cats, dogs, horses or any animal that is ill, injured or suffering, and sit with them all night if necessary. Many a lonely creature is looked after while its owner is ill; many a child's tears comforted away; many a sorrowful owner cheered, and often helped in a practical way when his own need is desperate.

And all this help is absolutely free. Voluntary contributions alone make it possible.

That so much is being accomplished is due in no small measure to the tireless, unselfish devotion of those who undertake P.D.S.A. work. Theirs is a purpose which can best be summed up by the simple P.D.S.A. policy: To relieve the sufferings of all dumb creatures, due to injury, sickness and ignorance; to feel with them, not merely for them; to share their pain, to be responsible for it.

"THE BUSY BEES"

P.D.S.A. staffs fulfil this purpose daily, but it is the public who make the work possible, and, by no means least, the co-operation of children everywhere. Children's staunch support helps and cheers the P.D.S.A. in many ways. Their enthusiasm led Mrs. Dickin to form the junior branch of the P.D.S.A., known as "The Busy Bees." To-day children of many nations belong to this energetic movement which works so industriously for the welfare of needy animals. They pay a membership fee of 6d., receive a badge, and have their own magazine, the *Busy Bees News*.

The great work which has been accomplished reveals how much there is still be to done.

Many countries have no P.D.S.A. centres at all, many have not enough to help more than a fraction of those who need it; and in Britain a great many areas are still pleading for P.D.S.A. help. It can be given only as funds are forthcoming, and it is the work of Busy Bees and generosity of animal-lovers everywhere which alone can make that possible.

The happy crews of PBK canoes which they have made themselves.

THE THRILL OF CANOEING

IN Britain to-day there are approximately 10,000 canoeists who paddle or sail their craft on rivers, canals, lakes or the sea. Many belong to the thirty-odd clubs which are affiliated to the British Canoe Union. This is the organisation that arranges international canoeing events, such as Olympic Games racing and slalom competitions, on rough waters.

It is quite easy to take up canoeing, and the sport can be very thrilling when rapid rivers are tackled after some experience has been gained on placid canals or quiet waterways. You can hire canoes cheaply along the chief rivers, or they can be sent by arrangement to the river of your choice. At Lechlade, on the upper Thames, the charge is 7s. 6d. per day or £2 per week. Folding canoes may be hired for £6 per month.

Nowadays real enthusiasts build their own craft from easily obtained materials, at a total cost of around £10. The best method is to work on an approved design or plan, which can be bought for a few shillings.

Rigid or folding PBK canoes (named after the designer, Percy Blandford, the K standing for kayak) are recommended. These boats vary in length from eleven to seventeen feet, and have a beam of between twenty-eight inches and thirty-two inches. Several are two-seaters and will carry loads of six hundred pounds upwards. Thus all necessary camping kit may be taken on a cruise, and one becomes independent of hotels or hostels.

Besides the canvas-covered canoes mentioned above, there is the ever popular Canadian type. This is roomier, owing to the absence of a deck, and long-lasting because of its stout cedar-wood hull. Canadian canoes have proved their reliability in the country from which they derive their name, and in France. They are propelled by single-bladed paddles used on one side of the canoe only; whereas all folding lightweight canoes require double-bladed paddles which are dipped alternately in the water on each side of the craft.

RACING IN CANOES

Racing is held annually on the Thames at Bisham, but special kayaks are usually used. The winners need to spend much leisure-time training. Ordinary canoes take part each Easter in the Devizes to Westminster marathon, involving a journey of 124 miles down the Kennet and Avon Canal and the Thames, with seventy-seven portages at locks. The record for this race presently stands at twenty-four hours and seven minutes! Every May there is a fifteen-mile race down the Great Ouse from Bedford. Here, again, numerous locks must be passed.

Slalom is a form of competition over a short course, either on a fast river or below a weir where the water is turbulent. Poles are hung from ropes suspended across the river to form gates. Canoeists must pass through these gates—perhaps a dozen—in the quickest time. Penalties are incurred for touching the gates, some of which have to be negotiated backwards. A dozen slaloms take place every year, the youngest entrants being only fourteen or fifteen years old. The best stretch of water for a slalom is probably on the Tay some miles above Perth, where heavy rapids mean plenty of capsizes, which spectators always enjoy!

Sea canoeing is a splendid form of the sport, but needs careful preparation beforehand, in view of the dangers. The English Channel has been crossed on a number of occasions by canoes, although conditions are treacherous, with short, choppy waves and tidal streams that set strongly. The fastest crossing yet made took four hours and seven minutes.

If you go sea canoeing, you should always be with a companion, preferably somebody experienced. Naturally you must be able to swim. Should you be capsized, it is essential to cling on to your canoe and not leave it in an attempt to swim ashore. It is often possible to right an upturned canoe and climb back on board—over the stern. But with ordinary care you should not capsize, particularly if your craft is well ballasted with plenty of gear.

CALLING OUT THE LIFEBOAT

Special items of equipment are required for

A competitor in a slalom race is guiding his canoe between poles which are suspended from ropes over the water.

paddling in salt-water if extended touring is undertaken. These include distress flares, which cost a shilling or two each and can be burnt to attract attention if the sea turns rough and you desire to be rescued. But don't let them off for fun, otherwise the lifeboat may be called out and you will be presented with a bill for £20!

A bailer is indispensable for your peace of mind, but canoes do not ship much water—they ride easily over the crests of waves. A compass fits conveniently to the cockpit coaming and is doubly valuable if luminous, for night canoeing is sometimes possible in settled weather.

A spare paddle is absolutely essential: if you had only one and that broke or was swept away you would be utterly helpless. A spray-cover to keep waves out of the cockpit is also vital. This must be lightly attached, however, so that you can free yourself instantly if a heavy sea bowls you over. In such an eventuality, the eskimo roll, if properly performed, will bring you to the surface still in the cockpit.

Every spring, classes are held in London swimming baths for those wishing to master the technique. It is certainly a useful accomplishment to be able to lever the paddle when one is submerged in such a way as to restore the canoe to its normal position on the surface.

Now a few words about the hazards of sea canoeing. Shipping lanes and busy estuaries should be avoided, owing to the risk of being run down by another craft or upset by its bow wave.

Rocky coasts are extremely treacherous with confused swells rebounding from the shore; therefore keep a reasonable distance from the land. It is preferable to go canoeing near a low-lying shore with flat beaches. Steep beaches near cliffs are distinctly dangerous landing-places, because such conditions invariably produce strong undertows that could suck you below the surface.

WHEN IN DOUBT, ASK A FISHERMAN

Never start when an off-shore wind is blowing, or you may be carried out to sea: wind has a big effect on a canoe, since most of it is above the water. Incidentally, few canoes need more than four inches to float. Ask local fishermen about any dangers in the locality. They are usually helpful, and like putting you wise. They will warn you of sunken wrecks, tide rips, overfalls (disturbance of water through tide passing over uneven sea-bed), irregular tides, and any jagged reefs that ought to be avoided at all costs.

Remember you must always know the whereabouts of the nearest safe landing-beaches, in case the weather suddenly worsens, and you have to come ashore. A surf-ridden beach offers a grand challenge to the canoeist attempting to land. Experts often come in stern first, checking the speed of their craft as each wave surges past, then jumping out in the shallows and dragging their boat through the foam to dry land. Split seconds make all the difference between a successful landing and a capsize.

The most exciting part for sea canoeing is undoubtedly along the western seaboard of Scotland, where basking sharks provide an additional hazard! Here are hundreds of fascinating islands teeming with bird life, many being uninhabited. Sheltered harbours on England's south coast offer a more leisurely holiday, with peaceful Cornish bays as the " Mecca " of many canoeists.

CANOEING ON CANALS

Inland cruising has infinite variety. Canoeing on canals is indeed a fine way of seeing the countryside. Of course, charges are payable on a mileage basis (minimum 3s.) to the Docks and Inland Waterways Board. But cheap season tickets can reduce this expense. Some

The canoe in the picture awaits the filling of the lock before being able to proceed.

canals lead one through lovely scenery, especially the Shropshire Union and Kendal Canals, and the " summit level " of the Leeds and Liverpool Canal, which crosses the Pennines in Yorkshire.

The main advantages of canals are that landings can always be made easily, and the canoeist need never get out of his craft and wade. Also, they are quite safe for beginners; and it is great fun working the locks and talking to the bargees and their families.

LAKE CANOEING

Lake canoeing is another alternative. This

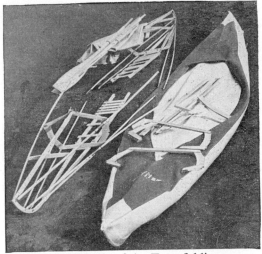

Here are the parts of the Tyne folding canoe partly assembled. This is a 15 ft. two-seater, which can be fully assembled in an hour.

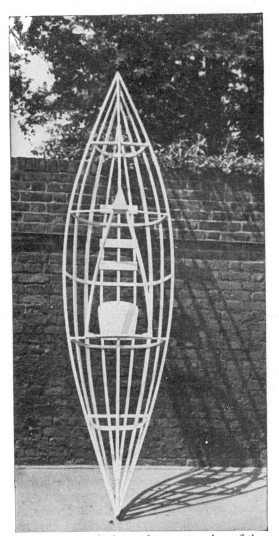

This photograph shows the construction of the framework of a rigid eleven foot single canoe of the Tyne Kit type.

is extremely pleasant, provided no strong winds arise. It is not really hard work if sails and leeboards are fitted. An inflated tube can be attached round the gunwale to minimise the chance of an upset. Thus launched on a sparkling lake, one may feel all the thrills of dinghy sailing. Scottish lochs, such as Lomond and Awe, will be found suitable for canoe sailing; while Bala Lake in Wales is another good place. In England, we have the Norfolk Broads and the lakes in Cumberland— Windermere, Ullswater, etc., all perfect playgrounds for canoes.

JOINING A CANOE CLUB

Although canoeing is emphatically an individual sport, you will derive vast benefit from joining a club. The Canoe-Camping Club is the largest, and issues a quarterly magazine, *The Canoe-Camper*, containing articles describing actual trips, and giving information on all aspects of the sport. Club members have access to a well-stocked library of canoeing books, and may purchase detailed itineraries of rivers; their insurance can be effected at reduced rates; and they attend meets or rallies in summer and film shows in winter. Attractive badges and pennants are available. This club is organised into local groups which arrange activities for the benefit of those living in the different areas. Other clubs include the Manchester Canoe Club, which specialises in rough rivers, and our oldest, the Royal C.C., founded in 1867.

CRUISING DOWN THE RIVER

The majority of canoeists believe that river cruising is the best form of their sport. They mostly use folding canoes, which can be assembled within an hour and dismantled in half that time. These consist of a skin or hull of rubberised fabric, with canvas deck sewn on. The framework of wooden rods slips neatly inside the hull and locks firmly into position. These craft are very steady on the water, and unlikely to overturn unexpectedly, since their centre of gravity is below the water-line. However, it is advisable to fix inflated bladders below decks at bow and stern, to give buoyancy in case of accidents. Lifebelts may also be carried for this purpose—or a big supply of ping-pong balls!

Folding canoes, when dismantled, are packed into two bags that can be taken on bus or train as passenger's luggage without extra charge. This portability is of enormous help, if one desires to visit many different waterways, while a stowage problem at home does not exist; the bags go under the stairs or in a cupboard. Nowadays folding canoes are rather expensive: they cost from £20 to £50, including all extras such as spray-cover (to keep the cockpit dry) and keel-strip (reinforced rubber material to give extra strength along the keel). However, second-hand bargains are often advertised in Club magazines.

Next to the paddle, the most vital piece of equipment is the two-wheeled collapsible trolley. This costs £2 and is essential for portaging the canoe on land past uncanoeable obstacles, such as steep weirs or dangerous rapids. Also, it comes in handy for transporting the dismantled canoe in its bags from station to river.

STOCKING THE CANOE

Other things needed on a canoe trip include a repair outfit in case you get holed; water-proof bags for spare clothing; suitable containers for food; maps (ordnance survey series are best); cooking utensils; small pressure stove and paraffin; kitbags and haversacks to hold full camping equipment—tent, sleeping bag, etc. And, of course, personal luggage, camera and ample rations. Regarding eatables,

dried foods such as prunes, apricots, porridge oats, and the like, are less bulky than tinned goods, and should, therefore, be carried whenever possible.

Canoe cruising is a specially pleasant hobby because it can be combined with other hobbies—bird-watching, drawing, photography, etc. And it can be adapted to suit individual requirements. You may paddle a few miles each day and linger in places of interest; or you can cover a considerable distance—thirty miles daily is perfectly possible. Average speed for canoes on rivers is three miles an hour, but this depends on the frequency of portages. With a weir every couple of miles you would be lucky to manage half this distance in a full day's canoeing.

You can choose whether to venture on easy, moderate or difficult rivers. Let us briefly survey Britain's canoeable rivers with reference to this broad classification. It should be remembered that most non-tidal rivers are private, and canoeing is therefore a privilege rather than a right. But land-owners generally do not object.

Canalised rivers, known as " navigations," are not private. An example of this type of waterway is the Weaver Navigation in Cheshire. The Wey in Surrey is another. Certain large rivers, such as Wye and Severn, are also open through boats having established rights-of-way throughout the ages—in fact, ever since the ancient Britons came down them in their coracles.

EXPLORING A RIVER

Our longest rivers all give over a hundred miles of eminently canoeable water. The Thames is an obvious first choice, from Lechlade to London (150 miles); the Severn from Welshpool to Gloucester (133 miles); the Trent from Stone, Staffs, to its junction with the Humber (150 miles); and the Great Ouse from Buckingham to King's Lynn (147 miles). Each of these long rivers takes about a week to explore by canoe, and the journeys are well worth while. Camp sites are always easy to find, except on the lower parts of the Thames as you approach the built-up areas.

Other easy rivers are the Medway between Tonbridge and Rochester, taking you through the delightful hop-growing districts; the Nene in Northamptonshire, but this has many

A canoe on the river Wharfe in Yorkshire. The Wharfe can be canoed for seventy miles of its course, but care must be taken in rocky stretches like this.

portages at old locks; the Evenlode, Loddon and Cherwell, all tributaries of Thames; and the Kentish Stour, which is possible for twenty miles from Canterbury to the old Cinque port of Sandwich.

In the category of moderate rivers, we have the Teme, which offers canoeists a seventy-miles trip as far as its junction with the Severn near Worcester; the lower parts of Wear, Tees and Tyne, all in the north-east and not much visited; some of the Yorkshire rivers including the Ouse and Derwent; the Exe, which goes south from the high ground of Exmoor in Devon. Dart and Tamar in the same county are reputed to be too awkward for canoeing, as they become very shallow in summer dry spells.

SHOOTING THE RAPIDS

Difficult rivers are a challenge to the adventurous, and it is fine sport tackling the tumult of their rapids. Some seem so severe that they must inevitably swamp or smash any small canoe. But the little craft can give a good account of themselves, and will stand up to lashing waves and heavy rapids without being stove in. It is incredible the way they bounce off boulders like a rubber ball. Rarely is any damage incurred, and then it is something minor like a fractured strut.

Extra care is necessary on fast, rock-strewn rivers. Lifebelts must be worn, and you should not attempt any rapids beyond your cabability. If in doubt, always portage or let the canoe drift down on the end of the painter, while you walk along the bank. It is advisable to stop and prospect all awkward stretches of river before descending them. A member of the party can helpfully be stationed lower downstream, while you attempt a rough rapid: then in the event of a capsize, he will be able to assist quickly with the salvage operations.

All rapid mountain-born rivers rise suddenly after rain, and conditions vary enormously from day to day. The British Canoe Union's *Guide to the Waterways of the British Isles* is a comprehensive book listing many such rivers, and gives advice for negotiating them. No serious canoeist travels without this valuable publication.

TRICKY RIVERS

Britain's difficult rivers are found in Scotland, Wales and the North of England: in other words, where there are mountains. Foremost are Tay, Dee and Spey. The Tay's course through Perthshire is amazingly beautiful, and it carries a great volume of water. "Highland" Dee gives the toughest canoe run in the country, forty-five miles of racing current from Ballater to Aberdeen with turbulent rapids enough to make the boldest tremble. The Spey is regarded as Scotland's fastest river and is canoeable for sixty miles from Aviemore to the Sea at Spey Bay.

Welsh rivers are smaller but decidedly tricky. Usk, Teifi and Dee are wild horses which can only be ridden by experts. Sometimes their beds are so boulder-strewn that no clearly-defined deep channel is apparent. Overhanging trees provide additional dangers, and the touring canoeist must constantly be on the *qui vive*. But one gets a deep satisfaction from conquering these rivers by coming down them in a canoe, with the feeling of being an explorer in unknown regions.

Fifty years ago, William Bliss paddled down all these rough rivers in his Canadian canoe, and several books about his experiences are widely read to-day. *Canoeing* outlines many trips possible, including a round tour of over 800 miles, using canals as connecting links between rivers; *The Heart of England by Waterway* describes in fine language both canal and river canoeing; *Rapid Rivers*, now unfortunately out of print, inspires in the reader the urge to paddle such exciting rivers as the Ribble, Lune and Wharfe.

Modern literature includes the *Canoe Errant* series by Raven Hart, who has paddled folding canoes 15,000 miles in many countries such as Burma, Egypt and Australia; the first post-war book, *Canoeing To-day*, by P. W. Blandford, is a concise beginner's guide to the elements of the sport; and *The Book of Canoeing* by Ellis is a favourite.

THE QUEEN OF ENGLISH RIVERS

Besides the rivers already mentioned, two others deserve to be drawn to your notice— the two best! The Hereford Wye takes you through the famous "Wye Valley" and is known as "The Queen of English Rivers": you can follow it for a hundred miles from Glasbury to Chepstow. That great salmon river in Cumberland, the Eden, provides a picturesque run (in one part through a gorge) and has fast, clear water all the way, with a three-mile stretch containing the testing Nunnery rapids that extend from Kirkoswald to Armathwaite. Yes, our English Eden gives a really sporting run, and to conquer it is a feather in any canoeist's cap.

The canoeist above is tackling a fast-flowing Perthshire river, in Scotland. The great thrill of canoeing is the mastery of rapid and rock-strewn rivers.

Seventy feet long, and with a long neck and small head and brain, the Brontosaurus once roamed the earth, long before the days of man.

THE WORLD THAT WAS
—And How it is made to Live Again

NO one need sit down and weep—as we are told Alexander the Great once did—because there are no more worlds to conquer. We are conquering new worlds daily. The world of germs and diseases is giving way before the patient work of doctors and the men who study bacteria. Before long all the make-believe stories of space will be regarded as rather feeble fairy tales, for someone will actually reach a star and give us facts instead of fiction.

And amongst all these new worlds is a very old one . . . the world of the remote past. People are no longer content to regard fossils as just curiosities, or the remains of giants and dragons. They want to know what sort of plants and animals they really represent, and how such creatures possibly behaved. For of course fossils are always in the making, and some of the animals and plants alive to-day may be in fossil collections half a million years hence.

There is one branch of science called Palæontology (a Greek word meaning a talk about old things) and its job is to piece together the remote past, and from fossils build up a living picture of days of long ago.

SEARCHING FOR FOSSILS

A modern fossil-collecting expedition can be a very elaborate affair when organised by a great museum. Its personnel will include not only scientists, but artists, photographers, museum modellers, and skilled miners and engineers to gather fossilised plants and beasts from the rocks with pick and shovel, and blasting powder. A whole fleet of lorries may be needed to transport this little army of scientific workers.

The treasures they bring home certainly look a little dull at times, just rows and rows of queerly-shaped rock. Little by little a picture grows, and models can be made and the scene set for these museum pictures. As a rule these three-dimensional museum pictures, or dioramas, are scale models, say an inch to the foot. But in the New York Museum, and the Field Museum of Chicago, there are models, and wall paintings made life-size, and it is very impressive to see Dinosaurs and Giant Sloths towering in their glass cases above the visitors.

The top picture shows a part of the Sussex Weald as it must have appeared between forty and a hundred and seventy million years ago. How science arrives at the time is too long a story to tell here, but it is possible nowadays to " date " very roughly the various rock layers. So here we have a picture of what is now peaceful agricultural Sussex as it was in the days of the Dinosaurs. From fossils we know it must once have been tropical or sub-tropical. This is proved by the plants, many of which still live in warmer climates. There were tree ferns and screw pines, horse-tails of the sort we see in damp ditches, but much larger, and all kinds of flowering shrubs.

FINDING FOSSIL FOOTPRINTS

As for the animals, we not only have complete skeletons of many species, but even fossil footprints and other marks on rocks which were once sand or mud, showing just how the animals behaved. In the foreground is a huge but harmless plant-eating Dinosaur, standing twelve feet high when on its hind-legs, and about thirty feet long from nose to tail tip. Fossil markings on the rocks tell us it walked on its hind-legs, but could squat like a kangaroo. When it walked it must have swung its tail from side to side in order to keep its balance, just as does a duck, or the living frilled lizard of Australia, which often runs on its hind legs. Birds and reptiles, after all, are very closely related. Both lay eggs—and feathers are only scales split up. And we know, too, that this Dinosaur was a vegetarian by its blunt, rather horsey teeth. An animal's teeth are very largely the key to its way of life.

At this period of the world's history there were also many other kinds of Dinosaur, besides turtles as big as billiard tables, great serpentine lizards, fifty feet long, flying lizards twenty feet across the wings, and the first true birds, about as large as fowls, and many more we have not had space to show.

STRANGE CREATURES OF THE SEA

In the lower picture is portrayed a piece of the sea floor as it must have looked during the last days of the Dinosaurs. If you walk along the rocks at low tide between Black Rock, Brighton, and Newhaven you will see shells just like those to the left of the picture.

Some of the prehistoric shells were about four feet across. As you see, each contains a strange-looking beast like an octopus swimming backwards at a great pace, just as the octopus does by blowing water out of its siphon pipe, a sort of jet propulsion.

It may seem rather bold of the model-maker to assume all this from fossil shells. But these shells are very like those of the pearly nautilus, a cousin of the octopus, and still abundant in the warm Pacific Ocean. So the scientists were not just taking a chance, after all. On the right is a fish exactly like the Coelacanth, that has been only lately found very much alive in deep water off the coast of Africa. And below the Coelacanth are glass-rope sponges, sea urchins, and other strange creatures not to be found in the shallow but chilly waters of what is now the English Channel.

Here then are two true pictures of a world that has vanished for ever. And how much more exciting than row upon row of lumps of queerly-shaped rock labelled with long, and not always easy to say, scientific names. Yet it is all sound fact, patiently built up by patient study, not only of fossils, but of living forms most nearly related to those now extinct. For the more we can get to know about the plants and animals around us, the better can we understand the fossilised remains of those that have had their day.

MODEL-MAKING AS A HOBBY

Model-making is one of the most popular hobbies, as anyone who has been to the Model-Makers' Exhibition, or the Schoolboys' Exhibition, held once a year in London, will agree. And if one has the good fortune to be at a school which owns a museum, model-making is fairly certain to be encouraged.

Though the two pictures shown may at first seem rather beyond the powers of a school museum, this is far from being the true state of affairs.

First of all, the glass cases are well within the scope of any carpentry class. As for the rest, let us take the Dinosaur landscape, from front to back.

The Dinosaur in the foreground is made of paper. First you make a model of the beast in plasticine or modelling clay, and from this you take a plaster mould. The mould is in

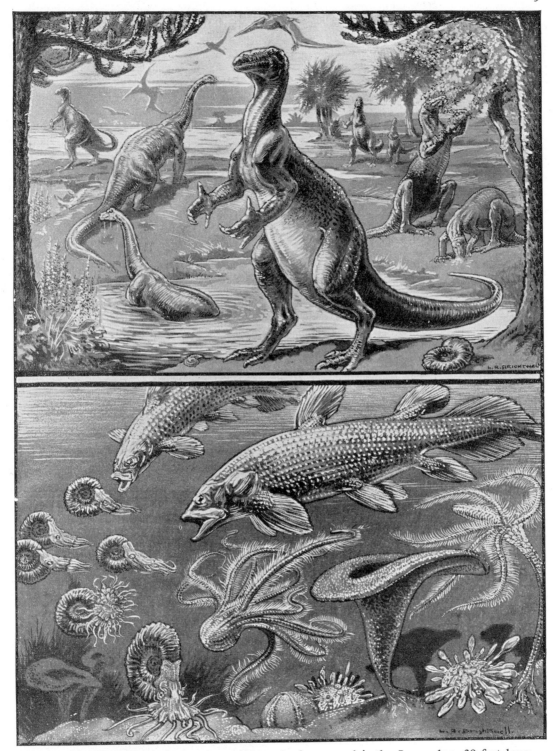

Life in Britain 80,000,000 years ago. Above in foreground is the Iguanodon, 30 feet long. Behind are other dinosaurs, while pterodactyls fly above. Below coelacanths are chasing ammonites. Coelacanths have been found recently in African waters, though long believed extinct.

A model of the Iguanodon—a gigantic lizard.

was in charge of the model-making studios attached to the New York Natural History Museum (the finest in the world to-day) a lady called Mary Cynthia Dickerson. On one occasion it was required to model a newt in the act of casting its skin. Presently a snag arose, how to suggest the old dry skin peeling off in shreds. No one could think of the right thing, for this was before cellophane and other plastics were in general use. Then Miss Dickerson thought of using some scraps of onion skin . . . and the problem was solved.

Model-making is like that. Cellophane, perspex, all the patent modelling substances such as plasticine and barbola, paper, string, paste, glue, beads, wire and coloured tinsels, all go to the making of museum models. The tools and materials are not expensive. The most important things are ingenuity, imagination and patient research in other museums and libraries, for of course one must make sure of one's facts. In making casts start with simple things like fishes and shells. Practice and experience that come from experimenting are more than half the battle.

In this business of making museum models there enters all the fun of stage craft, and stage property men are perhaps the most ingenious and undefeatable of all people. Moreover, in building museum groups you will realise as never before the wonderful panorama of plant and animal life that has passed across this world of ours, a tiny speck of solid substance spinning in the as yet unexplored vastness of interplanetary space.

sections and made by first greasing the model, to prevent the plaster sticking, and then putting on a fairly thick layer of plaster of Paris. When the plaster is set hard, you lift it off, in its sections, and there is your mould.

Next you make the cast; this is simple. Once more greasing with vaseline the inside of each section of the mould, you line it with about three layers of tissue paper and flour paste, with a final layer of newspaper, by way of stiffening. The best way to do this is to tear up the paper into half-crown-sized pieces.

When it is all quite dry (putting it not too near a fire will help) you will find each section springs out of the mould, and your pieces of Dinosaur are then joined together with more paper and paste. The artists in your school then get busy with paints and brushes, and some wire in the beast's legs, and glue on the soles of his feet will fix him securely to the mud bank made of brown paper and flour paste.

USING YOUR INGENUITY

The trees on either side can also be built of paper, and they will not only help to date the scene, but hide where the back cloth (more work for your artists) is fitted in. Remember there is no golden rule in making museum groups, any more than there is in making stage scenery, or some of those amazing and seemingly impossible scenes which delight us at almost any picture theatre. Anything and everything is fair . . . if it helps you to get the effect you are after. Some years ago there

A model of the Ostrich-mimic dinosaur.

HIGH ADVENTURE
The Thrill Of Climbing

WALKING along a knife-like ridge, with the scree slopes falling away a thousand feet on either side; inching up a narrow crack in a vertical rock face with the long thin rope snaking down behind you; or standing magnificently poised on the steep white slopes of a winter gully, your ice-axe sending splinters hissing down—if these appeal to you, if you love the freedom of high crags and the adventures of climbing, then you have the makings of a mountaineer.

Fell-walking, rock-climbing, and ice-work are the three branches of mountain craft which it is necessary to learn before you can be called a mountaineer, but in Britain, because our mountains are easily accessible and are free from snow in the summer, many climbers concentrate on just one or two of these crafts; usually fell-walking and rock-climbing. When it comes to Alpine mountaineering, however, snow and ice-craft become of supreme importance.

FELL-WALKING

Fell-walking is the best way for you to begin a mountaineering career. By walking and scrambling across rough country it teaches you the general layout of mountains and how to tackle features such as scree and bog. It also gives you experience of mist, and an opportunity to put your map and compass to good use.

Although there is nothing to prevent a large party of friends from undertaking a fell-walking holiday together, the sport is best done in pairs. Two people get along better than ten, and generally obtain more real enjoyment from the holiday. Of course, if an experienced fell-walker is willing to accompany you, so much the better, because by

93

Climbing the Cobbler, an example of a climb
that looks difficult but is really quite simple.

watching him in action you will quickly learn
the tricks of the trade. There is no reason to
be afraid of going with another novice, however. You will have a lot of fun and adventure,
provided you remember to *keep away from
crags at all times* and to try and avoid mists
until you are expert with map and compass.

Your equipment for the trip need not be
costly. The essentials are nailed boots and
a framed rucksack, to which might be added
map and compass, cape, wind-proof clothing,
and first-aid kit.

Since all our mountains lie in the northern
half of the country train fares are the greatest
cost to a mountaineer living in the south. The
excellent Youth Hostels, of which there are
many in the mountains, reduce the total cost,
however, and all young mountaineers should
join the Y.H.A. The best areas for beginners
to walk in are the Lakes and North Wales,
and these two regions also provide exciting
walks for the more advanced craftsman: the
Snowdon horse-shoe and the Scafell ring, being
examples of fine traverses. Skye offers more
to the experienced fell-walker who knows

something of rock-technique. For those who
hope to go on the Continent, Norway and the
Pyrenees are just two of the many good fell-
walking areas.

ROCK-CLIMBING

After a little fell-walking you will probably
become fascinated by the many magnificent
crags which are to be seen amongst the mountains, and you may even feel tempted to "have
a go" at one of them. Remember the advice
of the experts: *never climb alone.*

When you feel ready to tackle the crags,
persuade an experienced friend to lead you up
a few of the easier climbs, or if that is not
possible, then join a climbing club, of which
there are many. If there is an age limit to
your local club then simply go on storing up
fell-walking experience until you are old enough
to join.

There are several mountaineering courses
available for young people to-day, the best
known being those run by the Outward Bound

Scottish mountains in winter require considerable care when they are snowed over
and the rocks glazed with ice. The three small
figures, near the summit of the crest of the
Aonach Eagach ridge, Glen Coe, are all
experienced mountaineers.

Dangerous ground! A snow cornice overhanging the north corrie of Ben Lui. Wind causes the snow to pile up over these north-facing edges, and climbers who choose gullies often have to cut their way over a bulge to gain the summit.

Schools at Eskdale and Patterdale in the Lake District.

THE NECESSARY EQUIPMENT

A rock-climber needs to pay particular attention to two items of his equipment: his boots and his rope.

Climbers argue about the nailing of boots as much as fishermen do about bait! For all but the most specialised climbing the best type of boot is one which fits snugly over *two* pairs of thick socks without restricting the toes, and is nailed around the edge with *clinkers* and in the sole with *muggers*. *Tricounis*, nails which look like little saws, are vital in the Alps, but not really necessary for a beginner on British rocks, and this also applies to the rubber type " Commando " or " Vibram " climbing sole which can be seen in the shops.

On your wanderings in the mountains you will probably notice that many rock-climbers use gym-shoes to climb in. These give a better grip on most types of dry rock than do

boots, but they do not teach the proper use of *balance*, which is the secret of all good climbing, and unless you intend to become a rock specialist (in which case you will meet climbs where you *have* to use rubbers) they are best avoided.

Rope, that other essential for rock-climbing, is either manila or nylon, and can be obtained in three thicknesses up to 120 ft. in length. Because its stretch is greater and it is easier to manage, nylon is now regarded as the better of the two, and the novice, having decided that he likes rock-climbing, should buy 100 ft. of full-weight nylon rope. This will be quite adequate for all but the most severe British climbs.

It is surprising the number of people outside of climbing who still think that the rope is more of a danger than a help. " Surely," they argue, " if one falls off he will pull the others off with him." On the contrary; if one falls off the others will hold him. This is how it works.

Cutting steps in hard-frozen snow on the snow-cornice of Ben Lui. Careful positioning of steps is necessary to preserve the balance on such steep ground.

THE USE OF THE ROPE

Three climbers have reached the foot of their intended climb, and begin roping up. The most experienced man assumes the responsibility of *leader*, at the front end of the rope, so to speak. Next comes the least experienced —he makes up the middleman or *second*, and finally at the rear comes No. 3.

The crag which they face can be seen to be split by fissures and ledges into numerous stages, and the party will attack each stage, called a *pitch*, in turn.

The leader sets off and climbs the first pitch. When he reaches his ledge or stance he loops the rope around a convenient spike of rock and fastens it to his waistline in such a manner that he is securely fastened to the rock. This is called a *belay*. The second then begins to climb and the leader coils in the rope. You will see that if the second falls he cannot pull his leader off the stance because of the belay.

The second, in turn, repeats the act for No. 3 and then proceeds to pay out the rope as his leader starts on the second pitch. The second is still belayed.

A little thought will show you that a second

or No. 3 can never fall more than the length of the rope between himself and the man above. The leader, on the other hand, can fall *twice* the distance between himself and his second. That is one good reason why the leader should be experienced!

Rock-climbs are graded according to their " toughness ": EASY, MODERATE, DIFFICULT, VERY DIFFICULT, SEVERE, VERY SEVERE. A good climber is generally one who has worked his way *gradually* through this list over a number of years.

WINTER MOUNTAINEERING

For mountaineering abroad ice technique is of great importance and some practice in the use of the ice-axe and in judging snow conditions can be obtained in our own islands, usually around Easter. Scotland is the best centre, particularly Ben Nevis, but before you tackle winter mountaineering make sure that you are completely familiar with mountains and can use your map and compass accurately, because a winter expedition on British

An expert rock climber on a steep and exposed climb, calling for delicate grace and bold leadership on small holds. Note downward pressure by the left hand preserving balance.

Climbing Tubkal Arête, highest peak in the Atlas mountains, 13,671 ft.

Climbing one of the last great problems of Scotland. A picture taken on the first ascent of the Dalness Chasm, when its final 1,000 feet went to a strong party of climbers. Note the belay on the right. There is a similar one on the left, so that if the leader falls he will be held in mid-air. The rope on the right is threaded through a spike driven into the rock. Pioneering a new route, especially a difficult one, is the greatest reward in mountaineering.

mountains can be more severe than an Alpine climb on account of the weather and the short hours of daylight.

WHERE TO CLIMB IN BRITAIN

Rock-climbing is concentrated mainly in Scotland, North Wales, and the Lake District, although there are a few outcrops in other places such as Helsby, Cheshire. Each district has climbs for novice and expert alike, Tryfan being particularly good for beginners. For more expert climbers, Lliwedd, Gimmer, and Scafell Buttress have their own attractions.

Books will help you on your way, but the real way to become a mountaineer is to go to the mountains as often as possible.

W.W.N.   D

THE FORMATION OF THE STARS

*In the beginning God created the heaven and the earth. And the earth was without form, and void;
and darkness was upon the face of the deep. . . .*

Genesis.

NO FICTION is as fantastic as the truth of the Universe. The mere existence of the great galaxies with their countless millions of stars, and of the planets of our own Sun and probably of many others as well, is splendour enough, but even this pales beside stories of their creation.

Astronomers of the world to-day hold two main theories about the origin of the heavens: one, that the Universe has always been in existence and the other, that there was a beginning to everything.

Comparing the two theories, it is not only rather difficult to imagine everything having been in existence since time began, but scientists have, with their modern instruments, detected signs that strongly indicate that there was indeed a beginning—and not an impossibly long time ago. Our study of the stars indicates that our own galaxy—the huge group of stars which we call the Milky Way, of which the Sun is a member—came into being at some definite period in the past. And, not only does there seem to have been a definite beginning to the history of the galaxies, there also seems to have been a definite place.

THE MOVEMENT OF THE GALAXIES

One of many strange facts indicated by modern instruments is that the Universe seems to be expanding, that is, the galaxies are moving away from each other at enormous speeds. This does not mean that the stars of the individual galaxies are moving away from each other, it is the space between the galaxies that is getting larger. The effect is similar to that produced if a number of small balls are stuck to a balloon which is then inflated. As the balloon inflates, each ball will move away from its neighbour as the rubber between them stretches.

Now, what makes us think that all these galaxies are moving away from each other in this manner? If a ray of light from a star in one of these distant galaxies is passed through a prism it produces the familiar band of colours known as a spectrum. This by itself is what is expected but what has been noticed is that each band is moved towards the red end of the spectrum. Known as the " red shift," this indicates that the source of light is moving away from us.

This effect can, perhaps, be best explained as being similar to the familiar change in the note of a sound as it moves either towards or away from you. You probably know how the sound of a train whistle seems to rise as it approaches and fall as it moves away. The reason for this is that as the engine approaches the sound waves are compressed and shortened by the movement of the train, thus raising its pitch. As it moves away the waves are stretched out, resulting in a lowering of the pitch.

In the same way light waves from something moving towards you are compressed towards the blue, or short-wave-length, end of the spectrum, whilst those from something moving away stretch out towards the red or long-wave-length of the spectrum. Thus, because the light from the galaxies is stretched towards the red end of the spectrum, it is deduced that they must be moving away from us.

Nor is this all. Not only are they all moving away from us, but those farthest away have the biggest movement towards the red end of the spectrum, indicating the highest speed.

THE ORIGIN OF THE GALAXIES

Yet another surprise awaits us, for if the outward rush of the galaxies is accepted, and one assumes their direction and speeds to have remained unaltered during the æons of time they have been travelling, then the indications are that they all started from the same *place*. And calculations, made from their present estimated distances and speeds, indicate they all started at the same time, about 5,000 million years ago.

Andromeda—twin sister of the Milky Way and our closest neighbour in intergalactic space. The light which we now see from this galaxy started its journey thousands of years ago.

In other words, all the most up-to-date clues point to a time of creation when the cosmic fires were lit and the Universe as we know it came into being.

The galaxies, then, seem to have originated from a single, super-colossal explosion. An American Professor, Dr. G. Gamow, has suggested that perhaps in the beginning of time all the matter and radiation in the entire Universe was squeezed together in a dreadful inferno of fire and flame. The density of the mass would have been incredible with the temperature raging in the billions of degrees. Then, at the supreme moment, the stupendous mass of matter exploded with awful force, the debris of which we can still see—after 5,000 million years!

As the vast mass of gas swirled outwards into space, it gradually cooled. And, as it cooled, the force of gravitation was able to form immense clouds in which the stars condensed. The galaxies were dark at first, but gradually the stars were born to shine across the void.

THE LIGHT OF THE STARS

Astronomers using the big 200-inch telescope on Mount Palomar have been responsible for gathering much of the information on which this theory is based. The task has not been made simpler by the fact that we see the outer galaxies by light which started off on its journey thousands of millions of years ago, and the inner ones by light emitted a few million years only ago. Thus, when an astronomer looks outwards into space he views the outer galaxies not where they are now, for during the time their light has been journeying to Earth, they will have moved thousands of millions of miles from their visible positions. Because their light was emitted at an early stage of their development astronomers see the outer galaxies not as they are now, but as they were long before life stirred on Earth. The inner galaxies, however, because of their comparative nearness, are being viewed at a much more advanced age as their light does not take so long to reach us. The effect of this great age difference has to be taken into account when formulating the grand theory of the creation of the Universe.

The American theory is considerably more cheerful than older theories which envisaged the stars as a fixed number of huge bonfires slowly but surely burning themselves out, in that it assumes the formation of new galaxies and stars from the immense amount of space-dust that seems to fill the void between galaxies. This dust has been estimated to contain more matter than all the stars put together.

But, according to the American theory, there will still ultimately come a time in the dim and far distant future when the last dust cloud will condense into the last star. Then, with no gas to make new stars, the Universe will indeed slowly burn itself to ashes. One by one stars will cool and go out. Slowly the Universe would run down to become dead, dark and bitterly cold. Even though this will not happen for many thousands of millions of years the ultimate fate of the universe envisaged, bringing with it an end to Man if he survives as long, is not a happy one.

THE NEW COSMOLOGY

Another theory which is gaining considerable support has been popularly explained by Fred Hoyle, famous broadcaster and astronomer.

According to this New Cosmology, as this new theory is called, the galaxies did not appear in one awful explosion, but have always existed in the Universe.

What is thought to happen is that, as the space between the galaxies stretches—both theories are in agreement on this—so matter is being continually *created*. One moment there is nothing, the next a hydrogen atom has appeared. Hydrogen is the basic material of which the Universe is made and in time this continual process produces space-dust from which first a tenuous gas, then a cloud and finally the stars condense to form a galaxy. As one galaxy dies out, so at the other end of the cosmic time scale new matter appears to form a new one. Thus, the Universe is in a state of continuous creation. It has been since time began and will endure as long as time itself.

According to the American theory, in time the Universe as far as we are concerned will become emptied of galaxies—they will disappear from our sight. The New Cosmology theory agrees that the galaxies we now see will have disappeared from view in about 10,000 million years. But, an astronomer living then will still be able to see about the same number of galaxies as we do now. New galaxies will have condensed out of the background material at just the rate to compensate for those which are passing beyond the limit of our vision.

Although Hoyle's theory contradicts important parts of Gamow's and in some ways seems less feasible, because it foresees no end

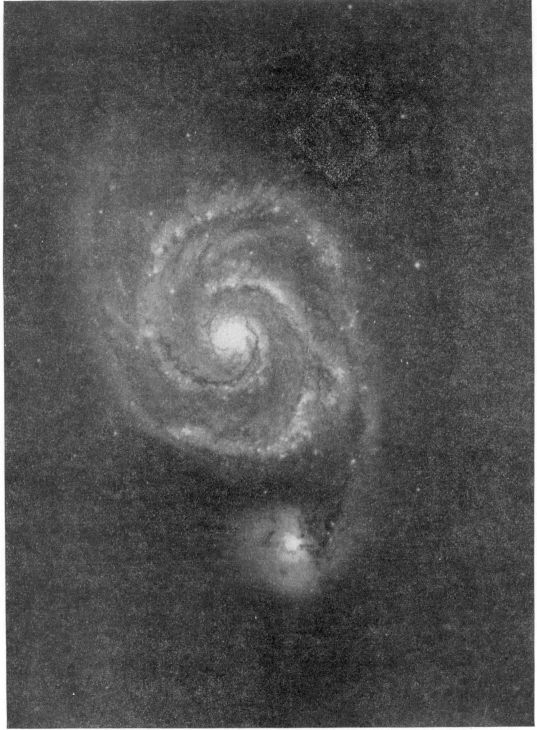

Shaped like a gigantic Catherine-wheel, the spiral nebula in Canes Venatica is only one of the countless thousands of galaxies that can be seen. Each galaxy, in the same way as our own, contains millions of stars and each is thought to have condensed out of the immense clouds of gas which are present in the depths of space.

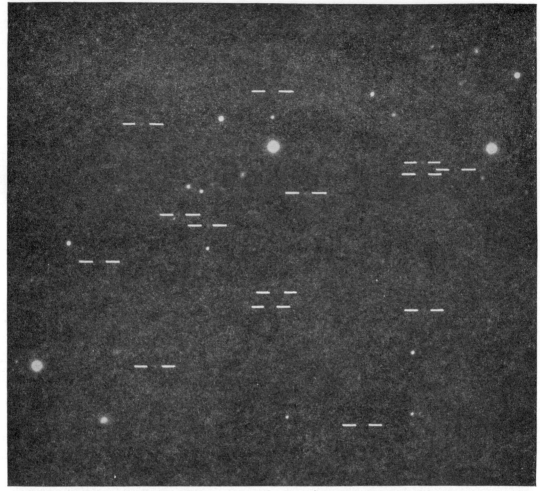

The dots of light showing between the gauge lines in the photographic plate took 2,000 million years on their journey to the Earth. They are the farthest galaxies we can see.

to the evolution of Mankind it is a much happier explanation.

A CHANGE OF OPINION

As far as the birth of the Earth is concerned, it was for long thought that it and other planets originated as bits of material torn or thrown out of the Sun, but two main factors have since caused a change of opinion. First of all, the planets rotate at an average distance of many hundreds of millions of miles from the Sun and it is difficult to imagine how the necessary material could have been thrown out so far. Secondly, if the planets came from the Sun one would expect them to be made of similar materials and this is very definitely not so. The vast bulk of the Sun is comprised of hydrogen, the simplest element of all and helium, the next simplest. All the other elements are extremely rare, amounting only to about one hundredth of the total material of the Sun.

On the Earth, however, the opposite is found. Whilst hydrogen and helium are relatively scarce, complicated atoms like iron, calcium, magnesium and aluminium are plentifully abundant. So, it is argued, the Earth at least cannot have come from the Sun, for its composition is quite wrong and the same is probably true of the other planets.

WAS THE SUN A DOUBLE-STAR ?

The material of the Earth is, in fact, extremely rare as far as the Universe as a whole is concerned and what astronomers have done is to try and work out a theory that gives a reasonable explanation for the presence of our strangely complicated materials. One thing they have noticed is the extraordinary number of double-stars that can be seen. A double-star is a pair of stars turning about each other and, in fact, there seems to be just as many of these as there are single stars like our own Sun. This being so there seems a good chance that, at one time, the Sun was part of such a double system. Anyway, the assumption is made that it was.

Having made this assumption, the next thing to do is to try to imagine what sort of distance separated the two stars. Elsewhere in the Milky Way the distance varies from about 600,000 million miles to a few hundred thousand miles. The average is about 750 million miles and this is the distance assumed as far as the Sun is concerned.

THE EXPLOSION OF A SUPERNOVA

Because the Sun's companion is not with us now something must have happened to it. And the explanation given is that it exploded. Not an ordinary explosion but a very special bang on a gigantic scale. It was thought to have exploded as a supernova. This is an extremely rare form of stellar explosion but one on which we have learnt much by watching the effects of similar explosions in galaxies far beyond our own across the void of inter-galactic space. What happens in a supernova is that the star concerned swells by sweeping up the extremely thin gas which exists throughout the galaxies. Then, having swollen, the star has to use up prodigious quantities of its hydrogen " fuel " in order to support itself. Such massive stars that are quickly burning themselves up are called supergiants.

When a supergiant has used all its fuel it still continues to radiate energy by " feeding " on itself. As it does so, it starts slowly to collapse inwards. As the star becomes smaller, two things happen; the centre begins to get hotter, and it commences to rotate more rapidly. And as its rotational speed increases, so there grows a tendency for the star to fly to pieces.

The stage is ultimately reached when the rotary forces become comparable with gravity itself and the star begins to break up through the power of its own rotation. Usually though, as the rotary forces only increase slowly, the star sheds material slowly, rather like a gigantic Catherine-wheel. Occasionally vast quantities of material are thrown into space at speeds of many millions of miles an hour and when this happens the hot inner regions are temporarily exposed which leads to an increase in the star's brightness. This is quite a frequent occurrence and such explosions are known to astronomers as ordinary novae.

But the explosion of the Sun's companion must have been on a much grander scale. Instead of spluttering away comparatively slowly, the star must have broken up in one colossal explosion known as a supernova. For this to happen, the tremendously hot inner regions of the star, instead of generating atomic reactions, must start to absorb energy. Once this state is reached the star collapses rapidly. Instead of the slow loss by radiation from the surface, the loss builds up as the inner regions absorb more and more energy. The final collapse is swift and dramatic.

HOW THE EARTH WAS PROBABLY BORN

In its dying stages the Sun's companion, in spite of its enormous amount of material, must have become smaller in volume than the Earth. Hard X-rays would have been radiated from the surface and it would have been so dense that a matchbox full of matter from the central core would have weighed about 1,000 million tons. The surface speed must have been in the neighbourhood of 100 million miles an hour.

The rotary forces increased rapidly until, with a stupendous upheaval, a large part of the star was flung out into space. The final break-up probably occupied a minute, but for a few days the accompanying blaze of light was as great as all the other millions of stars of the Milky Way put together.

Only three such explosions of stars have ever been recorded, the most famous of which occurred about a thousand years ago. Known as the Crab Nebula the remains of the star concerned can still be seen as an enormous cloud of tremendously hot gas travelling through space at a rate of 3 million miles an hour.

It was out of such a holocaust that the Earth was probably born.

THE EARTH IS BORN

" In the morning of time the earth was a featureless ball of anarchic matter, hurtling down the dusty corridor of its orbit. . . ." Life.

THERE are two popular theories as to how the Earth was born. One suggests the stupendous explosion of a supernova, as told in the article on " The Formation of the Stars " (page 167). If this is so then the force of the explosion seems to have blown our parent away from the Sun to some distant and unknown part of the galaxy.

A point in favour of this theory is that the incredible temperatures experienced during such an explosion are sufficiently high to cause the helium in the star to change into elements such as iron, calcium, magnesium and aluminium. These are, of course, just the elements found on Earth!

The cloud of gas thrown into space during the explosion remained near the Sun. Gradually it took the form of a rotating disc, the main part of which seems to have settled in the orbits now occupied by the bigger planets. This suggestion fits in readily with the estimated distance between the two stars at the time of the explosion—750 million miles. As the remains of the smashed star receded into space, so the temperature of the gas left behind dropped. As the temperature fell, the rarefied atoms of the gas tended to condense into molecules. For millions of years this process took place, and slowly the gas condensed into cloud forms. Once these had reached a certain size, the inherent gravitational pull of the cloud began to play an important part. This reached out and dragged particles of gas into the condensation. The effect was cumulative, for as particles were pulled in, the gravitational pull increased, resulting in a more rapid collection of particles. About 100 million years were probably required for a cloud to reach the mass of the Earth. But by this time the gravitational attraction was so powerful that only another 100,000 years were required for the body to build itself up to the size of the great planets like Jupiter and Saturn.

This raises an interesting question. If this is so, why did the Earth stop growing when it had reached its present size? Why did it not collect further gas and continue increasing in size? A possible explanation is that all the gas had been collected, although this suggestion is difficult to apply to the other smaller planets like Mars, Venus and Mercury.

THE BIRTH OF THE EARTH

What is thought to have happened is that the gas first condensed into a small number of very big planets which then broke up to form a larger number of smaller planets one of which was the Earth.

If this is what happened, then as the chunk of rock that is now the Earth swept round the Sun it passed through parts of the gaseous disc which had not condensed when the big primary planets were formed. This had two effects; one was to smooth out the Earth's motion so that it travelled round the Sun in a reasonably circular orbit, much closer than the big planets, and secondly, the material " collected " as the young Earth ploughed through the gas may well have been responsible for the formation of the upper, solid layers of the Earth's crust.

That is one theory. Now supernova explosions are very rare and if such a bang is indeed needed to form an " Earth " then planets like ours must be comparatively rare in the Milky Way.

THE FORMATION OF PLANETS

Dr. Kuiper of the famous Yerkes Observatory in the United States does not believe this is so. He thinks there may well be a thousand million systems like ours in our galaxy alone. According to Dr. Kuiper, the formation of planets may be a common occurrence. It may be that as our Sun condensed and contracted out of space-dust, there still remained around it a considerable quantity of dust. As the sun spun, the gas tended to rotate with it, being formed into a disc in the process. As the disc spun, getting flatter in the process, the effect of gravity created whirls of denser matter within

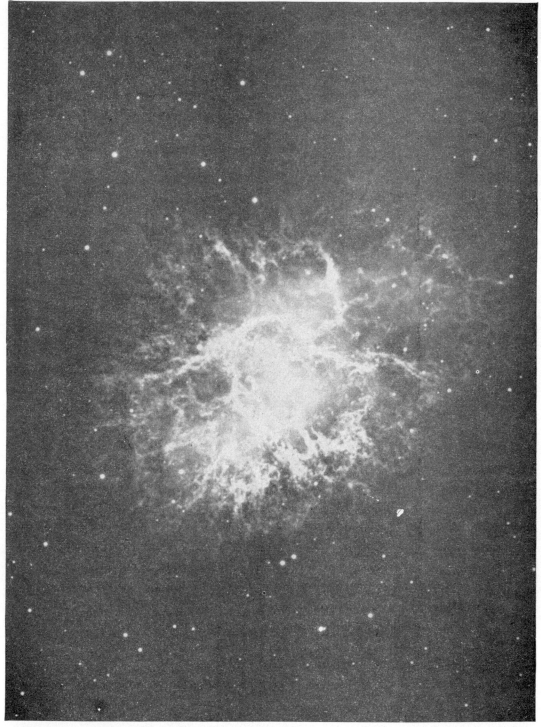

Another Earth? This gas cloud, known to astronomers as the Crab Nebula, is the result of
a supernova explosion in A.D.1054. Fantastic temperatures were experienced sufficiently high
to form iron, calcium, magnesium and aluminium—just the elements found on Earth. The
cloud is still expanding at about 3 million miles an hour.

it. In time the whirls condensed into the planets and their satellites and—the Earth and its Moon.

THE EVOLUTION OF THE EARTH

Whatever the true story of our birth may be—and we shall never know it for sure—it seems that in the beginning it was just a featureless ball of matter hurtling its way round the Sun. It was probably hot enough to be molten. While in the molten state the heaviest elements sank to the centre, leaving the lightest at the surface. Countless years ticked by and, with the passing of time, the crust slowly cooled. The process must have taken thousands or even millions of years, and as the young Earth cooled the first continents took shape—blocks of granite amid fiery seas of molten stone. The face of the young Earth spewed smoke and flame incessantly, but slowly the solidifying blocks of granite grew. No one knows if the continents then formed have the shapes we know to-day. Some think that they formed as a single mass, then separated and " floated " round the Earth. Those who hold this theory point out the remarkable similarity between the eastern coastline of South America and that of West Africa, which match each other like pieces of a jigsaw. It may be that the process is unfinished even yet, as matter is thrust upwards from the still molten interior.

While the continents were forming so also were the future seas. Spouting into the air were gases of carbon dioxide and water vapour. In the beginning the water must have condensed and fallen as rain, only to boil back at once as it fell on the still-red-hot rocks. For perhaps a thousand years this process continued until one day the temperature of the rocks fell below the boiling point of water and the rain fell and stayed. There followed countless years, perhaps centuries, of continual rain. Day after day, week after week and month after month it poured in the greatest deluge of all time. The low-lying areas of land filled to form the first primeval seas.

Slowly the grand process of cooling continued, and as the young Earth cooled, so it contracted, folding the outer crust as a dried apple shrinks and wrinkles its skin. The folds were mountains. This process too must have continued for countless thousands of years. Mighty mountain ranges were formed,

only to be eroded flat by torrential rain. Continents were worn flat until almost submerged by the seas.

THE LAURENTIAN REVOLUTION

Then about 1,000 million years ago, there came a particularly fierce period of contraction, the remains of which can be detected to this day. Known as the Laurentian Revolution, the foundations of some of the mountains then formed lie embedded in the hills of eastern Canada. The greatest volcanic fury of known time disgorged molten rock to cover two million square miles round Hudson Bay to a depth of two miles. This remains to-day—the great granite floor of the Canadian Shield.

About 60 million years ago the great ranges of the Himalayas, Rockies, Alps and Andes were formed. One million years ago up came the Cascade Mountains of West America, as indicated by the still smouldering volcanoes that stretch a thousand miles from Alaska to the Indies.

THE ICE AGES

This is perhaps an opportune moment to mention the ice ages—one of the great mysteries of geological history. It seems that several times in the course of history great ice caps have formed stretching from the poles half-way to the Equator, only to shrink and retreat to the poles.

Just what caused these ice ages is one of the past's biggest mysteries. An obvious suggestion is that the heat of the Sun diminishes periodically. An *increase* in the Sun's heat could, however, produce the same effect providing the increase was not excessive! The explanation for this strange suggestion is that a slight increase in the Sun's heat would produce an increase in the cloudiness at the poles. These clouds would then reflect a bigger proportion of the Sun's light back into space and prevent it from warming the ground, the general result being a raising of winter temperatures and, more important, a *lowering* of summer temperatures. At the moment plenty of snow and ice form in many places during the winter, but no glaciers are formed because the snow melts away during the summer. Snow would still fall if the winters were a little warmer, but would not melt if the summers were cooler.

A similar effect could have been caused by the ash from myriads of volcanoes which, if thick enough, would have blanketed off the heat of the Sun, allowing ice to spread.

The greatest series of ice ages began one million years ago. Four times since then great glaciers have descended from the North, the last occasion being barely 20,000 years ago. Since then the ice has retreated—and is still visibly retreating to-day. The great ice packs of the Arctic and Antarctic recede yearly.

Yet 5 million cubic miles of ice still cover one-tenth of the surface of the Earth. Were this to melt, however, the level of the seas would rise by more than 100 feet—enough to submerge London, Paris and New York, together with most of the great seaports of the world.

THE AGE OF THE EARTH

It was the glaciers of the ice ages, aided by repeated outpourings of volcanic lava and centuries of erosion by rain, that helped to hide clues regarding the age of the Earth. Up to a few hundred years ago most people thought that it was not much older than Man himself.

In 1654, an Archbishop of Ireland firmly announced that the Earth was born in the year 4004 B.C., on 26th October, at 9 a.m.! This is laughable now, but that date was regarded as official for more than 100 years. When discoveries such as fossil remains were made, indicating a much earlier origin, these were explained away as having been " planted " by the Devil to trick Man.

By the turn of the nineteenth century it became increasingly obvious that either the Devil must have been exceedingly busy, or else the clues of whalebones discovered in the middle of America, palm trees in England, or the remains of glaciers in Australia and New Zealand, were indeed pointers to ages long past, ages much older than 4004 B.C.

Yet, it was not until 1900, with the discovery of radio-activity that the age of the Earth could be estimated with any degree of accuracy. Measurements indicate that the Earth is far older, even, than was commonly supposed 50 years ago.

Radio-active elements such as radium and uranium decay at a certain rate, no matter where they are situated, or the conditions under which they exist. They lose a certain proportion of their atoms at a steady rate over certain periods of time and eventually end up as atoms of lead. The rate at which this takes place is calculable and it is possible to weigh the amount of radium in a piece of radio-active rock, compare it with the amount of lead present, and then estimate when the rock was formed. Measurements taken all over the world tell the same story to within remarkably close limits—that the Earth's crust was formed about 3,000 million years ago.

A volcano in action is an impressive sight. This one, 780 miles from San Diego, is the world's newest active volcano, and is thought to have an underwater link with the Hawiian Islands.

REPTILES AND AMPHIBIANS OF BRITAIN

SNAKES and lizards are reptiles; frogs, toads and newts are amphibians. All are cold-blooded. In the amphibians, the early part of their lives is spent in water as free-swimming tadpoles; as adults they can live in, or out of water. The snakes and lizards lay eggs which are enclosed in a skin, and at no stage of their lives can these reptiles live in the water.

THE ADDER OR VIPER

The only poisonous snake in Britain is the adder, or viper. This species does not grow to a great size. Most specimens are under two feet in length, and females are bigger than males. Adders of 26 or 28 inches in length are exceptions, and rarely met with.

Male and female adders can often be distinguished by their colour and, in cases like this, where each sex tends to have its own particular colour, we speak of sexual dimorphism. An adder with bold, contrasting colours is usually a male. Where the pattern is not well defined, and the colours are dominantly red or gold, the snake is usually a female. Greys, white, olives, creams and silvers, with clear black markings, are the sign of the male.

The adder is not a savage snake; nor is it prone to attack without provocation. It does not like being handled, and that is when it is most likely to bite, because then it becomes excited. When captured it will swell and hiss like escaping steam, but if gathered on a stick, or even a pencil, it will rarely make any attempt to bite. Snakes, by the way, do not sting; they bite. The forked tongue has nothing whatever to do with biting, stinging, or poison. Much has been written about the adder's venom, but in this country it is seldom really dangerous—to humans. I have been bitten twice in my life, in a country where adder poison is much more potent than it is here, and I am still able to write this. Apart from feeling sick, and having pains in my head and joints, I was none the worse of the bites.

All snakes are deaf. Yet they are quick to feel earth tremors, and that is why they are seldom taken completely unawares by anyone with a heavy tread.

Adders live on slow-worms, lizards, frogs, toads and mice. The slow-worm is the favourite and where there are slow-worms there are usually adders. Enemies of the adder, apart from man, are few. The hedgehog kills them. The mole can kill young ones. The roe deer is an adept at trampling them to death. He is nimble and cuts them to pieces with his hooves.

Young adders are generally born in August, escaping from the eggs just as they are being laid. They are about the length and thickness of a pencil. In their early days they live close together, and are fond of hiding under large stones.

The adder is the only snake found in Scotland. It does not do well in captivity, and, anyway, is not to be recommended as a pet to those who do not know how to handle them.

THE GRASS-SNAKE

The grass-snake, sometimes called ring-snake, is harmless. There is a great deal of variation in colour, but olive-green and olive-grey are common. Behind the grass-snake's head there is always a collar, which may be orange, yellow, white or pink. This species is found in England and Wales, and is the one most widely kept as a pet in this country. It feeds readily in captivity.

In the wild state it lives largely on frogs, and is most often found near water, on marshland or in woods. It is a lover of the sunshine, and will even climb into trees to bask in its warmth.

I have watched grass-snakes hunting and feeding. When they catch a frog it is usually by the hind-leg, so the frog is swallowed head last. The snake is a wonderful swimmer, and I have watched one hunting in a pool for small fishes, and coming out with one held cross-wise in its jaws. A grass-snake can stay immersed for a long time. I once timed one at twenty minutes.

The grass-snake mates in the spring, after coming out of hibernation, and lays her eggs in June and July. She is one of the few snakes which deliberately seek out warm places in which to lay their eggs. Manure heaps, old sawdust, rotting leaves, and such places are usual and the snake will return to them year after year. It is not unusual to find several female snakes laying together.

The adder is Britain's only poisonous snake, and the only snake found in Scotland. It is not savage or aggressive but, when handled, becomes excited and is sure to bite. The bite is, of course, poisonous, but seldom fatal in this country.

Grass-snakes are harmless. They lack the striking markings of the adder, but have a conspicuous collar of orange, yellow, pink or white. They are not found in Scotland.

Eggs take from six to ten weeks to hatch. The actual time varies with the temperature. The grass-snake sometimes shows attachment to her eggs by coiling round them, and displaying anger, which is not usual in snakes.

THE SMOOTH-SNAKE

The smooth-snake, which bears a superficial resemblance to the adder, is extremely rare in this country. It is, in fact, confined to the south of England, mainly Surrey, Hampshire and Dorset.

Like the grass-snake, the smooth-snake is harmless, and, like all British snakes, it hibernates. But this species mates before leaving its winter quarters. The main food is lizards, and the smooth-snake has the habit of coiling round its victim, just like the great boa constrictors; but the coiling serves to hold the prey during swallowing rather than squeeze it to death.

Young smooth-snakes are born late in the year, usually September and October, and are provided at birth with a layer of fat which helps to see them through the winter.

Smooth-snakes, by all accounts, are fierce fighters, and the males frequently engage in bloody combats in the early spring.

THE SLOW-WORM

The slow-worm is a snake-like lizard. It is not slow and it is not a worm. It is a lizard which has lost its legs and, if you were to watch one closely, you would see that it does not oar itself along on its ribs like a true snake, it wriggles.

Slow-worms are, of course, perfectly harmless. They are widely distributed and there should never be any confusion between them and any kind of snake. The usual colours are red, bronze, chestnut, grey and brown, and the skin has a burnished sheen. The most common length is a little over a foot, 14 or 15 inches being usual; but much bigger specimens have been found from time to time.

Though they can swim well enough, they drown quickly, and it is doubtful if they ever go into water of their own accord.

They have many enemies, furred, feathered and reptilian. In the early years of their lives they are even eaten by such creatures as frogs and toads. But young slow-worms are very secretive in habits, so in actual fact many survive to keep the race of slow-worms going.

Food varies with locality, but the main prey consists of slugs, worms, spiders and insects.

Mating takes place in the spring, when the males fight fiercely with each other. The young slow-worms are born in the autumn, August and September being the usual months.

LIZARDS

The more obvious lizards, with four legs and a clearly defined tail, are the sand-lizard and the common or viviparous lizard. The sand-lizard is confined to the extreme south of England, but the viviparous lizard is common throughout the British Isles.

The common lizard gives birth to living young. It is active and quite harmless If grasped by the tail it will usually leave the tail behind; it is brittle and breaks easily.

The common lizard, which is called viviparous, produces living young; the sand-lizard lays eggs. But the dividing line between a lizard which produces young and one which produces eggs is thin; in some places the common lizard will produce eggs instead of young.

The food of lizards is mainly insects and spiders. Sometimes lizards live in what one might almost call colonies. The common species enters water readily, and swims well. A feature of all our lizards is the brittle tail. If you snatch a lizard hastily by the tail you are always liable to be left with it in your hand. It breaks off readily, but the creature soon grows another, which may, or may not, be quite as good as the one it has lost.

NEWTS

Often mistaken for lizards are the little newts, which are, of course, amphibians. Like frogs and toads, they spend the early part of their lives in water, as tadpoles, and could not live out of it.

We have, in this country, three species of newts—warty, smooth and palmate. Only the smooth newt is found in Ireland. All three are distributed over most of the remainder of Britain. You have, of course, to go to ponds to seek newts. They are agile enough in the water, but on land they are rather sluggish. Yet they come ashore to hibernate; newts rarely hibernate in the water.

Courtship is in the spring, and then the females lay their eggs. In the smooth newt, which is the commonest species, the number varies from 200 to 350.

FROGS AND TOADS

Among frogs and toads, the commonest species are the common frog and the common toad.

Both produce their spawn in the spring, usually in March and April, and the eggs are not harmed by frost, even if the water actually freezes over. Frog spawn is laid in masses, which presently becomes like jelly owing to the absorption of water; but toad spawn is laid in chains, with the eggs in rows of two. In the same pond, toad spawn is usually later than frog spawn.

The tadpoles of both are black at hatching. They are active as soon as they are free from

Toads are easily distinguished from frogs by their warty skin and squat posture. They crawl and walk rather than jump.

the jelly, and at the same time become the prey of many hunters—the great water beetles, the dragonfly nymphs, birds and small boys. Tadpoles are extremely easy to rear in captivity, and are an excellent subject for study at home.

The croaking of frogs is a familiar chorus during the spring festival of spawning. Then you see them in the water, with only their heads showing, shoulder to shoulder singing their weird song. It is at this time that they are much sought after by their enemies—herons, foxes, otters, hedgehogs. A big frog is a fine meal for a hedgehog hungry after hibernation. An otter with cubs will skin every frog for her little ones, and frog skins and otter tracks tell you the identity of the hunter.

Female frogs and toads are bigger than males. The males take up what is called the amplexus position—which means that they fasten themselves to the females' backs, anchoring themselves by means of special suction pads on their wrists—and this has given rise to the belief that young frogs kill off old frogs. The females lay their eggs in the water, and only then are they fertilised by the males.

Frogs feed on all kinds of insects; toads are very fond of slugs and earthworms. In all cases the long, curled tongue shoots out like a flame and gathers the prey. The toad can always be distinguished from the frog by the warts on his skin and by his crawling gait.

There are a few other amphibians on the British list. The edible frog breeds in Kent and Middlesex; the marsh frog in Kent and Sussex; the natterjack toad in the south-east, and more rarely in the midlands, of England.

Two types commonly kept as garden pets are the Greek tortoise and the Brazilian tortoise.

KEEPING TORTOISES AS PETS

MANY people do not realise that tortoises make attractive pets. They become quite tame and give very little trouble, and if you get one you will soon discover that he has quite a character of his own.

BUYING A TORTOISE

Do not buy a tortoise if you haven't got a garden.

Age: This can be told by counting the rings on the shell.

Size: It is much better to get a small one because: (*a*) they are generally more active, and therefore more interesting; and (*b*) they live longer.

Cost: This is approximately five shillings. The most common breeds are Grecian and Brazilian.

Sex: If the underneath part of the shell is flat then the tortoise is a female, but if the shell is concave (i.e. curves slightly inwards) then it is a male.

Condition: Make sure that the eyes are quite healthy, and that there are no cracks in the shell. And, lastly, if possible choose a tortoise that does not seem as shy as the others.

Feeding: General favourites are buttercups, cucumber, lettuce, peas (raw), plantains, dandelions plus leaves, clover, chickweed, apple, and occasionally bread and milk.

Tortoises have no teeth but a sharp, horny structure with which they bite. *Water* is absolutely essential for your tortoise.

Summer: At night your tortoise should be shown a box full of straw, or dry leaves, and half-covered with a piece of sacking. When it gets really hot, he can be left under a dry bush (e.g. a lavender bush). If necessary you can keep him in a wire run on the lawn, but this should be at least three square yards. On the whole it is better if you do not keep him in an enclosure, but let him wander at will. This, of course, has one disadvantage and that is that tortoises are very fond of anemones and young lettuce seedlings—so beware of your parents' wrath!

Winter: See paragraph on hibernation.

HOW NOT TO LOSE IT

Get your father to drill a hole in the back of your tortoise's shell, where it is separated from the bottom part—just in front of the back leg. Thread a key ring, or piece of strong string (this is more advisable if your tortoise is very small), through this, and tie a long piece of string, or coloured bias-binding, on to this

This picture shows how the string and paper is attached to the hole in the tortoise's shell.

with a piece of white paper tied on the end. Your tortoise *may* still get lost, but you will be able to find him much more easily, and a precaution such as this is essential if your tortoise is loose in your garden.

CARE AND MAINTENANCE

It is good for your tortoise to have a bath occasionally, so try and persuade your mother to give you a very shallow, enamel butcher's tray. Fill this with luke-warm water and put your tortoise firmly in the middle—(the water

Tortoises usually like to have a bath in a shallow basin or tray of luke-warm water.

should not be more than about an inch deep). The first few times he will rush out of it, but he will soon realise that it is really rather pleasant. It is also good for him if you scrub his shell gently with luke-warm water occasionally. Afterwards if you want to make him look really bright, you can rub a little olive oil on his shell, but make sure you wipe off all the surplus, because otherwise bits of grass, etc., stick to it, and it becomes very uncomfortable.

HABITS

Tortoises are friendly creatures and so if possible keep two of them. They will probably be rather shy at first but after their first winter, they will become much tamer. They have

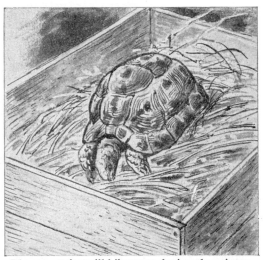

Your tortoise will hibernate during the winter.

keen sight, their hearing is very poor, *but* they feel the vibration of a foot passing close to them, and they *see* your shadow. They like propping themselves up against something so as to catch the full sun.

HIBERNATION

By the middle of September, you will notice that your tortoise has lost his normally large appetite and has begun to hide even more. At the beginning of October you should bring him into the house at night, and when it begins to get really cold (about 15th October or so) put him in his straw box in your attic, or cellar, covered with a sack, leaving a tiny airhole. There you should leave him till the end of March, or preferably the middle of April.

If he is woken up, or disturbed, in the middle of the winter he will probably die. When he wakes up in April you must not take him outside immediately, but keep him in a warm kitchen, where the sun shines into his box, and make sure his eyes are quite all right. If one, or both, are stuck shut, bathe them with some warm, weak boracic acid solution, with a camel-hair brush.

If after a few days there is no improvement I advise you to take him to your local vet, or, preferably, a People's Dispensary for Sick Animals as they know a great deal about tortoises. Also bathe his mouth with this solution and prise it gently open. The first thing he should be offered is water every day. Of course, you can offer him a lettuce leaf or two, but he may not eat for the first week or so.

If your parents are fond of gardening they may have some glass cloches. If so, try and get hold of one on a sunny April afternoon and pop your tortoise inside, plus food, for a few hours—he is more likely to eat out-of-doors. On dull days he probably will not be at all active. Do not let him spend the night out until the end of May, when there is no further risk of frost, and then make sure he is safely in his box or enclosure at night. As a matter of interest, he probably lost about 1 oz. in weight during the winter.

ILLNESSES

Ticks: These are fat, blue insects—sometimes quite large. It is a good idea to search your tortoise's face, throat and feet occasionally. Ticks are often picked up where sheep have been. To get rid of these, cover them (the insects, not the tortoise) with medicinal paraffin or castor oil, and then pull out carefully with a pair of tweezers and a slight twisting motion.

Round Worms: These may be found in the droppings, and if so, it is advisable to take your tortoise to the vet; but if you cannot do so, the best treatment is one grain of santonin in his food, once a week for six weeks.

Shell—Broken, Bleeding or Peeling: The first two are a sign that your tortoise has had an accident (trodden on?). You should clean the injured part with warm water and apply some Friar's Balsam or weak permanganate of potash (make sure you keep the flies away). After this I should take him to the vet if you are not very happy about his condition. Peeling is a sign of old age.

Other Illnesses: Take your tortoise to the vet, the People's Dispensary for Sick Animals or the Royal Society for the Prevention of Cruelty to Animals.

BREEDING

Tortoises very rarely breed in captivity, but if they do, the female buries the eggs about five inches deep in some loose soil. She covers them so carefully that it is quite impossible to find the nest unless you have watched her. If you want to hatch the eggs, dig them up very carefully and then re-bury them the same way up in some fine damp sand. They should then be put somewhere where the temperature is at least 80° all day. If they are going to hatch they will do so from four to eight weeks—but do not be too disappointed if they do not hatch.

You must keep the young tortoises in a fern case or vivarium with a saucer of water sunk in one corner. They should only be allowed tender, young lettuce or dandelion leaves (N.B. *No* bread and milk). When they have got into the habit of eating regularly, you can take them out of the vivarium, but put them in a conservatory, or indoors, at night. Baby tortoises are only about one inch square; they have soft shells like putty. And one last thing —I do not expect your tortoises will breed unless they themselves are of the same breed (e.g. both Grecian tortoises).

KEEPING REPTILES AND AMPHIBIANS

IF YOU go to the London or any other good Zoo, you will find the Reptile House one of the most popular places in the collection. People do not shudder at reptiles now, or think that they must be dangerous just because they *are* reptiles. Books, zoos, museums and films have taught us to see them as they are. All are useful, many beautiful, and only a very few harmful to man or domestic animals.

There are two ways of keeping reptiles and the reptile-looking creatures called amphibians, i.e. frogs, toads, newts and salamanders. They can be kept indoors in cages called vivariums (places for keeping live animals) or in outdoor enclosures called reptiliaries.

for few of us want to keep expensive and delicate tropical reptiles until we have had some years of experience. A reptiliary is simply a rockery enclosed by a wall of concrete with a turnover top (see drawing) to prevent escapes. In fact, it is very like a garden pond, but without the concrete floor, and so requires far less cement. There must be a pool, and if you are keeping frogs or newts, as large a pool as space will allow. Also beneath some of the rocks there should be good deep holes in which your pets can hide when winter or an unseasonable cold snap comes.

In Great Britain we have few reptiles. The only dangerous one is the adder, and until you

GARDEN REPTILIARY CONTAINING POND, MOAT, AND ROCKERY. WITH UNDERGROUND SHELTERS ALL ROUND IS A LOW CEMENT WALL WITH AN "OVERHANG" TO PREVENT ESCAPES. THE OWNER IS SHOWN FEEDING HER WATER TORTOISES.

A vivarium can be made out of a big box, but a fern case is better. The cage should be at least eighteen inches long, with a slate floor, one big glass window, a perforated zinc cover (most reptiles are climbers) and some perforated zinc at either end to permit a flow of air. The floor should be covered with sand, with a mossy rock for shade, and earth pockets to contain plants; a vivarium can be a little garden as well as a cage. There must be a little pool (say a pie-dish sunk in the sand floor), for most reptiles are thirsty and many like a bath. The temperature of an ordinary living-room will as a rule be warm enough.

But if you have a garden, even a small one, the outdoor reptiliary is by far the better plan,

have had plenty of experience and other folk raise no objections, leave it alone. As you can see by the picture, it is quite unmistakable. It has poison fangs connected with poison glands, and they work just like the hypodermic syringe the doctor or dentist uses.

HOW TO HANDLE A SNAKE

An adder bite is much worse than a wasp sting, and people usually get bitten on the ankle or hand. If bitten, don't panic. Unless one is already in bad health, the bite cannot be fatal; suck the wound and spit, and if you swallow the poison it will do no harm, for it will pass out of your system very shortly. Should you live in a very addery county, always carry with you some permanganate of potash crystals for rubbing into a wound. This has cured bites from really deadly serpents. Adders are mostly fatal to dogs. If you *must* kill an adder, the slightest tap with a stick will suffice. The picture shows how to handle any snake.

The adder brings forth five to twelve babies alive in August, and they start at once to eat insects, first paralysed by their poison. Older adders save us from plagues of mice and frogs.

A much safer pet is the grass-snake. This is a frog-eater and, as a result, a water lover. Its bite is quite harmless, and if it seems to hang on, there is no need for terror. Once a snake has bitten it cannot let go, for all its teeth point towards its throat; this is why in zoos snakes sometimes swallow a blanket put there to keep them warm. The grass-snake soon becomes tame with handling, and in mid-summer lays from a dozen to fifty eggs, in moulds or even in manure where the sun hatches them. A big grass-snake may measure a yard, and the rarer smooth snake grows to about the same length, but lacks the staring yellow collar by which you may always know the grass-snake.

Our native lizards all make charming pets and are perfectly harmless. They love sun-light, and outdoors will keep themselves well fed on flies. Indoors they will thrive on flies (which you must catch in a balloon fly-trap) and can also be fed on meal-worms, purchased at any bird shop and bred quite easily in a mixture of bran and oatmeal.

In our country we have the slow-worm, the common lizard, the sand-lizard, and you can always buy at a pet shop the lively and gorgeously-coloured South of France wall-lizard. The first does not look like a lizard; it has lost its legs and resembles nothing so much as a piece of polished bronze or a scrap of dried bracken stem. It lives largely on worms and slugs.

The others eat worms, caterpillars, spiders and insects of all kinds. Save when sun-bathing they are never still, soon become tame with gentle handling, and learn to take food from one's fingers. In winter they go to ground in some snug retreat, and there you must leave them until spring sunshine lures them forth. The forked tongue is used for drinking and feeling their way about. They are brim-ming with curiosity and full of amusing tricks. About a score of young are hatched from soft transparent eggs that break soon after being laid; the shell is broken by a tiny " egg tooth " fixed on the snout. It is very like the egg tooth of an ordinary farmyard chick.

With the first hint of frost lizards go to ground and, though a particularly warm, sunny day in winter may lure them out for an hour or two, they generally stay hidden until spring. In a very lizardy part of the country, heathland with sandy soil, you may light on a hibernating lizard when digging the garden. It will be curled up, with feet on chest and tail wrapped over all, in a sort of parcel. Put it back carefully where you found it, to enjoy its winter sleep in peace.

WHEN IS A REPTILE NOT A REPTILE?

Amphibians, frogs, newts, etc., are often mistaken for reptiles, but they are very different

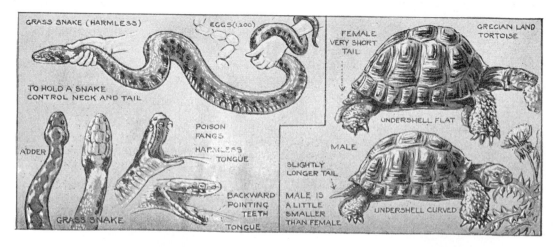

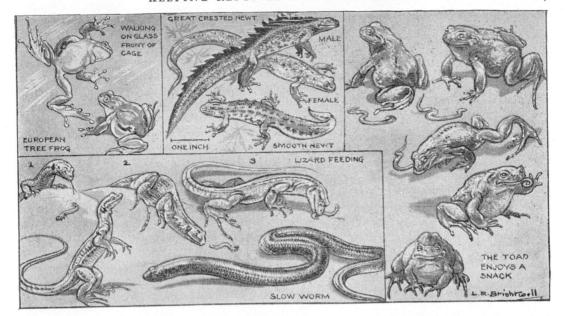

n many ways. Their skins are soft and moist, not covered with hard scales, and the young are hatched from jelly-like eggs laid in water. At first the babies have long tails, often no limbs at all, and breathe by means of gills worn in two red tufts, one on either side of the head. In fact, amphibians have much in common with fishes, and are a connecting link between the fishes and more highly organised reptiles.

Most of our native amphibians do far better in an outdoor reptiliary than in an indoor cage or vivarium. If you have a garden pond, the frogs and toads will soon find it in spring, and toads come to the same pond year after year to lay their eggs. You may hear people say that frogs and toads attack goldfish, but this is wrong. At breeding-time a male toad clutches automatically at anything in its path, and so sometimes a fish is accidentally strangled. But the toad's long strings of eggs and the frog's big wobbly masses of spawn are pleasant things to see, for they mean that another brood of frogs and toads is on the way; and there are no more hard-working creatures when it comes to keeping our gardens free of slugs and plant-destroying insects.

Toads soon become very tame and learn to take worms from their owners' hands. In winter these, like all our native reptiles and amphibians, hide away underground until warm weather returns. It is always fascinating to watch the annual transformation of the tadpoles into perfect frogs and toads.

The natterjack toad is smaller and less pimply than the common species, runs rather than crawls or hops, and like the common toad can, when alarmed, squeeze from its tail-end a few drops of thick yellowish fluid. This has an irritating effect if it gets into a cut, or falls on a dog's nose, and it is a natural protection. But both frogs and toads are perfectly harmless to humans and amongst the gardener's best friends.

At pet shops you can sometimes buy the little bright green tree-frog of Europe and N. Africa. It is a charming pet, but must be fed on flies and kept in an indoor vivarium. The sound of heavy rain will cause it to sing —a loud clacking noise which can be heard many yards distant.

Our three native species of newts should be left to make their own ways in a garden pond, or an outdoor reptiliary with a good-sized pool and plenty of plants, such as hornwort or Canadian weed, amongst which the newts can lay their bead-like eggs. Though lizardish in general shape, newts are close cousins to the frog and toad, must breed in water, and come ashore in winter to hibernate. Frogs can often winter in deep mud at the bottom of a pond, but the toad must have dry quarters. Stories of toads living for years walled-up are nonsense. A toad can, if it comes to the worst, fast for quite ten months, but *must* have food sooner or later, and also plenty of moisture.

DANCING AN UNDERWATER BALLET

The largest of our native newts is the great crested newt or Triton, nearly six inches long, the male usually slightly smaller than the female. In spring he dances in front of his partner a wonderful sort of underwater ballet, a sure sign that presently one may see the new tadpoles. They are more advanced than the frog's babies and begin life with beginnings of front legs.

Two kinds of tortoises can be kept in a reptiliary but require very different treatment. The common garden tortoise comes from the hot, dry parts of N. Africa, Palestine and Persia. When buying one, see that the eyes are wide open, black and shining, and the animal should hiss and draw back quickly into its shell when touched. The picture shows how to tell a he from a she tortoise, but they do not breed in this country.

There are very few records of a captive tortoise laying two or even four white, hard-shelled eggs and then being hatched out in hot sand. Food—cabbage, lettuce, grass and dandelion. It will touch no animal food of any kind. It should have plenty of water to drink and a deep winter retreat; but it may very likely dig a hole for itself in a lawn where it will sleep from October until next April or May. It soon gets to know anyone who treats it properly, and there is at least one record of a garden tortoise living for over fifty years. Occasionally one may find a hard-shelled, eight-legged insect-like creature, as big as one's little fingernail, sticking to the reptile's skin. It is a " tick " and should be picked off with a pair of tweezers.

SUN-BATHING IN THE WATER

The pond tortoise of Europe and Asia Minor must have a pond, and see that there are no fish in it or they will soon vanish. This handsome reptile, with its black shell covered all over with bright golden dots, like all tortoises, loves sun, and spends hours in the water with just its head showing. It soon becomes tame and you can drop worms, small dead fish, or scraps of raw fish and meat into its widely-opened mouth. In winter it needs deep cover until sunny days return.

Remember all these creatures have very tiny brains. One must not expect too much of them, but, like nearly all animals, they respond to kind treatment. Get to know their habits, meet other pet keepers, and study all the books you can, for of even the commonest animals, there is always something more to learn.

Puzzle Picture: what is it ? Solution on page 345.

KEEPING TROPICAL FRESHWATER FISHES

IN 1906, nearly fifty years ago, the London Zoo showed a small tank containing some tiny fishes from the West Indies. They were "guppies," named after a Dr. Guppy who first brought them to Europe, or "millions fish," famous in their own land for destroying mosquitoes. That little exhibit was the beginning of what is now a world-wide industry. You can see a Tropical Aquarium almost anywhere to-day. In a friend's house perhaps, a cinema entrance hall, a tea-room or a hospital ward. There are thousands of different kinds of small fishes living in lakes and rivers throughout the warmer parts of the world, and at least two hundred kinds, a few of which are shown in the picture, can be kept together in the same tank quite safely. A community tank, as such a gathering is called, makes a lovely picture, and it is a living picture too.

A tropical tank needs more attention than a cold water one, but if one observes a few simple rules all should go well. A few tropical fishes will be happy in the temperature of an ordinary living-room, about 60° Fahrenheit, but most need warmer conditions, so the tropical tank must be provided with a thermostat, which is hung in the tank and keeps the water at whatever temperature is needed. The aquarium shop people where you buy this, and a water thermometer, also very necessary, will show you just how to regulate it. The tank is always covered with a hood holding one or two lights to make the plants grow, and these plants should be planted in an inch or two of sand. It may be necessary to siphon off accumulated dirt about once a month, but if you keep some of the little tropical snails shown on the illustration, they will burrow into the sand and help to clean it. They come out chiefly at night.

KEEPING THE FISHES HEALTHY

The tank must have plenty of plants, for they not only help to make the picture, but in full light give out bubbles of oxygen, without which no animal can live, and provide nests for those fishes which must attach their eggs to something. When buying these aquarium plants always carry them home wet, for they are more delicate than the plants of our native ponds and rivers.

Some "trops," as tropical aquarium fishes are now called, lay eggs on the water plants, some build nests of bubbles, some hatch the eggs in their mouths, and others even bring forth their young alive, just as do cows, dogs and all the beasts we know so well.

Hardiest and cheapest of these live breeders is the guppy, first of all trops to reach Europe. It is so easy to breed that any tropical aquarist will give you a few guppies with which to make a start. The female is about two and a quarter inches long; the male less than half her size. Females vary little in shape, but breeders have produced male guppies with all kinds of quaintly-shaped tails.

If the tank water is kept to about 78° Fahrenheit, young will be produced within a month, but below 68° three times as long. You will soon know if a guppy is about to become a mother by a big black patch appearing above the under fin near her tail. This dark patch is caused by the heads of the babies all pointing towards the opening that will soon let them out into their little world. A brood varies from six to fifty. A guppy can breed when six weeks old, and lives about two years.

THE FISHES' DIET

For these or other trops various dry foods, sold at any pet shop, can be given, but all fishes grow faster on live foods. You can buy water fleas (daphnia) by the canful, or dip them up with a fine muslin net from a stagnant pond or canal. Pet shops also sell red worms, and a tiny worm called tubifex.

But one excellent worm food you can grow yourself. This is the white worm, or enchytrae. Put just a pinch of these worms (any aquarist will give you some to start with) on a slice of stale bread, or some cold porridge laid on a panful of damp earth. The worms if kept in the dark will soon multiply so fast that you need never be without a supply.

Another method of feeding is to hang a scrap of white meat, liver, fish or boiled spinach by a thread in the tank, being careful to remove it when the fishes have eaten their fill. A few fishes do better if the tank is supplied with an aerator, or pump, a simple " plug in " contrivance, which uses so little electric current it does not register on the meter. But a large

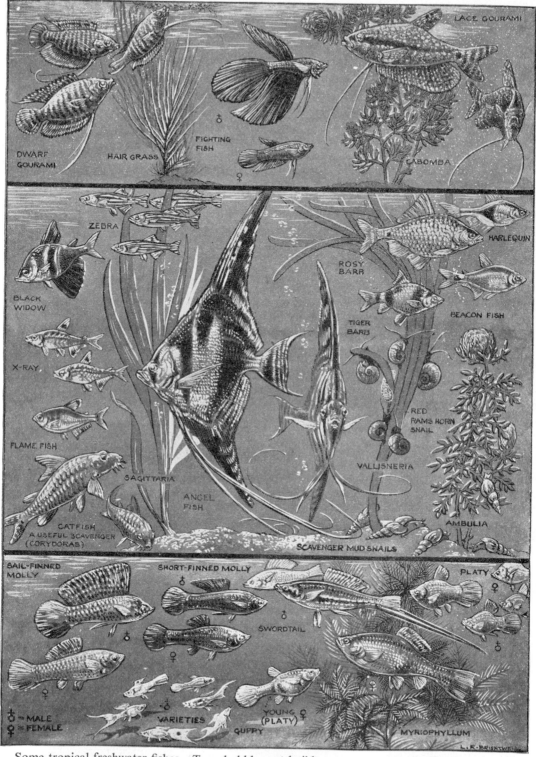

Some tropical freshwater fishes. *Top:* bubble nest builders; *centre:* fishes that lay their eggs on water plants; *bottom:* fishes that bring forth their young alive.

number of trops are quite used to stagnant water, the plants and their own movements keeping it sufficiently well aerated.

THE ANGEL FISH

Once you have made a success with guppies (and you can hardly fail), your ambition will be fairly roused, and you will want to try your luck with that joy and pride of every aquarist, the angel fish. It was discovered in the River Amazon, Brazil—in waters frequented by big electric eels, and a terrible little fish called the caribe, which goes in great shoals and with its sharp teeth has been known to cut large animals and even men to pieces. In the same country lives the fierce jaguar, a huge snake called the anaconda, and dangerous warlike natives so that we owe much to the courage of the explorers who first brought us this lovely aquarium pet.

Like other trops it likes the company of its own kind, and may at first be a little shy, requiring to be fed separately. As with many fishes the courtship of two angel fishes looks more like a dog fight than the usual signs of love.

The tank water should be very clear, and plenty of plants handy for anchoring the sticky eggs. A temperature of 75° and strong aeration are also vital, and the eggs when laid removed to a separate tank, for most, but not all, fishes tend to eat their own eggs, and even the newly hatched young or fry. Young angels hatch in from five to six days, and with plenty of daphnia to nourish them, soon look just like their beautiful parents.

THE SIAMESE FIGHTER

Possibly the most famous and gorgeous of all aquarium fishes is the Siamese fighter. Though only two and a half inches long, this fish is, in its own country, what the race-horse is to most Europeans and Americans. The Siamese have for centuries put male fighters together and then staked enormous sums of money on the result. Before the law stopped it, a Siamese would, after having lost all he possessed on " backing a loser," even stake his own liberty on the result of a fight, agreeing to serve as a gardener or house-boy to the owner of the winning fish, for a period of months or even years.

But in our country, of course, the fishes are only bred for their beauty, and two adult males are never kept together. So pugnacious is a male fighter that he will even offer combat to his own image in a mirror. No butterfly or tropical flower can excel a male fighting fish as regards splendour of colouring. Though such a " bruiser," one male fighter can be kept safely with fishes of any other species. Like a human boxer he scorns to hit a non-professional.

The male fighter does most of the nest-building, though his smaller and drab-coloured mate may help. The nest is about three inches long by a quarter of an inch wide. A temperature of 78°, and strong lighting all help in the making of this ideal home, or rather cradle for the eggs. The nest is made of twigs held together on a mass of bubbles blown by the fish.

When all is ready the male rushes at his bride, wraps himself round her, and holds her tightly perhaps for an hour until up to three hundred eggs have been laid, each wrapped in a separate bubble. After about two days the parents should be removed, when the eggs will hatch out. As soon as this happens keep the water steady at 72–82° and also cover the tank with a sheet of glass, to prevent dust settling on the surface.

EXOTIC FISHES

A well-known clan of tropical fishes is that of the gouramis, some of which grow to a large size and in India and Africa are used for food. But there are some charming dwarf gouramis and one of the loveliest is the lace gourami, about four inches long. Just below the head are two fins drawn out into long threads with which it feels its way about the tank floor, like a man feeling his way over a swamp by means of a long pole. It likes water of from 73°–77° F., and has one great advantage in that it will eat hydra, should this enemy of baby fishes appear in the tank.

Like the fighter, it builds a bubble nest, but is very choosy as to its surroundings and must have a tank quite two feet long, and plenty of plants, particularly the Cape water-lily, or vallisneria which does well in both cold and warm water. Take away the female once the eggs have been laid, but the father fish can be left with his family for a few days after the fry have hatched, which they should do in about

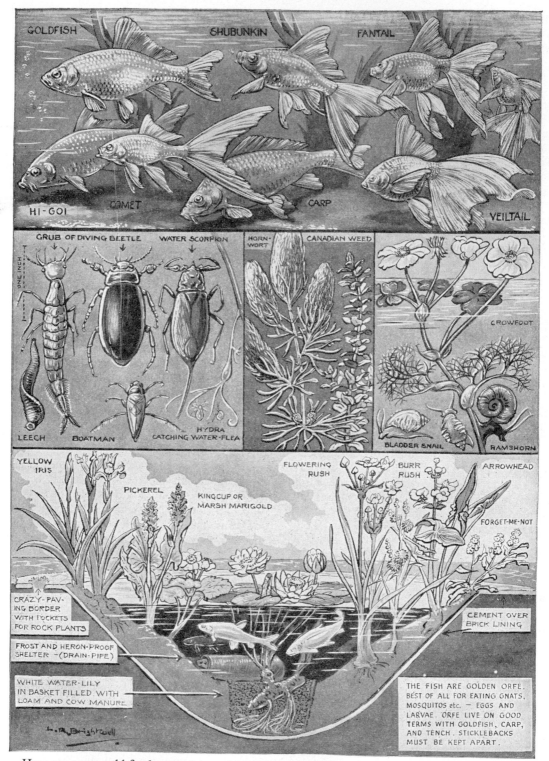

Here are some cold freshwater fishes which could be kept in a large garden pond. *Centre row left:* some of the fishes' foes; *centre and right:* some useful plants and animals.

twenty-four hours. Keep the tank free of dust and draughts with a glass cover until the fry are at least eight weeks old. A sure sign of the male gourami being ready for family affairs is a bright red spreading over his breast and feelers. The female becomes fuller and rounder about the same time.

THE FISH THAT IS LIT UP

Other fishes which do well in a community tank are such live bearers as the swordtail, the platy, and the molly. Good egg layers are the pearl danio, harlequin, zebra, black widow and white cloud mountain minnow. With experience you will in time learn to breed the neon tetra which looks just as though lit up by neon light.

But, as with keeping cold freshwater fishes, there is nothing like joining the junior branch of your local Aquarium Club. For such a club is a Mutual Aid Society, where everyone is ready to help and advise everybody else. There are outings, lectures, and often a good library. In fact everything you can want to add to the pleasures of a hobby that can never grow tiresome, for there is so much to learn.

DO YOU KNOW?

Who is " the old man in the fur coat "?

" The old man in the fur coat " is the polar bear. He was given this name by hunters who went to his cold Arctic home to seek him.

His fur coat protects him both from the extreme cold and from his enemies. It is a creamy white in colour and is difficult to see against the background of his snowy home.

Other protections against the cold are the thick hairs under each foot. These not only keep his feet warm but prevent him from slipping when he walks on the ice.

" The old man in the fur coat " is a very fine swimmer, and loves to splash about in the icy water. His small head and long neck make it easy for him to swim quickly.

He is also a fine fisherman, and has a cunning way of catching seals. He finds a hole in the ice where they come up to breathe and lies down beside it, keeping very still. When a seal comes up the bear pounces on it and stuns it with a blow of his strong paws. Then he drags it out of the water and takes it home for supper.

Why are birds' eggs not all the same colour?

Nature shows her wisdom in many ways. She has caused her bird family to lay eggs of different colours so that they will be safe from prying eyes.

For example, the birds whose nests are in the sand or among rocks lay eggs with spots and blotches on them, so that they fit into their background and are not easily seen. The eggs of the tern look so like the pebbles among which they lie that it is almost impossible to see them.

You will find that the birds who nest in hedges usually lay eggs of greeny-blue. But birds who nest in obscure holes, where no one is likely to find them, lay white eggs.

It is interesting to find that many of the birds who nest among rocks lay eggs that are pointed at one end rather than rounded. This prevents them from rolling off the narrow ledges of the rocks. In this clever way Nature has saved many of her bird families.

Why do factories have tall chimneys?

Great factories are worked by steam power. The steam is made by means of heating large boilers. Coal is used for this purpose, and, as you know, the smoke from coal is very black and full of soot.

If the smoke from all the factories in a large town came out of low chimneys people would scarcely be able to see or breathe.

So tall chimneys have to be built to take the smoke a long way above the streets. Then the wind is able to carry the smoke away. Long chimneys make a stronger draught through the boilers, and thus make the fires hotter.

Even with tall chimneys the black smoke from the great boilers of factories makes large towns very dirty. So there is now a law making factories take as much soot as possible out of the smoke before it leaves the chimney.

Then there is another law which says that no factory chimney may send out black smoke for more than a few minutes in each hour.

THE WONDERFUL WASP

OVER two thousand years ago, the great Greek dramatist, Aristophanes, wrote a comedy called *The Wasps*. Though it is seldom played to-day, a noted British musician, Dr. Ralph Vaughan-Williams, born in 1872, has made that almost forgotten comedy famous by composing an over-ture to it. It begins with a whirring, high-pitched buzzing sound which, when rendered by many skilled violin-ists, has a quite terrify-ing effect, so perfectly does it mimic the angry noise made by a suddenly aroused wasps' nest.

Most people think of wasps going in great swarms like bees, but most wasps are sol-itary, or at least live in quite small colonies. The majority agree, however, in wearing a rather striking dress of black and yellow arranged in a variety of ways. It is what naturalists call " warn-ing coloration," and is such an arresting

A worker wasp emerging from the nest to set off in search of food.

mixture that it has been adopted, for peaceable and helpful purposes, by the Automobile Association.

There are many hundreds of kinds of wasps, some tropical kinds being almost as large as the smallest humming-birds and capable of giving very dangerous stings. About twenty-three kinds are found in our islands, but only seven, including the large hornet, live in big colonies sharing one nest. The picture shows you how to tell these seven wasps at a glance.

HOW TO CURE A WASP STING

Nobody loves the wasp, but it is still one of our insect friends. As you will see in the picture, it destroys all manner of pests and also prevents some other insects from becom-

ing too numerous. The wasp is disliked mostly for its sting and this can be painful, but if dealt with at once is soon cured. When a wasp stings, it squirts acid into our blood with an instrument just like that used by a dentist when he " numbs " the gum before taking out a tooth. Since the fluid which the wasp squirts into one is an acid, the best cure is an alkali, i.e. some such sub-stance as common soda or ammonia. A poultice of ammonia and bicarbonate of soda, if applied im-mediately, will give instant relief.

A bees' nest or comb is made almost en-tirely of wax, but a wasps' nest is built up very largely of paper, and paper of the most up-to-date kind —wood pulp. The an-cient Egyptians made paper of a sort out of the tall reed called papyrus at least three thousand years B.C. Judging by the rather few fossil remains of insects at present known, it is safe to say that wasps were making modern paper at least thirty-five million years before civilised man thought of cutting down trees and turning the timber into a pulp, which he afterwards rolled out into sheets of the stuff on which these words are printed. The wasp makes the paper by biting off rotten wood and chewing it.

MEAT-EATING WASPS

A wasp colony or swarm lasts only from spring to autumn, and though managed roughly on the lines of a bee-hive, it differs in a variety of ways. The young grubs, for example, are not fed only on honey. Animal food plays a big part in their nourishment,

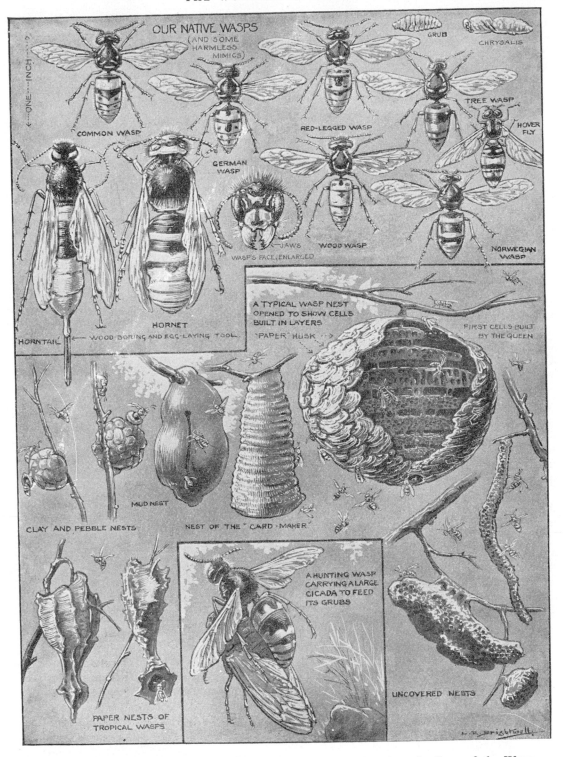

OUR NATIVE WASPS (AND SOME HARMLESS MIMICS)

ONE INCH

GRUB

CHRYSALIS

COMMON WASP

GERMAN WASP

RED-LEGGED WASP

TREE WASP

HOVER FLY

JAWS

WOOD WASP

WASP'S FACE, ENLARGED

NORWEGIAN WASP

HORNTAIL

HORNET

WOOD-BORING AND EGG-LAYING TOOL

A TYPICAL WASP NEST OPENED TO SHOW CELLS BUILT IN LAYERS

"PAPER" HUSK

FIRST CELLS BUILT BY THE QUEEN

MUD NEST

CLAY AND PEBBLE NESTS

NEST OF THE "CARD-MAKER"

A HUNTING WASP CARRYING A LARGE CICADA TO FEED ITS GRUBS

UNCOVERED NESTS

PAPER NESTS OF TROPICAL WASPS

Every picture tells a story. This one gives a fascinating glimpse into the lives of the Wasp family, showing their different homes and how they are built. There is no doubt that we have much to learn from these industrious insects.

and it is this which makes the wasps so useful to man. They can be a great nuisance when they raid the honey or jam pot, but they do good work in killing caterpillars and keeping the spider population within reasonable bounds.

The hunting wasps are mostly solitary, or living in very small parties, and most are specialists, i.e. they keep to one particular kind of prey on which to feed their young. For instance, one sort of hunting wasp uses only spiders. Having laid her eggs in a paper-built nest, she seeks out a suitable spider and stings it just enough to paralyse but not to kill it, so that its meat will keep fresh for days or even weeks. As a result, the wasp grub, when it hatches, finds beside its cradle a food supply that will last it until it is ready to turn into a chrysalis, and finally creep out into the open as a perfect wasp.

This all sounds rather horrible to us humans, but it must be remembered that the insect has a most minute brain, and it is more than unlikely that any real pain is felt. It is certainly very unpleasant to see a crushed insect still kicking, or a wasp's head cut from the body, still eating jam; but these movements are quite mechanical, and very like the wheels of a clockwork engine still turning over long after the engine has been thrown on to its side or upside down. The wheels just turn until the spring or the supply of oil or steam has run its course.

When some of the social wasps build a big underground nest near an occupied house or a school, it must be got rid of by pouring in some strong poison at night when the insects are asleep, and then plugging all the entrances with earth in order that the poison may do its work. But to kill every wasp just because it *is* a wasp would soon mean plagues of all kinds of insects and other creatures.

FILLING THE FAMILY LARDER

For instance, in most warm countries there abounds a wonderful plant bug called the cicada. If you go to the South of France or Italy you can hear these big-winged insects making their loud " chick-a-chicka-chick " noise high above the hum of passing traffic. One could have too many cicadas, and, to correct this, a family of hunting wasps feeds its babies entirely on cicadas. The mother

wasp first paralyses a cicada, much larger than herself, by stinging it; but now comes the problem how to get it home to a cluster of eggs that will soon hatch out into hungry wasp maggots. She overcomes this difficulty by dragging the heavy cicada up to the top of a rock, or hauling it to the edge of a window-sill. This gives her a good take-off, and so at last she brings her bulky prize to the family larder.

Another group of wasps feeds the young only on different kinds of beetle grubs, and yet another wasp family specialises in hunting spiders. The largest of all the wasps, a very fierce creature called salius, even attacks the great hairy bird-eating spider which is shown in another picture capturing a banana opossum.

Although the spider has a body much larger than that of a house mouse, and is armed with powerful poison fangs besides having eight legs to the wasp's six, the wasp nearly always wins. Often there is a desperate fight in which the two roll over and over together, locked amongst each other's powerfully clawed legs; but in the end the wasp's sting proves stronger than the spider's fangs, and the ogre of the banana grove is dragged away, leaving its prey, the banana opossums, locusts, humming-birds and lizards, in peace for the time being.

The homes of these wasps are as varied as the creatures they hunt. Some of the smaller kinds make a few cells inside any handy shelter, such as a cotton reel or a blind tassel. Others, called mud-daubers, make nests of clay, and one shown in the picture covers the clay with quite heavy pieces of stone. Some of the paper nests, as you see, take quite beautiful shapes, and even the nest of the common wasp, whether underground or hanging from a branch, makes a charming pattern not unlike those handsome fungi we meet fringing old tree-stumps in the autumn woods. The English hornet, largest of our native wasps and disliked because it sometimes raids bee-hives, nests chiefly in rotten wood; but like most wasps, though well armed, it is not really malicious and will seldom sting unless it is first attacked.

A HARD-WORKING QUEEN

A wasps' nest and colony is always set going by a queen. The first few top cells or layers of comb shown in the picture of the

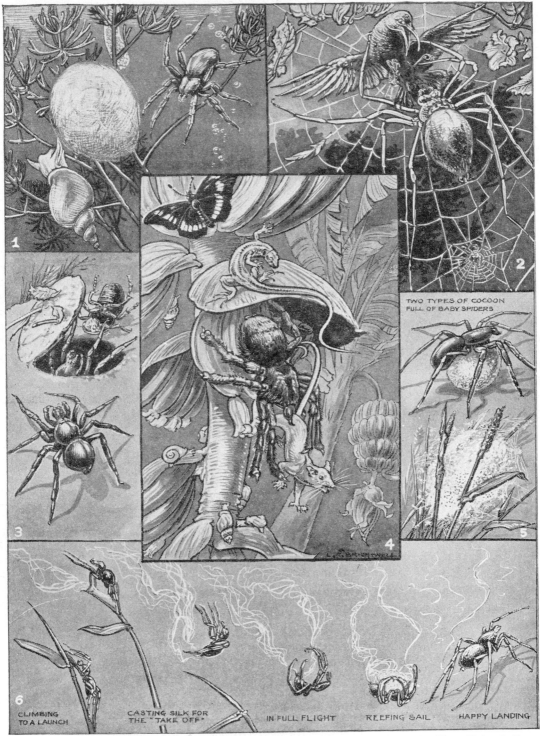

CLIMBING TO A LAUNCH   CASTING SILK FOR THE "TAKE OFF"   IN FULL FLIGHT   REEFING SAIL   HAPPY LANDING

One of the wasp's victims, the spider, lives an exciting life. 1. Spider with silken diving bell. 2. A bird-eating spider. 3. Trap door spider catching beetle. 4. Indian spider catching banana opossum. 5. Spider caring for its young. 6. Gossamer spider.

half-opened nest are the work of one queen, who, having started the town, so to speak, lays a batch of worker wasp and drone, or male, eggs. Once these have turned into perfect wasps she ceases to be a labourer and becomes a queen indeed, and spends the rest of her life laying eggs and so founding a big and prosperous hive.

One of the most wonderful things in the story of animal life is the manner in which some quite harmless creatures escape from or scare off enemies by imitating animals which are well known to be dangerous. A number of flies that cannot sting mimic the warning colours of the wasp. Now a fly cannot say to itself, " I am harmless and the world is full of enemies, so I will dress up as though I was one of those dangerous wasps." What really happens is that a fly which chances to look a little like a wasp is avoided, and those of its children which inherit the wasp colouring from their parents have a better chance of living. So the more like wasps these flies look, the more they will be avoided. It is rather like blue eyes or red hair being handed on from grandfather to father, from father to son, and so on.

A HARMLESS GIANT

The largest of all our wasp-coloured flies is the horntail. It is bigger than a hornet, makes a loud buzzing sound, quite a roar when flying, and is altogether quite a frightening beast. But the " sting " at the end of its tail is not a sting: it is only an instrument for boring tunnels in wood and then for laying eggs at the bottom of the tunnel. So strong is this egg-laying tool that it can even bore deep into wood that has been covered with a sheet of lead. People have been surprised to see one of these false wasps crawl out of a table-leg made from unseasoned timber.

But some friends as well as foes have adopted the wasps' warning attire. A large handsome ichneumon fly, dressed wasp-fashion, finds where the horntail has been and, with an even longer and stronger egg-laying tool, plants its own eggs on the grub of the horntail, and so the work of wood destruction is nipped in the bud. Yet another wasp-coloured friend is the hover fly which we see standing in the air above the flower-beds like a miniature helicopter. Never harm one. Its ugly children spend a long and greedy infancy eating green-fly. So the wasps are wonderful insects, never to be destroyed except when so numerous as to be a plague. They do their part in keeping the balance of Nature—a very uncertain balance at any time.

JERUSALEM

And did those feet in ancient time
    Walk upon England's mountains green?
And was the holy Lamb of God
    On England's pleasant pastures seen?

And did the Countenance Divine
    Shine forth upon our clouded hills?
And was Jerusalem builded here
    Among these dark Satanic mills?

Bring me my bow of burning gold!
    Bring me my arrows of desire!
Bring me my spear! O clouds, unfold!
    Bring me my chariot of fire!

I will not cease from mental fight,
    Nor shall my sword sleep in my hand,
Till we have built Jerusalem
    In England's green and pleasant land.
                                    William Blake

THE HAND BEHIND THE TRAWLER

IT is only about eighty years since the great scientist, Thomas Henry Huxley, when writing of the riches of the sea, declared "Fish where you like, when you like, and how you like." But vast as the sea is, we now know that catching enough fish to feed the world's fast increasing population is not so easy as it may sound. In Huxley's day there were few big trawlers, and the sea was not poisoned by the waste oil thrown out of diesel-driven ships' engines. Neither were rivers poisoned with all sorts of chemicals from bankside factories, and there was far less sewage poured into the sea near big ports and holiday resorts. With the invention of the big deep-sea steam trawler the finding of new and unspoilt fishing grounds

in Bute, Port Erin in the Isle of Man, and others also at Aberdeen, Conway and Lowestoft. Usually a "lab" also has a big public aquarium attached, and if ever you get a chance you must certainly visit one. For not only is the aquarium cared for by scientists, but every laboratory has a specially equipped vessel which does nothing but collect plants and animals for study, so that a "Marine lab" aquarium is always the very best of its kind. Every tank is a lovely picture of the sea bed, and as full of colour and beautiful forms as any flower garden.

JIG-SAW PUZZLE OF SEA LIFE

The laboratory is not open to the public;

THE BUSY LIFE OF A MARINE "LAB" :— GENERAL VIEW OF A TYPICAL RESEARCH LABORATORY WHERE STUDENTS AND OFFICIAL MARINE BIOLOGISTS OF ALL NATIONS CAN MEET AND WORK TO SOLVE THE ENDLESS PROBLEMS OF THE SEA, IN THE CENTRE IS A LARGE TABLE TANK, AND ON EITHER SIDE CUBICLES OR TABLES, ONE TO EACH WORKER

became a serious problem. Also the trawler quite unavoidably kills more fish than are wanted. Young and undersized fish are caught and killed along with big marketable fish.

So it came about that in 1872 scientists realised something must be done to prevent wastage. To do this one has to study every kind of life in the sea, how one kind of animal affects another, how they travel and at what times of year, and how animals multiply. A first step was to build aquariums and laboratories for the study of sea life. The first two big aquariums were at Naples, and Brighton. Brighton Aquarium is now little better than a ruin, but Naples has become world famous. Fourteen years after Naples Aquarium was opened, there was built the now equally famous Marine Laboratory at Plymouth, and soon after there were set up similar "labs" at Cullercoats in Northumberland, at Millport

it is for workers only. But let us, in imagination, push through this door marked "Private", and explore what lies beyond. We pass through room after room filled with rows of tables, and alongside each table is a sink, a chair, and many shelves crowded with bottles and jars full of chemicals for preserving sea beasts and plants. Scientists interested in special branches of study pay so much a week to rent a table, and here they strive to piece together the life histories of the sea's vast population. In the sea round Plymouth alone there are over a hundred and fifty kinds of fish, more than a thousand sorts of shellfish, two hundred sorts of corals and anemones . . . altogether nearly four thousand kinds of animals, besides over seven hundred sorts of seaweed. When you consider that many of these creatures are very difficult to keep in confinement, and are most active after dark, you will see that piecing

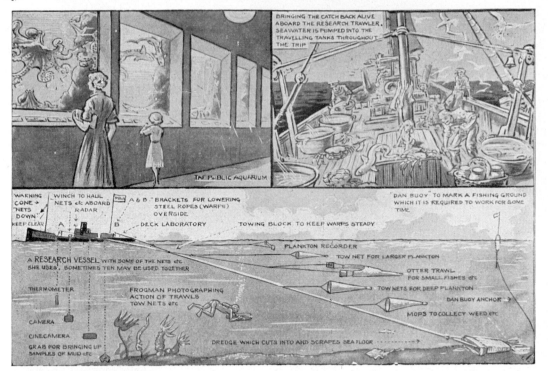

together the great jig-saw puzzle of life in the sea is not easy. To-day we still know very little, sometimes nothing at all, of the private lives of thousands of kinds of quite common sea animals.

"But," say some people gazing at all the "lab" workers bent over their microscopes, and "messing about" with all kinds of tiny animals, which, one must agree are quite uneatable, "how does all this help to fill my pantry?" It helps a great deal. In the "food chain" picture you will see how one animal may eat only microscopic plants, but in its turn is eaten by some other creature, which is eaten by one of our food fish, such as a herring or a plaice. Very rightly the scientist argues that if the microscopic plants are increased there will in time be bigger and better plaice. This was tried out in a Scottish loch. Tons of phosphate and other chemicals known to be plant foods, were tipped into the water, and sure enough the plaice grew twice as large and fat as the plaice leading a haphazard, eat-what-you-can-find sort of life in the sea outside.

INTERESTING DISCOVERIES

That is just one example of the useful discoveries now being made every year in our marine laboratories. But that is only a fraction

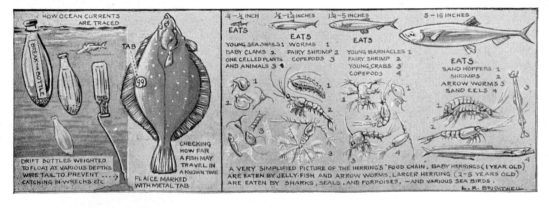

of a "lab's" work. How far do fish travel for example? To find out, the Research Vessel dredges up thousands of some particular kind of fish and each is marked with a numbered tab, rather in the way that birds are ringed, or whales marked with little harmless silver harpoons. When a marked fish is caught by an angler, or picked up by a fishing vessel's net, the fish is sent by post back to the "lab," and there the staff can tell at once how far the fish has swum in so many months or years, and how much it has grown on its travels.

A fish does not always travel by sheer fin power. Often it is carried about by ocean currents. But what currents? To find out, the Research Vessel throws overboard hundreds of " drift-bottles " rather like those used for soda water. Inside each bottle is a folded card, asking any one who finds the bottle to fill in on the card where it was found, the direction of the wind, and other useful details. This card is posted back to the "lab", O.H.M.S., and so useful information is obtained about ocean currents.

All life in the sea, with the exception of sea birds, whales, and some big fishes, begins as plankton. Plankton is a Greek word meaning the " wanderers," and it is used to cover all the minute floating life which on a dark night sometimes makes the sea look as though it was burning with a weird bluish light. The big jelly-fish we find cast up on the beach, the seaweeds growing on the rocks, and all the creatures we see at the fishmonger's, whether they be oysters and lobsters, or cod, plaice, herring and so forth, all begin life as plankton. In the tropics plankton is so thick it can be used as a sort of fish soup or even spread, like meat paste, on bread and butter.

COLLECTING SPECIMENS

Since most animals and plants when in the plankton stage look quite unlike their grown-up selves you will see how important it is to know just what little plankton beast is the young of some particular animal. To find out all this every "lab" has a staff of specially trained experts, working out plankton problems the year round. To collect this plankton for study the Research Vessel uses either a fine meshed net, rather like a butterfly net, or a curious piece of apparatus called a Plankton Recorder. It is very like a roll of camera film,

and so arranged that as it is towed behind the vessel the film is steadily wound off one spool, and wound on to the other, the film picking up plankton as it unwinds. The receiving spool automatically preserves any plankton caught, and so the scientist knows just how much and what sort of plankton has been caught in some particular part of the sea.

These are just a few of the jobs going on the year round in our marine laboratories in order to learn something of the harvest of the sea, for it must be remembered the harvest of the sea is a harvest which man has not sown. But though we cannot sow and cultivate sea crops, as we can grow vegetables and breed cattle and poultry on land, we can to some extent control it.

LAWS FOR SAFEGUARDING FISH

For example we can make laws which give various animals a " close season," a time during which they may not be caught, and so give them a chance to breed and multiply in peace. On the Sussex coast it is unlawful to collect winkles between the 17th of May and the 17th of September. Another way in which sea crops can be protected is to " fix " the size of the mesh in fishing nets and so give young fish a chance to escape and grow into big marketable fishes. A plaice less than seven and a half inches long must not be sold, neither must a crab under five inches across the shell.

When a "lab" finds certain fishing grounds are being swept clean of fish it tells the Board of Fisheries in London, and the grounds are closed for a time, to give them a rest. Gunboats of the Royal Navy police the seas to see that these laws are obeyed. So you will realise that a "lab" is a very busy place. There is always plenty happening, life is never dull. I work a great deal in marine "labs," and have had many strange experiences. Late one night I met an escaped octopus solemnly walking downstairs, and on another occasion a conger eel tank burst throwing ten seven-foot conger into the public corridor. They had to be put in a big reservoir while the tank was being mended. When the time came to return them, the only way to get them out was by angling with rod and line. There were some iron girders in the reservoir, and if a conger twists his tail round a girder he just stays put. A lot of fishing tackle was broken, until the very hungry conger (we really had to starve them out) gave themselves up.

To-day there are a hundred or more "labs" spread along the coastlines of the world, for everyone now realises how important they are to our food supplies. But it was not always like this. In the early days of "labs" old fishermen were suspicious of the scientist, and regarded him as a rival, not, as they now know him to be, their best friend. I remember once an old salt giving me the " bearing," i.e. the exact point on an ocean chart, of a particularly good fishing ground. But when I came to work it out on a big scale map, it led me fifty miles inland!

Those days are gone for ever, and when you see a marine "lab," standing—as most do—high up on the rocks above the sea, you will know it is a sentinel, safeguarding our larders, and taking care we shall always have good meals of tasty sea-foods.

The trawlermen laying the trawl nets in the sea.

The motor trawler *Princess Elizabeth*, a modern type of vessel suited for work in the deep seas. The trawler crews are brave men who sail hundreds of miles out to sea in order to catch the fish we need for food. Cod is one of the chief catches they take from the depths.

THE MIRACLE OF SPONGES

WHAT is a sponge? To most people it is a complete mystery. It looks so like a plant, and indeed it is so plant-like that to grow plenty of bath sponges for the market you can take cuttings from a living sponge and each will in time grow to be as large as the parent sponge from which it was cut. All the same, a sponge is an animal. But what is an animal? The up-to-date definition is any living thing which must feed on organic (i.e. growing) matter to keep alive. A sponge cannot get its nourishment from soil, air or water as can plants, except a few parasitic kinds. It must feed on stuff that is either alive, or once was alive. Therefore it is an animal, though very low in the animal scale.

If you take one of the small sponges, or even a piece of one, shown in the drawing, and place it in a dish of sea-water you can see it behave very differently from any plant. Scatter some dust on the water, or better still put a little carmine in it, and at once the dust or the carmine will be seen to swirl about. The sponge is doing something to the water.

The microscope can show us just what is happening, for it reveals a piece of sponge as a sort of maze. It is full of galleries leading to little rooms, and in each room will be a number of tiny whips, much too small for the naked eye to see. These whips are perpetually lashing the water, and the currents they set up bring in minute floating plants on which the sponge feeds.

These currents also bring in fresh sea-water full of life-giving oxygen, and the stale sea-water emptied of its oxygen and full of stale food scraps is sent shooting out through larger galleries or canals. And so the rather dead-looking sponge is full of life and as feverishly busy as a factory with its lathes and engines of many kinds.

THE SPONGE HAS A SKELETON

This wonderful discovery was made by a Dr. Grant only a little more than a century ago. He found too, that a sponge, which when alive is full of soft pulpy matter, is held together by a sort of skeleton, made of calcium carbonate, silica (flint) or horn. And this skeleton is built up of beautiful little structures called " spicules " and taking the most fantastic shapes, suggesting darts, feathers, snow crystals, anchors and many other familiar objects.

The sponge we use in the bath is simply the horny skeleton of a once-living sponge, after the soft pulpy matter has decayed, been washed away, and the skeleton left to dry and bleach in strong sunlight.

There are a few fresh-water sponges. A very lovely bright green one is common in our country and often seen on the lock-gates of canals. But most of the many thousands of kinds of sponges known are marine, and, judging by fossil remains, some sorts were abundant more than two hundred million years ago.

About a hundred kinds are found in home waters and a few of these are shown in the picture. One of the commonest is the Crumb or Bread Sponge, which forms thick sheets, fawny brown or bright yellow on the under-sides of rocks left uncovered at extreme low tide. It looks very like a mass of tiny extinct volcanoes, such as one sees on photographs of the moon. But these little volcanoes on the sponge are far from extinct. They are the out-flows, part of the sponge's feeding, breathing and drainage system.

The inflow openings are much smaller and dotted all over the surface generally. Deep down in the tissues of the sponge are minute chambers which at certain times of year release enormous quantities of eggs, that are shot out and for a short while swim by means of rows of restlessly-moving hairs. Gradually they settle down on the sea-bed, and give rise to colonies of Bread Crumb Sponge.

There is still much we do not clearly understand about sponges. How long, for example, do they live? This probably depends on the size of the sponge. The Bread Crumb Sponge is believed to be an annual.

Another pretty sponge you will find attached to the fine red seaweeds fringing tidal pools is the little Flask Sponge (Sycon), a good species for testing the breathing and feeding currents, as already described. Another too common sponge is the Boring Sponge. Often you will have picked up oyster shells or even pieces of

Some queer sponges: 1. Bath sponge; 2. Branching sponge; 3. Flask sponges; 4. Breadcrumb sponge and a slug that lives on it. 5. Neptune's Bath; 6. Venus Flower Basket; 7. Tufted sponge; 8. Glass Rope sponge; 9. Inset, in circle: magnified slice of breadcrumb sponge.

limestone, riddled with hundreds of small holes. These are the work of the Boring Sponge, which gradually rots to pieces any stony substance it attacks and so does great damage to limestone breakwaters. No definite remedy for this dangerous pest has yet been found.

THE CRAB WHO CARRIES A SPONGE

Though only a few kinds of sponge are of use to man, all play a big part in the complex jigsaw puzzle of life in the sea. Sponge eggs serve to nourish some of our food fishes in their baby days, and many big sponges form safe retreats for crabs, prawns, sea-worms and all manner of shellfish. One of our hermit crabs always tucks its soft defenceless tail into a sponge, and another fairly common crab actually carries a sponge over its back like a small boy hiding for fun under a tin bath.

In tropic seas and the Ocean Abyss are many picturesque sponges, some of enormous size. A beautiful one is the Venus Flower Basket, found at a depth of 540 feet (90 fathoms) off the Philippine Islands, and even more wonderful is the famous Glass-Rope Sponge of Japan and Portugal. It is anchored in deep mud by a tuft of enormously long spicules that look exactly as though made of the finest spun glass, and are immensely strong. Some sponges are so densely packed with spicules as to seem almost as if made of stone. But the sponges we use are all of the horny kind, and are cultivated on a big scale in the West Indies and the Mediterranean.

A bucket with a glass bottom is used for peering down into the water, and the sponges are fished up by means of a spike on the end of a long pole. Great care must be taken when growing sponges by means of cuttings, to keep a piece of the outer skin attached to each fragment. It takes about seven years for a cubic inch of sponge to become big enough for a place of honour in the bathroom. No wonder a good bath sponge is rather dear.

WRITTEN IN MARCH

The cock is crowing,
The stream is flowing,
The small birds twitter,
The lake doth glitter,
The green field sleeps in the sun;
The oldest and youngest
Are at work with the strongest;
The cattle are grazing,
Their heads never raising;
There are forty feeding like one!

Like an army defeated
The snow hath retreated,
And now doth fare ill
On the top of the bare hill;
The ploughboy is whooping—anon—anon:
There's joy in the mountains;
There's life in the fountains;
Small clouds are sailing,
Blue sky prevailing;
The rain is over and gone!

William Wordsworth

THE FIRST LIVING THINGS

ABOUT half-way between the birth of the Earth and the present there occurred the most momentous event in the history of time. In some unknown place, through some unknown process, life appeared.

For countless millions of years the Earth was far too hot for anything to live. There were no rivers or seas for the rain that fell vaporised as soon as it came near enough to the hot surface. Even when the temperature fell below the condensation point of steam, and water remained on the surface, millions of years must have passed before it was cool enough for anything to live in it. The primeval oceans were probably fresh water, until rivers had carried into them sufficient minerals to give them their well-known salty taste.

WHAT IS MEANT BY " LIFE "

In the beginning there were many things that formed, moved and probably had the appearance of something alive. But when we come to consider the advent of life, it is as well to remember that we are largely playing with words. What, in fact, do we actually mean by " life "? If it is the capacity of movement, then all matter is " alive," for everything expands and contracts when subjected to heat and cold. If it is the capacity of growth, then crystals must be " alive " for they certainly grow. And, like us, they grow to a certain size and then stop. Their variety and beauty stagger the imagination. Ask your science master to show you some ordinary snowflakes under a microscope the next time it snows.

It is not in fact easy to say just where living matter begins and inorganic matter ends! And so, in the middle of time, there was probably no spectacular change-over as it were, but a gradual process.

As the ages went by and the seas cooled, more complex molecules formed and then parted, formed and then parted. This was repeated an infinite number of times until one day the first one-celled organism representing life, as we now know it, appeared. Just what caused it is not known. Perhaps it was brought about by solar radiation, or a stray lightning discharge, or even pure chance. The first life-cell probably survived only a short time before it succumbed to excessive heat or cold or the vibrations of a primeval earthquake. Hundreds, perhaps, thousands, of years passed before the ever-changing pattern of molecules again fitted together to form life.

ONE-CELLED ORGANISMS

Many times in those early days the world must have alternatively been with and then barren of life! Finally, however, one-celled organisms formed and did not fade away, and since that day, many millions of years back in the dim and distant past, Earth has had life. That is to say there have been things exhibiting the four basic signs of life: movement, growth, food digestion and a capacity for reproduction; living things, that is, with an instinct for self-preservation, a capacity for development and a tenuous thread of heredity.

The first one-celled things were probably made of protoplasm such as exists to-day, a substance rather like a thin jelly, and contained within themselves a darker spot, known as the nucleus, which was concerned with reproduction.

They were exceedingly small—much too small to be seen with the naked eye—and were probably about the size of a present-day microbe, a thousand of them end to end would have measured only 1/32 inch. An area measuring 1/32 in. by 1/32 in. could have contained one million of them, and a 1/32 in. cube could have held 1,000 million of the first inhabitants of the Earth.

The first living things may have formed in sheltered waters exposed to sunshine and were probably more plant than animal although here, as in the case of living and non-living matter, the distinction between the two great kinds of life, animal and vegetable, is very loosely defined.

ANIMALS AND PLANTS

Animals are born, grow, reproduce and die —but so do plants—plants eat, drink and breathe and are sensitive to warmth and cold like animals. Most plants possess chlorophyll, a green substance, but animals never do. It is the chlorophyll which, with the help of sunlight, enables plants to make foodstuffs from water and carbon dioxide gas. Animals, on the other hand, can only consume foodstuffs already made by plants or other animals. Plants show relatively little movement compared with animals, as their chief food is readily available in the air. Plants have a skeleton made of cellulose, a substance no animal possesses. This is, perhaps, the only difference between animal and plant to which there is no exception.

There would be no movement amongst the first plants on Earth. They had neither the need, nor the ability to swim. In time, however, movement became essential if plants were to keep their position against currents and, later, were to escape from enemies. These early blobs of jelly (like the amœbæ of our ponds to-day) probably moved by extending part of their bodies in the direction they wished to go and then closing up again. Similarly, food would be eaten by pushing out lobes from their bodies to encircle the tiny particles, which would then be absorbed.

THE APPEARANCE OF MOLLUSCS

After the jelly-blobs came the molluscs, soft-bodied jelly-fish, starfish and oysters, and arthropods, different in that they had segmented bodies with jointed limbs, one or more pairs of which in front acted as jaws.

The shape of the creatures in the fast-running rivers became more and more stream-lined. Fins became more flexible and jaws and teeth appeared. In time such creatures found their way down to the sea, where the ability to move gave them immediate superiority over the slower, crawling molluscs and arthropods. As a result they not only survived but thrived, and by to-day have evolved into 20,000 different species, including cod, herring, mackerel, bass, sharks and skate—the common fish of the sea.

THE STORY OF THE EARTH

Our knowledge of the past comes to us in traces of early life preserved as fossils; that is, imprints in rocks revealing to us the external shape of creatures long since extinct. This record in the rocks resembles a gigantic book

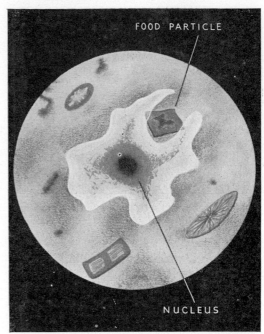

FOOD PARTICLE

NUCLEUS

This diagram shows an amœba, greatly magnified, life's simplest form on earth to-day.

—a story book telling us the story of the Earth. It is not a complete book, nor is it easy to read. Some of the pages are creased, some are torn and a good three-quarters are missing completely—lost in changes that saw great continents thrust up, then eroded away, thrust up again and eroded away, time and time again. Even the story of the continents we know to-day is not at all clear; the pages are creased, torn, folded, out of place and badly smudged.

It is not surprising then that of the earliest life forms no trace remains. The coves and ponds which sheltered them have vanished in the mists of time.

For more than 1,000 million years of life no record remains. Creatures existing during this time are thought to have been invertebrate, that is, boneless, and were too soft to have left any mark which could survive the ravages of time. But life there must have been, for by the time we come to the continuous fossil record, a wide variety in life forms is evident and nervous systems, digestive tracts, body cavities and sensory organs had all evolved.

THE CAMBRIAN PERIOD

To find the first outlines of living creatures we have to turn the pages to the period called

Fossilised bones, petrified by the chemical action of the rocks which covered them.

the Cambrian, which started 500 million years ago. Cambrian is the name given to very old rocky layers found in Wales and it has also been given to similar rocks found elsewhere in the world. Perhaps the most important development of this period, which lasted 100 million years, was the appearance of the protective shells and skins which enabled fossils to form, and so we have the first well-filled pages of our book. Bacteria, minute globular organisms, generally regarded as the lowest form of life, are the earliest living things that have left traces in the rocks. Apart from the bacteria, the next oldest remains are those of so called sponges. These sponges, organisms very different from any now living, formed colonies, united by their body walls. They were covered with a fine hair which extracted from the surrounding water the nourishment required for survival and for a while they covered the earth. They spread across the oceans, building reefs along the continental shelves from pole to pole. Then, sometime in the middle of the Cambrian era, the sponges died out.

Another early creature was the lamp-shell, so called because of its similarity to an ancient Roman lamp. This species total about one-third of all Cambrian age fossils discovered. Then came a greater variety of molluscs, the snails, jointed worms, and the even more successful arthropods. The most familiar of these were trilobites, a cross between a lobster and a crab. Most of them were about 1 inch long though some exceeded 18 inches. They were the giants of their time and flourished on

earth for a span 75 times as long as Man's whole existence.

THE ORDOVICIAN AGE

After the Cambrian period, came the Ordovician age, which lasted from 425 million to 350 million years ago. This period is notable for its tremendous floods which at times may have covered the entire land surface. It saw a great increase in the invertebrate species and by the time the age drew to its end most of the animals had acquired thick defensive shells. The reign of the trilobites passed to nautiloids, a type of mollusc resembling a cross between a squid and octopus but protected by shells up to 15 feet long.

In the Silurian period, which followed the Ordovician, sea scorpions attained domination of the earth. It is fortunate that these are now long extinct. Horny-coated and living by preying on other animals, some attained a length of nine feet. The first true jawed fish appeared in this period, the acanthodians. Although only a few inches in length they had a strange resemblance to a modern shark. Their appearance meant that fish were well up the ladder of evolution.

As the Silurian Age drew to a close about 325 million years ago, life itself began the second most important chapter in the record of the rocks. Then, for the first time, evidence appeared of life on land.

Trilobite—one of the earliest creatures of which fossilised remains have been found.

The formation of coal. An impression of a primeval swamp of the Upper Carboniferous period. about 250 million years ago, the remains of which formed the great coalfields in Britain.

The Evolution of the World

THE GREAT AGE OF REPTILES

FOR millions of years life on earth existed only in water. Then, towards the end of the Silurian age, about 330 million years ago, there occurred the Devonian period of great geological change. New mountain ranges were thrust upwards and new continents appeared. Over vast areas the ocean bottom appeared above sea level leaving the sediment of untold years of marine life high and dry.

For something like 1,000 million years marine plants had drifted aimlessly in the primeval seas. With the appearance of large areas of richly fertilised dry land, however, the earth witnessed a transformation the like of which has not been repeated. Within the comparatively short space of 50 million years there was a spectacular spread of great plants across the then barren surface of the earth. Ferns and leafy plants sprouted everywhere. Simple seaweeds evolved into magnificent trees. At first the plants were restricted to moist lowlands but, in time, seeds evolved permitting reproduction without water and growth spread to the dry highlands. This great age of plant growth saw the appearance of the lycopod,

which, reaching a height of as much as 100 ft., was one of the mightiest trees ever known.

THE BEGINNINGS OF COAL

The trees of this period are of particular interest and importance to-day, even though the last of them decayed and rotted hundreds of millions of years ago. We call their remains coal! The best coal is composed of compressed bark, stems and roots, and to form the rich seams we now mine the accumulation of the remains of decayed trees must have reached incredible proportions whilst the forests were growing. Century after century the trees grew, died and rotted, until their remains attained a thickness of a hundred feet or more. The carpet of decaying matter must have been so thick that it is a wonder how the plants that came last managed to grow at all. Perhaps fierce floods uprooted trees in one place and laid them on top of the earliest plants. But whatever happened with the passing of time the rotting vegetation became heavily compressed, partly by its own weight and partly by layers of rock which came to cover it in later ages. These great coal-forming ages are known as the lower and upper Carboniferous periods.

THE DEVELOPMENT OF AMPHIBIANS

The spread of vegetation across the surface of the planet meant that for the first time a source of food was available to tempt creatures from the seas on to land. The first step was the appearance of fish which could breathe. From these air-breathing fish it was a small step to the first amphibians, creatures with fish-like tails but with feet instead of fins. For a long time—perhaps 50 million years—such creatures thrived in the immense swamps which existed at that time. In this humid era also the first primeval insects appeared. To-day, these have evolved into more than 800,000 species. The early amphibians were perhaps more fish than land animals and, although some learned to feed entirely on insects and land plants, they still returned to the water to lay their eggs. As this period drew to a close some 200 million years ago, the next great evolutionary step occurred: an amphibian, the ugly crocodile-like eryops, learned to live most of its life on dry land.

REPTILES APPEAR

About the same time great geological changes were once again reshaping the surface of the earth. Great new mountain ranges appeared and the climate became much colder with the result that glaciers slid down from the poles covering vast tracts of the surface. The newly-formed amphibians had a hard time; some died out, some returned to the water and some, the hardiest, adapted themselves to the new conditions, becoming in the process reptiles. That is, cold-blooded creatures laying their eggs on dry land. This brings our story of the evolution of the world to the Jurassic period which ushered in the great age of reptiles.

During this period the most important line of development centres round reptiles that learned to stand on their hind legs and use their front legs as forearms. These were to

These fossilised tree stumps, in Victoria Park, Glasgow, are the remains of a mighty forest of the Upper Carboniferous period.

evolve into the largest and most dangerous land animals of all time—the famous dinosaurs— a Greek word meaning " terrible lizards." And terrible they were too! Many were vegetarians but others were savage flesh-eaters. One of the fiercest was the dreaded allosaurus, a terrifying creature, over 30 feet long, with several rows of razor-sharp teeth in a tremendously strong jaw. This was the tyrant of the day, preying on the often much bigger vegetarian dinosaurs, using its fore-limbs to hold its prey and then tearing it to pieces with its teeth.

Biggest reptile of all was the huge brontosaurus —another Greek word, meaning " thunder

one specimen of the Indian crocodile, *crocodilus porosus*, which, when measured, was found to be 33 feet long, with a circumference of 13 feet 8 inches; no other extinct crocodile grew as big as that. Other reptiles alive to-day include the East Indian, lizard-like *varanus salvator*, which grows to a length of 10 feet.

SOME PREHISTORIC REPTILES

The reptiles rapidly evolved into a wide range of varied types, one being the turtle. These soon reached their present state of evolution and since then for some unknown reason have descended down the ages—century after century, for millions of years—virtually

England—120 million years ago. In the centre is an iguanodon. A pterodactyl flies over a brontosaurus in the background; in the right foreground is the strange stegosaurus.

lizard." These incredible beasts weighed up to 30 tons and measured a good 70 feet from nose to tail. They were so heavy that evolution gave them four massive and tremendously strong legs, but even so they spent as much time as possible half-floating in the water to relieve their feet of the weight.

A COMPARISON WITH THE PRESENT

As a matter of interest it can be pointed out that, big as these monsters were, the record for sheer size is held by creatures alive *to-day*. The blue whale, growing to a length of 80 to 85 feet and weighing close on 150 tons, is superior not only to all land or marine mammals of the past, but also to everything else that ever moved, including the dinosaurs! So far as reptiles are concerned, though the past certainly outdoes the present, there was

unchanged. Thus, when you gaze at a turtle next time you are in a zoo, you have the unique opportunity to study a type of animal which roamed the Earth millions of years ago! The ancestors of the modern snakes and lizards also appeared about this time.

One of the ugliest dinosaurs was the stegosaurus. Nature seems to have played a joke on this ponderous beast. To start with, it was badly proportioned. Although weighing a good 10 tons it was only 20 feet long. Its hind-legs were several times bigger than the forelegs, making the small pointed head come close to the ground and giving it a peculiar humpbacked appearance. Running along the middle of its back from the back of its head to the tip of its tail was an array of heavy muscular triangular plates, which appear to have served no useful purpose at all. In spite of its size

These rather frightening creatures are the pterodactyls, the extinct flying reptile.

the brain of this odd creature weighed about 2½ ounces, or about as much as that of a small dog.

Other bizarre creatures of this bygone age included the ankylosaurus and triceratops. The ankylosaurus, which looked like an enlarged version of a modern armadillo, was protected by a heavy shell of bony armour with a wicked array of spikes jutting outwards just above ground level. These were purely defensive and the ankylosaurus used to stun his enemies by clouting them with his tail, a terrifying bludgeon of solid bone. The triceratops also had defensive armour. It resembled a modern rhinoceros except that, as the name implies, it had three huge horns projecting from an enormous frill of bone surmounting a ponderous seven-foot skull.

But the most fierce and terrifying dinosaur of all was the tyrannosaurus. These flesh-eating monsters were about 50 feet long and carried their huge heads a good twenty feet above the ground. They had tremendously powerful hind-legs ending in great taloned claws. Their jaws, of huge proportions, were literally filled with sharp fangs about 6 inches long. These were used with terrible effect on all other creatures alive at the time.

THE DISAPPEARANCE OF THE DINOSAURS

Their reign of terror, however, was relatively short and they vanished from the face of the Earth. And all the other big dinosaurs vanished too. Vanished utterly and completely in a way that has left us with one of the biggest question-marks in the book of the rocks.

For perhaps 100 million years, through the Jurassic to the end of the Cretaceous period 75 million years ago, the dinosaurs dominated life on Earth as no other creatures had, before or since. What caused them to die out suddenly is one of the great mysteries of the past. Perhaps a dreadful plague swept them away. Or perhaps a great change in plant life may have brought starvation to the vegetarian dinosaurs which could not get used to the new plants. Then, as these died, so did the flesh-eating carnivores. Another suggestion is that climatic changes proved too severe for the warmth-loving reptiles. But this does not explain the equally sudden disappearance of the great sea monsters of the period which had plenty to eat and could have migrated to tropical waters.

Yet another theory is that mammals (warm-blooded creatures giving birth to live young) may have eaten the eggs that were laid, but not protected, by the giant dinosaurs. Perhaps the monsters were too stupid to survive because, in spite of their immense bulk, one feature common to all dinosaurs was an incredibly tiny brain. But this, by itself, cannot be the complete answer to the sudden and complete extinction of these great beasts that roamed the face of the Earth 100 million years ago.

THE PAST COMES TO LIFE—
MONSTERS OF A BYGONE AGE

These fiercesome monsters exist now—as full-size, and most realistic, concrete models in the Crystal Palace grounds, London—and provide a unique opportunity to see in what may be described as jungle-like surroundings some of the inhabitants of the great age of reptiles; their size and frightening aspect can be readily appreciated.

Top left: the fearsome megalosaurus. *Top right:* a labrinthodon pachygnathus, which, apart from its size, resembled a frog. *Right:* a giant sloth. *Below:* These two monsters are iguanodons (so named because their teeth resembled those of the American lizard, the iguana).

LIFE IN THE CRETACEOUS AGE

This article and our artist's colour plate have been based on information obtained from fossil remains found and extensively examined in the United States of America. The scene is laid some ninety million years ago in the Cretaceous Age, so called by geologists because of the vast expanse of chalk then laid down.

THE principal animals were the dinosaurs, a family of lizards whose sizes varied from two to eighty feet in length. Some of the larger ones walked upright on their hind-legs and preyed on all other animals, and some, both two- and four-footed, spent their lives trying to avoid being eaten up!

In the picture, on the left, you can see two of the larger dinosaurs, the *Tyrannosaurus* and the *Gorgosaurus*, fighting. An evenly-matched pair, with well-developed teeth and claws, they were both large and could run with considerable speed on their strong hind-legs, using their short forelegs only for grasping their prey. To give you some idea of the size of these animals the *Tyrannosaurus* was over 40 ft. long from snout to tail; the skull 4 ft. long and the teeth from 4–6 in. long with sharp saw-like edges.

In the centre of the picture are the " duck-bill " dinosaurs, known as the hadrosaurs, who ate only grass, leaves, roots, etc. They used these " beaks " to search for roots and plants in the water as well as on land, and, although standing upright on their hind-legs and used to moving about on land, they had also webs of skin between the " toes " and " fingers " and a long muscular tail, slightly flattened from side to side, like an otter's, for speed in swimming.

The *Trachodon* and the *Anatosaurus*, shown in the picture, were both about 30 ft. from beak to tail end. They had about 2,000 teeth, which they had developed because of the harshness of the food they ate.

In the right foreground is an armoured type of dinosaur, the *Ankylosaurus*, 20 ft. in length, some 5 tons in weight, and, despite its fierce appearance, a placid plant eater, its armour used for defence and not attack.

Behind the *Ankylosaurus* on the river bank stands a smaller dinosaur, the *Struthiomimus*. About 10 ft. in total length, its mouth toothless, its skin and tail like those of a reptile, it

had many of the characteristics of the ostrich of to-day.

In the right background there is yet another variety of armoured dinosaur, the *Triceratops*. Its armour was only on its head, which was nearly 6 ft. long, with a bony frill over the neck and the 3 ft. long spikes over each eye and a lesser one on the nose. The body measured over 20 ft. and the heavy skull formed a beak for cropping vegetation. When attacked this animal had only to stand still with lowered head and its enemies were in danger of being impaled on its sharp horns.

There were also flying lizards, the pterosaurs, the largest of which, the *Pteranodon*, can be seen flying in our picture. It had a wing span of 25 ft. and was as light in weight and probably as capable of sustained and effortless gliding as the modern albatross. It had no feathers, skin like a reptile and the wings were thin webs of similar skin attached to the body, legs and arms, and largely manipulated by the enormously lengthened fourth finger. The bones were thin and hollow, and their beaks toothless, as in modern birds. Capable of long flights over the sea, they are the largest flying creatures that the world has so far seen.

Other birds at this time, were the *Hesperornis* and the *Ichthyornis*. The former was a large swimming bird, no longer capable of flight. About 4 ft. long, it had all the characteristics of the divers of to-day, except that its jaws bore teeth, which no modern bird has.

The *Ichthyornis*, smaller and something like a tern in appearance, had well-developed wings, and perhaps also teeth, though this is not known for certain.

At the close of the Cretaceous Age, the dinosaurs and pterosaurs disappeared from the earth completely, never to return, leaving only their skeletons to tell us what manner of creatures they were and how they lived. The birds alone lingered on and are the direct ancestors of the birds of to-day.

THE CRETACEOUS AGE. Some of the amazing animals which lived some ninety million years ago are pictured here in their natural surroundings. The numbers in the key at the bottom of the page

refer to the following animals: 1. Tyrannosaurus. 2. Gorgosaurus. 3. Pteranodons. 4. Triceratops. 5. Trachodons. 6. Anatosaurus. 7. Struthiomimus. 8. Ankylosaurus. 9. Hesperornis. 10. Ichthyornis.

Much of a farmer's success depends on his ability to judge the weather.

THE COUNTRYMAN'S WEATHER LORE

Read the Skies and the Living Barometers

ON TELEVISION you will see experts interpreting the scientific weather charts and predicting as far as they are able—and Nature occasionally makes fools of us all—the probable weather and prospects for the next day.

But the most they can foretell is general prospects, dividing the country into a few large areas. The farmer and the other workers who depend upon the weather are guided by these expert forecasts, but much more by their local observations. While an area covering several thousands of square miles may have, in the main, a fine day, there will be places within it that have a very far from fair day—and the farmer is not interested particularly in what's happening even twenty miles away; he is concerned with his particular farm.

It's the personal touch, the understanding of local conditions that count, and fortunately there are many signs in Nature to help the farmer to make a correct forecast.

A few of the old weather rhymes are thought by some to be merely superstitions; but superstitions, even, have a reason, and are generally the result of perhaps centuries of experience. Of course, a weather rhyme may be wrong occasionally—but so are the experts, with all their scientific equipment.

"READING" THE SKY

The farmer spends a good deal of his time looking at the sky. An intelligent reading of it may save him thousands of pounds and many, many hours of wasted labour.

What does he say about the sky?

Perhaps one of the most familiar rhymes is:

Red sky at night, shepherd's delight;
Red sky at morning, shepherd's warning.

There is a variation:

If red the sun begins its race, be sure the
rain will fall apace.

Again:

When the clouds of the morn to the west
    fly away,
You may be quite sure of a fine, settled
    day.

The nature of the clouds is also significant:

Mackerel sky, mackerel sky;
Never long wet, never long dry.

When goats' hairs are flying,
It means the winds are drying.

Mackerel sky is mottled, like the markings on this fish.

The " goats' hairs," called in some counties " horses' tails," are the wisps of clouds which float like floss across the sky.

The rainbow, if it appears at eve, is a sign that " it will rain, and leave." There is a quaint saying in some parts that if it rains while the sun is shining, the devil is beating his grandmother; he is laughing and she is crying.

Thunder is never a blessing and the farmer takes warning from the clouds:

Angry cloud with edges that glower,
That means thunder within the hour.

The one good word I have heard for thunder is in the saying " If it thunders on All Fools' Day, it brings good crops of corn and hay."

BIRDS AND BEASTS FORETELL THE WEATHER

The birds, of course, are particularly sensitive to the weather; it may affect their very life, and it will certainly affect their food. So the farmer watches them for weather forecasts.

Seagulls and wild geese fly inland when they sense that there is a storm approaching, so:

Seagull, seagull, stay on the sand;
It's never long fine when you're on the land.

If swallows fly high, dry weather is forecast, and the reason for this is apparently that in a dry, light atmosphere insects fly higher. When the air is moist and rain is expected, swallows seek their food nearer the earth.

When rooks stay at home and chatter noisily in the trees, the farmer expects a change to bad weather.

When rain is near, snails come out of hiding, and while this is not likely to be observed by the farmer, the result is: ducks begin searching eagerly among the long grass.

Pigs, too, become agitated just before a break in fine weather, and sheep will huddle together and bleat frequently.

THE MOON IS THE BEST BAROMETER

The moon is perhaps the farmer's favourite and most trusted barometer, and while the scientist has sought to discredit some of the old sayings, the farmer still sticks to his beliefs. And who shall blame him, for they have

" Seagull, seagull, stay on the sand ;
It's never long fine when you're on the land."

An unwelcome sight in the sky, a Cumulo-nimbus cloud, described by the countryman as,
" An angry cloud with edges that glower ; that means thunder within the hour."

crystallised through centuries of experience and observation, and many of them were accepted and followed long before weather science was known.

> *Pale moon doth rain*
> *Red moon doth blow,*
> *White moon doth neither rain nor snow.*

> *Plant the bean when the moon is light,*
> *Plant potatoes when the moon is dark.*

Says a Scottish proverb:

> *When the moon is on her back,*
> *Gae mend the shoon and sort the thack*
> (thatch)
> *When round the moon there is a brugh*
> (halo),
> *The weather will be cold and rough.*

Most farmers pay careful attention to the habits of bees. If they go about their business quietly and unconcernedly, the land-workers will be confident of fine weather, whatever the reports may be. If the bees seem agitated and quarrelsome, then most surely the temper of the weather is rising also. Many farmers claim

A settled evening sky on the coast giving hope of fine weather on the morrow.

that worker bees are so careful when collecting honey that they will return swiftly to the hive if a cloud obscures the sun.

> *A swarm of bees in May is worth a load of*
> *hay;*
> *A swarm of bees in June is worth a silver*
> *spoon;*
> *But a swarm in July is not worth a fly.*

The winds, of course, have each their whispered message for the wise man's ear:

> *When it rains with the wind in the east,*
> *It rains for twenty-four hours at least.*

> *A whistling March will make the plough-*
> *man blythe,*
> *And moisty April fits him for the scythe.*

Many a fruit farmer says fervently:

> *September blow soft*
> *Till the fruit's in the loft.*

The countryman learns much useful weather lore from the bees.

Nothing is too small for the farmer's observant eye. Well before the human can detect a freshening of the wind, spiders are seen strengthening their webs. Moles surface before the approach of rain, sure that there will then be a feast of worms and small insects.

LEARNING FROM NATURE

The tiny scarlet pimpernel, the daisy and the dandelion are wide open if fine weather continues; closing at the approach of rain. But don't consult these particular barometers too early in the morning, for they will be closed then, whatever weather is ahead.

If, on a summer afternoon, there is a sudden calm, a stillness that can almost be felt, you will see that the birds are in the trees, and silent save for an occasional twitter. Then you can be sure that a storm will break quickly; probably within an hour, however innocent the sky may appear at the moment.

Fishermen have several sayings about storms, but they are not very poetic. They have, however, paid their respect to the effect of the winds in this rhyme which is centuries old:

> *When the wind is in the east,*
> *Then the fishes bite the least;*
> *When the wind is in the west,*
> *Then the fishes bite the best;*
> *When the wind is in the north,*
> *Then the fishes do come forth;*
> *When the wind is in the south,*
> *It blows the bait in the fishes' mouth.*

An English proverb:

> *Onion's skin is very thin, mild winter*
> *coming in;*
> *Onion's skin is thick and tough,*
> *Coming winter cold and rough,*

reminds me of a very quaint custom I heard of in France. On Christmas Day twelve onions, of the farmer's own growing, are set on a shelf, representing the twelve months of the New Year. A pinch of salt is placed on the top of

This fascinating photograph proves that every cloud has a silver lining, and that even on the stormiest and gloomiest day the sun can break its way through.

This skyscape, showing "the gentle weather clouds of a summer's day," is one which the countryman would love to study. His conclusion, no doubt, would be : "In for a settled spell."

each. At Epiphany, which is January 6th, the onions are examined, and if the salt on any onion has melted, its place in the row of twelve is noted and the corresponding month of the year ahead is forecast to be wet. If the salt remains firm, then that onion's month will be fine.

I was never there long enough to check the results, but many farmers put much faith in this home-made barometer for the year.

Indeed, there are few months that are without a particular rhyme or belief. The Welsh say " A warm January means a cold May." February used to be called " Fill-dyke," but in fact records in recent times have proved that it is by no means as rainy as it seems.

March has many rhymes:

A dry March, wet April, and cool May
Fill barn and cellar, and bring much hay.

March borrowed of April, April borrowed of
* May three days, they say:*
One rained and one snew, and the other was
* the worst day that ever blew.*

A peck of March dust and a shower in May,
Make the corn green and the fields gay.

Robert Browning said:

    Oh, to be in England
    Now that April's there,

but apart from the promise of spring, it can be a maddening month; promising one moment and darting back to wintry weather the next. "April weather, rain and sunshine both together," in fact.

In April the cuckoo sounds his bell; in May
he sings all day; in June he alters his tune;
in July away he'll fly; in August away he
must.

The country saying claims that the third of April brings the cuckoo and the nightingale, but their appearance seems to vary with the district, if not with the season.

"If cherries blow in April, you'll have your fill; but if in May they'll go away."

A MONTH OF MIXED BLESSINGS

In fact, May seems to be a month of mixed blessings, as far as the farmer is concerned. It may smile—or it may frown. A misty May and a hot June, bring cheap meal and harvest soon. A red, gay May, best in any year, says another tradition. On the other hand:

He who bathes in May will soon be laid in clay;
He who bathes in June will sing a merry tune;
He who bathes in July will dance like a fly.

June, " the month of roses," is expected to provide calm weather, for that sets corn in tune, and " a dripping June brings all things in tune "—except, perhaps the holiday-makers.

An ancient saying, current in the days of the old calendar, claimed that rain on the eighth of June foretold a wet harvest. By the calendar of to-day, that would mean the 18th.

The next month starts rather badly, for:

If the first of July be rainy weather,
It will rain, more or less, for four weeks together.

There is another risk, for 15th July is St. Swithin's Day and the weather then is said to set the weather for the forty following days. As, however, it is seldom a completely beautiful day, or a thoroughly bad one, the forecasters have plenty of scope for the prescribed period. The old saying, " Ne'er trust a July sky," has not been disproved by the scientists,

Winter frost on a lovely woodland lane. The tiny frost particles form a crisp carpet on the ground, and cling to the grass and trees.

and it is a month in which no one wisely makes confident forecasts or plans too far ahead.

August hasn't too good a reputation, in fact Byron went so far as to say that the English winter, ending in July, recommences in August. But perhaps he was recovering from 'flu, when even poets lose their sense of humour. A dry August, and warm, does the harvest no harm. Indeed,

> If the twenty-fourth of August be fair and clear,
> Then hope for a prosperous autumn that year.

MISTS AND MELLOW FRUITFULNESS

In September we approach the autumn, which Keats so beautifully called the " season of mists and mellow fruitfulness, Close bosom-friend of the maturing sun . . ." We look for a fair First, because that means " fair for the month." The morning mists bring mellow days and you will do well to remember in all aspects of life the farmer's wise words that " ripe fruit may grow on a rough wall." And " he who would have the fruit must climb the tree." You cannot eat the fruit while the tree is in blossom, and when, by careful toil you have come to hope for a good harvest, remember there may be one ripe fruit between two green, just as there may be a rose between two thorns.

With October the farmer is prepared for frosts, and, indeed, at the right time he welcomes them. They are not likely, yet, to be of long duration.

> If hoar frost comes on mornings twain,
> The third day surely will bring rain.

Make a note, and see how often this comes true.

THE NEGATIVE MONTH

November is a month about which there are few rhymes. It is not a month that lends itself to poetry, though the farmer realises its particular purpose in the rhythm of Nature.

For city dwellers it is a month of few merits. Indeed it was a great London-lover, Thomas Hood, who wrote the most often remembered lines about it:

> No warmth, no cheerfulness, no healthful ease—
> No comfortable feel in any member—
> No shade, no shine, no butterflies, no bees,
> No fruits, no flowers, no leaves, no birds,
> November.

December's dreariness is lightened by the bright star of Christmas; " a green Christmas, a white Easter," is the country rhyme. " A foot deep of rain, will kill hay and grain; But three feet of snow, will make them come mo'." So they say in the West Country.

There are two days which, for centuries and in many countries, were held to reveal the character of the whole year ahead.

ST. PAUL'S DAY

The first was 25th January, the Feast of the Conversion of St. Paul. Fair weather on the day promised good weather and a prosperous year; snow or rain indicated a year of scarcity, and clouds were an omen of disease among cattle. High winds on 25th January were thought to be a sign of approaching war.

The significance of the day was summed up in an ancient rhyme:

> If St. Paul's day be fair and clear,
> It shall betide a happy year;
> If it chance to snow or rain,
> Then will be dear all kinds of grain;
> If clouds or mists do mask the sky,
> Great store of birds and beasts shall die;
> And if the winds do fly aloft,
> Then war shall vex the kingdom oft.

The second all-important day was 2nd February, the Feast of Candlemas. From pagan times it has been a season of festivity, one of the milestones of the year. It was a public holiday and therefore, not unnaturally, a day of significance and forecasting. Unlike St. Paul's Day, the weather was interpreted in reverse:

> If Candlemas day be dry and fair
> The half of winter's to come and more;
> If Candlemas day be wet and foul,
> The half of winter is gone at Yule.

In some parts of Europe farmers say that if a badger looks out of his hole on Candlemas day and finds snow, he ventures abroad with confidence in the swift coming of good weather. If he sees the sun shining, he retreats into his hole, because the sun is a delusion; there is still rough weather to come.

"RAIN'S MY CHOICE"

There is a German proverb which bears out this belief—the shepherd would rather see the wolf enter his stable on Candlemas day than the sun. " A fair day in winter is the mother of storms."

Farmers, of course, always grumble about the weather; it would never be right for them unless there were sunshine in one field, gentle rain in another, shade in a third and a freshening wind in the fourth. And when they have a festivity at home, they want sunshine everywhere—all the time.

The happiest farmer I have met was a very wise man. He said, and he had learned it from his grandfather: " When God sorts out the weather and sends rain, then rain's my choice! "

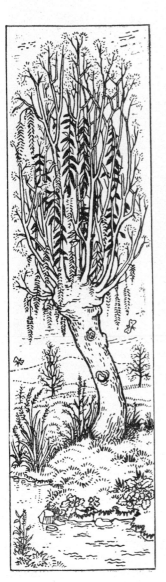

THE VOICE OF SPRING

I am coming, I am coming!—
Hark! the little bee is humming.
See, the lark is soaring high
In the blue and sunny sky;
And the gnats are on the wing,
Wheeling round in airy ring.

See the yellow catkins cover
All the slender willows over;
And on banks of mossy green
Star-like primroses are seen;
And, their clustering leaves below,
White and purple violets blow.

Hark! the newborn lambs are bleating,
And the cawing rooks are meeting
In the elms—a noisy crowd;
All the birds are singing loud;
And the first white butterfly
In the sunshine dances by.

Look around thee—look around!
Flowers in all the fields abound;
Every running stream is bright;
All the orchard trees are white;
And each small and waving shoot
Promises sweet flowers and fruit.

Turn thine eyes to earth and heaven
God for thee the spring has given,
Taught the birds their melodies,
Clothed the earth, and cleared the skies,
For thy pleasure or thy food—
Pour thy soul in gratitude!

Mary Howitt

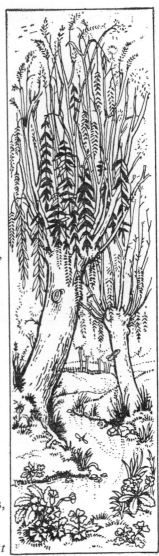

Ready for the saddle. These young riders are correctly dressed for a canter, in well-fitting jodhpurs, hacking-jackets, and tight caps. Both look neat and business-like.

SADDLING UP

HAVING decided to learn to ride, the first question is that of what to wear.

Buy the best it is possible to afford. Well-cut riding clothes of durable cloth are never cheap, but the better they are the smarter they look, the longer they last, and they do have to stand considerable strain and wear. Jodhpurs are usually the first choice of the intending rider. Jodhpur boots should be worn with them for correctness and comfort, but a beginner anxious to avoid expense can manage very well with woollen socks and flat-heeled, lace-up walking shoes. A school blazer, woollen cardigan or pullover will spare the cost of a hacking jacket for a while, but a really storm-proof mackintosh is an absolute necessity, and for safety's sake a head-covering should always be worn, preferably a velvet hunting cap or bowler.

Girl riders will be well advised to buy or

borrow a boy's shirt for wearing with breeches or jodhpurs, since the extra length of tail tucks well down and will not ride up as blouses do, leaving a wide " smile " of exposed under-clothing across the rider's back.

Everything must be well secured. Whatever the weather or pace, a rider should remain neat in appearance, with hair fastened tidily under a well-fixed hat, tie pinned firmly into place, neither fluttering into the face nor flying over the shoulder, and jodhpurs secured by strips of elastic under the insteps if there is any tendency for the legs to work upwards towards the knee. If a cane or crop is carried it should be held as unobtrusively and close to the rider as possible, not sticking out and waggling in such a position that it catches the sight of every horse, causing the animal to shy away from this—to them—peculiar, protruding object.

CHOOSING YOUR MOUNT

After the clothing comes the horse.

In the case of a hired mount this is an easy matter, and a visit by appointment to a local stable will find a steed standing saddled and bridled in the indoor school or paddock ready to introduce yet another aspirant to the pleasures and thrills of riding.

These old-timers are rarely exciting. They may be old, fat, placid, queer-shaped, or even downright ugly, but they are invariably honest and kind. They suffer the kicks and pulls and wriggles of their novice rider patiently and surely with understanding; when things go wrong, they stop; when pupils fall off them they stand still to be mounted again. They know the words of command almost as well as the master who gives them. They are always wise and usually greedy, nuzzling hand and pocket at every opportunity for a well-deserved reward.

Never disparage these equine instructors. Having progressed a little, neither scorn, nor let others scorn them as " mug's mounts." Be grateful to them for their patience, kindness and tuition. They are the true, long-suffering friends of man.

If the horse or pony to be ridden is privately owned, it may be turned out in a paddock, and then the problem is to catch, groom, bridle and saddle it. Every rider should know how to do these things, and the handling of a horse in the paddock and in the stable will inspire greater confidence when mounted.

FIRST CATCH YOUR HORSE

To bring a horse readily, bribery is the best, in fact, the only way. An animal in a field should be visited often and regularly, and always with a tit-bit to tempt and reward him. Never try to cheat with an empty hand or bucket. This trick may succeed once in a while, but the horse soon becomes aware of it, and will no longer come eagerly to a call. And never, never throw the bucket or head-collar at him in a temper!

The head-collar should be put on quickly and quietly with no unnecessary fuss, just slipped upwards over face and head. A good plan is to grasp an ear with one hand whilst adjusting the head-collar with the other. Once the head-collar is in position the horse can be led easily by the rope attached to it, but care must be taken not to loose the rope, or away may go horse, head-collar and all!

Never under any circumstances, should the free end of a rope be tied or knotted to the waist or wrist of the person holding it. If, through fright or any other reason, the animal should decide to canter off, a serious accident could result. Far better to have the trouble of catching the horse over again than to risk being dragged at the rope's end with every likelihood of major damage.

ACTING AS VALET

Once the horse is caught the next move is to groom it.

Good grooming is beneficial to the horse and excellent exercise, though rather tiring, for the groom. It is the process of cleaning the skin and hair by means of brushing and massage. The first essential is a place to tie the horse, and necessary equipment is the body brush, curry-comb, hoof-pick, rubbers or dusters, and a wisp made out of hay or straw. Other useful articles such as dandy and water brushes, mane and tail comb can well be added to the list, but the first-named articles it is absolutely impossible to do without.

The curry-comb is not really a comb at all, but a metal instrument used to clean dust out of the body brush, not the horse, except on rare occasions when it may be used very gently to scrape a thick mud-plastered coat.

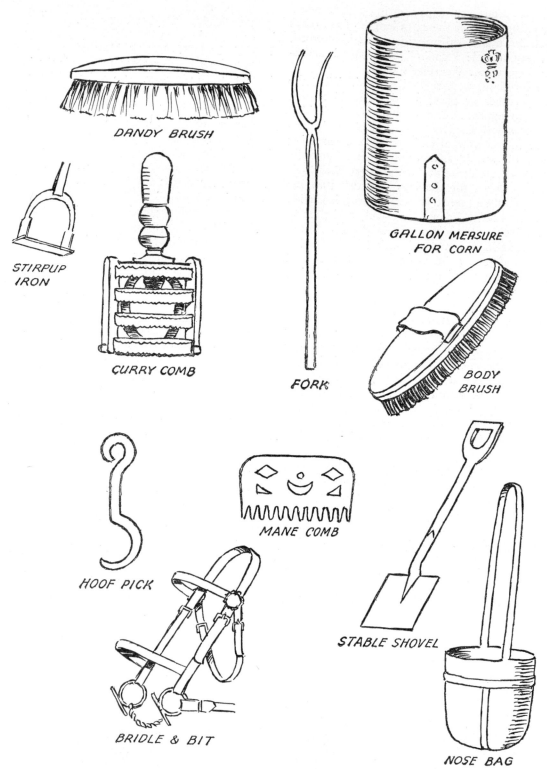

DANDY BRUSH

STIRRUP IRON

CURRY COMB

FORK

GALLON MEASURE FOR CORN

BODY BRUSH

HOOF PICK

MANE COMB

BRIDLE & BIT

STABLE SHOVEL

NOSE BAG

Here is the necessary equipment for the care of the horse.

There are many Pony Clubs where young riders can learn, not only how to ride, but also how to groom their horses. At this Pony Club Camp at Somerley Park, Ringwood, Hants, an instructor is giving the members a lecture on grooming

The hoof-pick is a hook-shaped piece of iron curving from a handle into a thin, blunt point. One should be owned and used by every rider for cleaning out the sole of the foot, the frog, and the cleft within it, when grooming, after exercise of any kind, first thing in the morning and last thing at night. " No foot, no horse," the saying goes, and a dirty foot is soon an unsound one.

Grooming is best learnt by first watching someone else, and then by working under instruction. Important points to remember are that one grooms with the weight of the body, not the strength of the arm; that the stroke always follows the lie of the hair, never brushing against it; and that the brush must never be banged down on the skin, but brought against it with a glancing movement in itself a part of the brushing stroke.

The groom should stand away from the horse, leaning on him so that the full weight of the body lies behind the brush. After every few strokes the brush should be cleaned by drawing the teeth of the curry-comb through it, then the dust tapped out of the curry-comb on to the ground. The usual place to start grooming is on the left, or " near " side of the horse well up on the neck behind the ear, working in wide, sweeping strokes along the back and side towards the tail. The underside of the belly and inside the thigh and forearm must be brushed carefully and well, but gently, since these are sensitive places. After the near-side the process must be repeated on the right or " off " side of the horse.

Having well done the body, each leg should be brushed in turn, great care being taken not to bang the bony structures with the wooden back of the brush.

THE HORSE'S BEAUTY TREATMENT

The face and head are next to need attention. Brush these slowly and very gently. Wipe the eyes and nostrils carefully with a damp rubber. Do not ever cut or try to pull out the long, coarse hairs on a horse's lip or about his eyes. The roots of these hairs are full of nerves and act as feelers to help the horse select his food and prevent him from bumping his head about in the dark. To interfere with them will not only rob the animal of something he needs, but also hurt him very much.

Brush out the forelock, mane and tail, separating the hairs and using the brush on them gently but firmly. Wipe the dock and sheath with another damp rubber. Then give a final polish to the coat with a dry rubber.

All grooming tools should be kept as clean

as possible.   Rubbers should be regularly washed, so should brushes, and the curry-comb dusted out every day.

Grooming should be quiet and controlled with no shouting at the horse, no unnecessary clatter, no jerking at the tethering rope, and no slinging about of brushes. The average horse enjoys his grooming and is only too pleased to greet a visitor to his stable, but not if his head is jerked about, his face and legs bumped with the back of the brush and his skin banged with its bristles. He will soon begin to hate the process and start to lay back his ears, and bite, and kick, habits of which it will not be easy to break him, and caused entirely by the incompetence and roughness of his owner or groom.

The bridle is the earliest of all items of saddlery or " tack." It came early in history, the very first means man devised for controlling and taming the wild horse, for his use and pleasure. Its object is to support the bit in the horse's mouth, since the bit, with the reins, is the primary means of controlling a horse.

In its simplest form it is a strap looped over the horse's head, passing behind the ears and down either side of the face, with the ends attached to the rings of a bit on each side of the mouth. Another strap, the brow-band, passes in front of the ears and holds the top part, or " head," in position, while the head itself is split at the sides so that a narrow piece passes under the neck buckling on the side of the face. This is called the " throat-latch," pronounced " lash."

These few straps form the simplest form of bridle and the basis of all bridles. The use of more complicated forms of bridling means the addition of more straps. Sometimes these additions are decreed by fashion, as in the case of the noseband which, though generally worn, is really only needed when a martingale is being used, and sometimes by the necessity of obtaining greater control of the horse, but it is well for the rider, both novice or more expert, to remember that sympathetic hands

One of the aims of Pony Clubs is to instil into young members the necessity for taking proper care of their animals. Here, a lecture on harness is in progress.

Many Pony Clubs hold Championships in which their members compete. Here is a competitor in a dressage competition.

front, or pommel, of it falls just behind the rise of the withers, in a position which ensures that the withers will not be pinched and there will be no interference with the free movement of the shoulders. The padded undersides or panels of the saddle, rest on the muscular pad of the back, leaving a distinct channel down the centre of the saddle so that no part of it presses on the spine. The saddle must not be placed so far back that the panels rest on the loins. If the girth is left to fall loose from one side of the saddle it should hang down the side of the horse just behind the elbow.

The girths should be tightened gradually, and care taken that the loose skin behind the elbow is not pinched. A horse should never be girthed too tightly. It should always be possible to slip two fingers in between the body and the girth.

In spite of the safety catches on them, stirrup leather bars should be left open so that in the event of an awkward fall the whole thing would come away, permitting no possibility of being dragged.

It is the responsibility of the rider to see that girths are sufficiently tightened before mounting, although the final adjustment must be made by the rider from the saddle.

and a secure seat, not some weird bit, are the key to a horse's mouth.

PUTTING ON THE BRIDLE

The successful and comfortable control of a horse depends on the correct choice and fitting of the bridle and the bit, and a beginner should acquaint himself with the action and severity of the various ones in use.

The secret of putting on the bridle is to get the co-operation of the horse, and this is only gained by sure and gentle handling. Any horse will object to being poked in the eye with a strap end or buckle, or being banged on the jaw with iron bits. The would-be rider must achieve the knack of drawing the bridle carefully and quickly up the horse's face and over his ears, slipping the bit gently between his teeth, prising his mouth open by pressing a thumb against the corner of his lips. Once the bit is in, the throat-latch can be buckled easily, and if a curb chain is being used it can be adjusted at leisure.

The saddle is placed on a horse so that the

LEARN THE ANATOMY OF THE HORSE

A careful study of the anatomy and points of the horse, and a thorough knowledge of the parts and correct assembly of the various pieces of saddlery, are essential to good horsemanship. Ignorance, idleness or carelessness means misfitting tack and consequent discomfort for the horse, in which circumstances even the most honest and willing animal will become restive, resentful, and even unmanageable. Though a horse cannot speak, he will convey clearly to his rider that he is uncomfortable or in pain, but the rider must be wise to understand this equine language of dumb sign, and knowledgeable enough to find out what is wrong and put the matter right.

One of the most important steps in learning to ride is to mount properly.

To do this stand on the left, or near, side of the horse, facing the flap of the saddle. Take up the reins in the left hand, and, still grasping them, lay it on the base of the horse's neck.

Facing his tail, hold the stirrup in the right

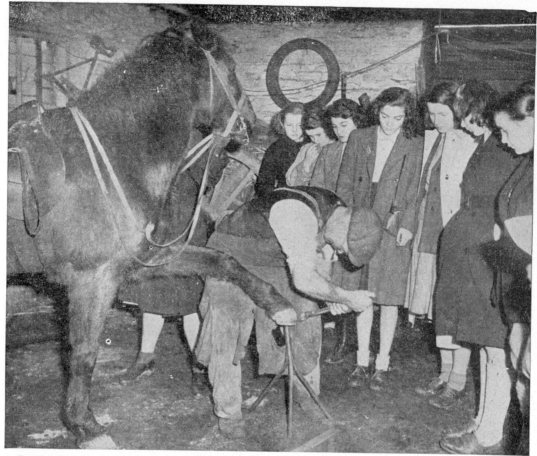

Instruction is given in Pony Clubs in all branches of riding, watering, feeding, shoeing, and everything that helps the well-being of the horse. Here, a farrier cuts the nail ends off a horse's hoof, watched by interested members of the Club.

hand and turn it to receive the left foot. From that stance spring up to a standing position in the stirrup. Swing the right leg over the saddle, at the same time carrying the right hand forward to the front of the saddle. Sink down quietly into the saddle. Never bump down on the horse's back. Slip the right foot into its stirrup and take up the reins quietly in both hands.

This correct way allows no possibility of the rider being caught by a cow-kick from the horse, and if the animal moves off whilst only half-mounted the action will swing the rider in towards the saddle rather than away from it.

THE THREE L'S

Education has its three " R's," and riding has its three " L's " also.   Look—Listen—Learn—but make sure the tutor is competent and understanding, and remember that true knowledge may be found in unexpected places. The man with the loudest voice and coat is not always the cleverest fellow.   Experience often speaks with a quiet tongue and walks in shabby clothing.

Every rider must make mistakes, and learn to profit by them.   He must fall, to mount again; fail, to ride better; school himself to surmount the obstacles in his path with quiet determination and unswerving courage.   He must ask the utmost from himself, but never too much from his horse.

> " Be to his virtues ever kind,
> And to his faults a little blind."

Fully conscious of the importance of the occasion, Christopher, the week-old baby camel born at London Zoo, accompanies his mother on his first outing.

THE CHILDREN'S ZOO

THERE is scarcely a Zoological Gardens in the world that does not devote some part of its grounds to a place where children may play with carefully-selected animals. But, in 1935, London could boast that it possessed the one and only Zoo to experiment with an attraction of this kind.

It is true that the idea sprang into the mind of Mr. Julian Huxley, then Secretary of the Zoological Society of London, when he was on a visit to Berlin in 1934; but the " Pets' Corner " in the Zoological Gardens of that city was, at that time, only a faint indication of what the London Zoo was to achieve in the years to come.

What Mr. Huxley actually saw in the Berlin Zoo was a paddock in which a few rather sad-looking sheep were roaming about, and where children were allowed in to play with them. The day he was there the animals were trying to avoid some small boys who were teasing them. It could hardly have been called an ideal plan, but it set Mr. Huxley thinking, and when he returned to London a definite scheme was beginning to take shape in his mind. What Berlin had attempted London would turn into a working proposition. The Regent's Park Zoo should have a properly organised " Pets' Corner " where the animals would be able to enjoy themselves just as much as the children.

The authorities at the London Zoo were so attracted by the idea that they decided to put it to the test. Wheels were set turning and, by 19th August, 1935, " Pets' Corner " was all ready, stocked with animals, and only

Wobbling, but still upright, this day-old giraffe takes a good look round.

waiting for the moment to come when it could open its gates and let in young members of the public.

PETER, THE CHIMP, STEALS THE SHOW

A grand opening ceremony took place at which about a thousand people were present. Most of them were Fellows and Members of the Zoological Society of London, and their friends. But the most important feature of that assembly was the animals. They included Nigger, a baby yak; Brownie, an eland; three Georges, a lion cub, a camel and an alligator; two Peters, a chimpanzee and a python; Iris, a Shetland pony; Monty, a banded mongoose, who had already attained fame on radio and television; The Marquis of Regent's Park, a parrot; Thunder and Lightning, two flying squirrels or phalangers; a giant tortoise; some kinkajous; king penguins; white rabbits; and guinea-pigs. Most of these creatures only attended for the opening ceremony, and were taken back to their

Not a lesson in table manners! Drinking out of the teapot is not very polite, but at the Chimpanzees' Tea Party nobody cares very much as long as everyone enjoys himself.

This fallow doe and her young fawn await the visitors' arrival at the Children's Zoo.

own enclosures by their keepers when the day was over. But Nigger, Iris, Monty, Thunder and Lightning, The Marquis, the tortoise, the rabbits and the guinea-pigs were allowed to remain in " Pets' Corner " as its first permanent residents.

Several speeches were made on this August day in 1935, which must have made it pretty boring for the animals. But they were all on their best behaviour. It is true that Peter, the chimp, climbed up on to Julian Huxley's shoulder, while he was addressing the crowd, and sat there making faces while thoughtfully rumpling the speaker's hair with one paw. But this only added the right kind of touch to the occasion. The moment " Pets' Corner " was declared open children and animals met, and the fun began.

RIDES ON A GIANT TORTOISE

One of the most popular creatures on that memorable day was the giant tortoise which gave rides to any boy or girl who felt inclined to sit astride his horny shell. He had to be labelled " This End Bites " to warn off any adventurous child who might put his fingers too near the snapping end.

For the first two years of its life the Zoo's new experiment was called " Pets' Corner." And experiment it certainly was. At the outset some of the inmates were housed in pens round which it was possible for the public to circulate. But the presence of so many people trying to attract their attention from all sides at once was too bewildering for the poor creatures, and it was found necessary to make new pens with at least one side against a wall.

The idea behind " Pets' Corner " was to make it possible for children to get to know certain animals at close quarters. It took some time before an ideal arrangement could be arrived at. Some of the wilder baby beasts tended to bite and scratch if handled too roughly, and, eventually, they all had to be replaced by more domesticated creatures, such as sheep and goats. Now baby bears, lion cubs and the like are only introduced into the Children's Zoo by their keepers on short visits.

King penguins, with their amusing ways, always attract a large crowd.

" BOLT-HOLES " FOR ANIMALS AND CHILDREN

The successful development of Mr. Huxley's idea depended not only on protecting the children from the animals, but also protecting the animals from the children. To give the former opportunity for escape, when circumstances became too much for them, low pens were built so that the occupants could jump in and out as they pleased. It was found, however, that this was too much for the smallest among them, so " bolt-holes " had to be added. These consisted of openings into the pens just large enough to provide a means of escape for baby animals. For the more complete comfort of the inhabitants of the Children's Zoo dens were built at the backs of the pens where an animal could retire for a little respite, if it wanted to dodge the limelight for a while.

When " Pets' Corner " entered its third year a big change was made. It was decided to re-christen it the " Children's Zoo," and to re-build upon the site it has occupied ever since, in one of the old Park paddocks, not far from the South Entrance, behind the Lion House.

All the uncaged animals were of the domestic type, such as goats, sheep and llamas, Shetland ponies, donkeys, rabbits, squirrels, dormice, hamsters, guinea-pigs, mice, rats, tortoises, foxes, deer, doves, budgerigars and parrots were also on show. Most of the rodents were kept in glass-fronted cages because it was found that they were apt to bite the poking fingers of children. The donkeys and ponies were obliging enough to give free rides to all who wished to mount them, and were led about for that purpose by some of the girl attendants. Foxes and deer were kept in ordinary cages, and the ponies lived in loose-boxes.

A MODEL TOWN FOR MICE

One of the most fascinating exhibits in the Children's Zoo is a complete " Mouse Town." This was designed by a Mr. Spaj Atkinson and is on show in the Exhibition Hall at one end of the paddock. Here, in a long glass case, nearly 400 mice of many colours run in and out of miniature cottages, built to resemble a model town. There is a river running through the estate with a bridge over it; a community centre; some tall towers; and a group of swing-boats. The tiny dwellings have to be made of concrete, or their inhabitants would nibble them to pieces. They are made in one solid block, with a passage passing through the middle, so that the mice have no chance of congregating where they cannot be seen. Feeding-time in " Mouse Town " takes place at each end of the show-case and, as if by instinct, the tiny creatures divide themselves up into two equal parties for the occasion. In this same Exhibition House are housed some rodents and tanks full of tiny fishes.

At the beginning of its existence " Pets' Corner," or as it is now known, the Children's Zoo, was opened every season by a different notability. This habit was discontinued after the war. Among famous people who have taken part in these functions are Sabu, the elephant boy; Sally Ann Howes, when a little girl; and the Kennedy family, when Mr. Kennedy was United States ambassador to this country.

NURSING THE SICK ANIMALS

The Children's Zoo depends for its efficient day-to-day management upon a team of girls, whose ages range from sixteen to twenty-five. They are presided over by a " head girl," aided by a deputy. No special training is needed for this work, although a love of children and animals is essential. All new recruits are gradually instructed in their duties by the head attendant, and given jobs for which they seem best suited. These girls are entirely responsible for the smooth running of this department of the London Zoo. They have to attend to the toilet of the animals where grooming, washing, clipping, etc., is concerned; to the cleanliness of the pens; and to the feeding arrangements. In addition, they must be ready to doctor their charges, under veterinary orders, when they fall sick; check any animal that is behaving badly; and keep a sharp look-out for any teasing that may be taking place.

Their duties start at 8.30 a.m., when the animals are fed and made ready to receive visitors. At 11.30 a.m. all the girls change out of their working kit into the uniforms in which the general public always sees them. These consist of yellow or green blouses, jodhpurs, brown cardigans and brown shoes. They are also issued with short brown duffel coats for cool days, and wind-cheaters with hoods for wet weather. They are then inspected, together with their charges, and all is ready for releasing the turnstiles of the Children's Zoo to the general public at 1 p.m. During the winter months a nucleus of this staff is retained to look after the animals, which continue to occupy the same quarters.

One of the most pleasant things about the Children's Zoo is the absence of many rules and regulations. If any exhibit is fed upon special food a notice to this effect is hung on its enclosure. But it is permissible to feed all the others without stint. When a young

Although they are well protected from visitors, mother sea lion " Tiny " defiantly " warns off " the watching crowds as her three-week-old baby makes his first public appearance.

Only a few months old, yet already these young lion cubs are too rough to play with children.

animal is first introduced into the Children's Zoo it is liable to suffer from stomach-ache brought on by over-feeding, and has to be taken away to recover. But when it comes back into circulation it is generally found that it has learnt its lesson and will not accept anything more to eat when it feels it has had enough.

EATING PAPER-BAGS AS "ROUGHAGE"

The appetites of the goats seem inexhaustible. But these wise creatures counteract the effect of sweets and biscuits, fed to them by visitors, by devouring paper-bags as well. These act as "roughage," and save the animal from indigestion. There is seldom any litter to be seen in the Children's Zoo because the goats eat it all up! Less admirable is their partiality for hair-ribbons. Any little girl entering the Children's Zoo with bows on the ends of her pigtails is quite likely to lose them to a goat before she has been inside the place

five minutes. Another less likeable trait of all goats is their love of sucking people's clothing.

There is not the slightest doubt that the Children's Zoo is a success. The fact that now nearly every Zoo in the world has followed London's example is proof of that. If anyone should challenge this fact figures can be produced to prove how valuable Julian Huxley's idea has been on the financial side alone. Two hundred and fifty thousand is the average attendance per season, and this means that the Zoo funds are increased by an extra £10,000 every year. Could anything be more definite than that?

Yet what are figures when measured by the pleasure shared by the thousands who visit the Children's Zoo every year? The laughter of children, and the sudden exclamations of delight at the antics of the animals are true rewards for the amount of thought and work that has been expended upon this very profitable branch of the Zoological Society of London's activities.

Ski-ing in Norway. This photograph was taken on a Youth Hostels Association Tour which cost only £20 for ten days. The mountains are high above Rjukan in the Telemark district where the peaks are approximately 6,000 feet and are buried in 6 feet of snow.

YOU WANT TO TAKE UP SKI-ING

IF you want to take up ski-ing, then you are another recruit to a sport which, by its growing popularity, has not only altered the mountain faces of Europe, but is now beginning to alter the hills of Scotland with pylons and wire ropes to tow skiers uphill and so take the drudgery out of climbing.

Thanks to ratchet-railways, chair-lifts, overhead cable-cars and tracked vehicles, skiers on the Continent can now put in more downhill running in a day than they could in a month thirty years ago; hence the reason why ski-ing has become the most popular outdoor sport in Europe, demanding the quickness of eye of a fighter pilot and the muscles of an athelete to control the narrow boards at racing speeds from 40 to 80 m.p.h.; while ski-jumpers fly through the air, arms outstretched, in flights that take a quarter of a minute as they curve 400 feet through the air.

But not many ordinary individuals reach this high standard of championship ski-ing, though everyone may obtain the same sort of thrills, because swooping down through the frosty air on skis is one of the greatest joys of life. Fortunately for us in Britain it is more accessible to us to-day than it has ever been before, now that the Scottish Youth Hostels Association promotes cheap courses in Scotland and Norway with instructors and ski equipment provided at cheap hire rates.

LEARNING TO SKI

I began to ski myself by going on a Youth Hostel course to Norway one February some years ago at a cost of £20 for ten days, arriving in a world of Christmas trees and mountains sparkling with deep snow. The place was called Rjukan in the Telemark district, and we stayed in a cabin in the mountains where the slopes were flood-lit at night. None of us knew anything about ski-ing, but inside a day or two we were hurtling down steep slopes, taking terrific purlers, but more gradually gaining confidence. No instructor was provided to teach us, but by the end of the week we were no longer slaves to the nursery slopes, but could climb the mountains and taste the thrill of swooping down several thousand feet at a time, going over wild glens so deep with snow that they would have been impossible to a foot slogger. One day three of us covered 26 miles on skis, climbing over one mountain range and coming back over another. At the end of our wonderful holiday we felt we were no end of skiers.

Of course we still had a terrible lot to learn, as I discovered when I went to Switzerland a year or two later and was told that I was very bad. My skis were the wrong kind; my boots were unsuitable; nor was I using my body in co-ordination with my legs but wobbling all over the place. In short I had to begin all over again. All this because I had not had an instructor in Norway to correct my bad habits, or guide me in the correct choice of skis.

THE INSTRUCTOR AND EQUIPMENT

It is worth emphasising that the instructor is nearly as important as the skis, because in the last twenty years the 4,000 year-old practice of sliding on two wooden boards has become an exact science, so exact that ski races are won by fractions of a second, as speeds get faster and faster by cunning design of the ski, by the plastic finish of its sliding surface and by the method of attachment known as the " binding," which fastens the ski so tightly to the boot that the merest flick of the body controls the skis.

How then do you choose a pair of skis? Of course you should get an expert to help you to make the purchase, but a good test for length is as follows. Stand upright with one arm extended vertically and measure the ski against your stretch. Your hand should crook easily over the upturned end of the ski. Skis that are too long by this measure are harder to manage on turns but faster on the straight. Skis that are too short will be more manageable on turns but slower on descents. Short skis are becoming popular among amateurs on the Continent and are easier to master for a beginner, but I do not recommend them for a young person who wants to be a fast skier. There should be plenty of flexibility in the ski,

Instead of football or school sports, these children of Rjukan, South Norway, get an afternoon off two or three times a week to go ski-ing. They are going off into the mountains now.

so that when you stamp it on the ground you see the point quiver. Such a ski, with steel edges, will run well on hard as well as on soft snow.

Next in importance to the skis are the boots, which are square-toed to fit the binding and so rigid that they do not buckle under the tight pressure of the cable which fastens them to the ski. They should be close-fitting, with support straps giving protection to the instep and ankles. Boots that are wobbly are no good except for running on gentle slopes. Now you want a pair of sticks to propel you when walking, or as an aid in climbing. A good test for length is to measure them roughly against your arm-pits. Metal is better than wood, and they should have reasonable-sized baskets or they will sink in too deeply in new snow and be of no help.

THE POSITION

Now you are all set to ski, but, before you try out your equipment, you should look at a good text-book on ski-ing showing the modern technique. By diagrams and photos you will see how you should look on your skis, body leaning forward from the ankles, skis close together, shoulders relaxed. Now stand on your skis and try to assume this position, and when you think your knees are bent, bend them a bit more, and get forward from the ankles.

My advice to you at this point is to choose a gentle slope and keep running down it until you feel you are leaning purposefully forward at each run. Every time you sit down will remind you that you are not leaning forward. Examine your ski tracks, for they constitute your examination paper, and if you see what looks like a pair of wobbly tram lines you know you have failed to keep your skis properly together. Concentrate on keeping the skis together, because when you fall there is less chance of hurting yourself. But always bend the knees, and lean forward from the ankles. In this way you avoid sticking out your back-side, however convenient that may be for sitting down upon.

TURNING

I am not going to deal with the refinements of ski technique here, but define what I consider to be the best course for a beginner. You have been running straight downhill.

Try running across the hill now in the position known as the traverse. All the weight should be on the lower ski, with the body inclining down the slope, not leaning into the hill. To stop one merely needs swing the downhill shoulder and downhill ski stick forward with an easy knees-bend motion. The effect of this is to turn the ski tips gently uphill in the movement that is known as the into-the-hill Christiania.

Turning on skis is an art that has gone a very long way since the early days of leaning on the sticks and forcing the body round. It was an invention of the British, the slalom race, that did more to perfect the fast turn than anything else. The slalom is an arrangement of poles and gates on a steep mountainside through which the skier must twist and turn. Watch a good skier weave in and out through these posts shooting from one to the other with accuracy and perfect poise and it looks easy. What you are watching is the result of some sixty years of intensive study of the science of ski-ing, as decade by decade the bad habits which hindered perfect control have been ironed out into this technique of grace and speed. That is why a good teacher should direct your first tremulous attempts at turning, for it is the most difficult thing in ski-ing.

You can learn a lot by watching, but whenever you yourself try turning you will discover you have half a dozen things to remember at once. There is, however, a sequence of movements that is taught at all the best ski schools in the world. First you begin with the legs steering the skis by transferring the weight from one to the other to make them go right or left; then when this has been mastered you speed it up, until at last you are doing an entirely different kind of turn where the legs do nothing but remain flexible while the swing of the body levers the skis in the desired direction. This turn, known as the Christiania or parallel swing, is the most stylish turn in ski-ing and is the turn which has knocked the minutes off ski race times. It is the hallmark of the really polished skier, though it polishes the trousers more than the skier in the initial stages as one sliding fall leads to another until it is mastered. The sequence of learning, to give technical names to the turns, is (a) snow plough, (b) the stem, (c) stem-christie, (d) parallel swing.

Because it is such a thrilling sport it is not

The age to take up ski-ing is not necessarily as young as this little girl in the photograph,
but ideally the younger you start the easier it is.

hard to understand why there are more people in Europe who ski nowadays than play football. Indeed the Norwegians are a nation on skis, but it was the British who were pre-eminent in the field of ski racing until 1939 and who first conquered the highest peaks in the Alps on skis.

DOWNHILL RACING AND SKI-JUMPING

I have mentioned the slalom race between sticks as a test of precision and skill. The only other race that approaches it for excitement is the downhill race where no holds are barred and reckless daring is given its head on sensational courses down mountains where a slip can mean death. Britain has been left very far behind in this sort of racing of which they were pioneers, because our men and women cannot get the constant practice necessary, whereas so many people on the Continent can get to the snow any week-end, from the big cities.

The same applies to ski-jumping or ski-flying as it is more properly called. You have probably seen it on television or in the cinema, and know that the skier leaps out from a prepared runway with the intention of leaping into space and flying through the air for as long as he can stay above ground, gradually falling twice the height of a tall city building in his fifteen-second flight through 400 feet of space. Most who engage in this exciting sport are professionals using specially heavy skis to withstand the tremendous shock of landing.

CROSS-COUNTRY RACING

The other type of race, more popular in Scandinavia than anywhere else, is the cross-country race, such as is held from Lillehammer to Rena every year, a distance of 35 miles which is known as the " Birch Leg Ski Race." This marathon commemorates an event of 750 years ago when the two-year-old King of Norway was saved from falling into enemy hands by two fast skiers who sped across the mountains carrying the infant to safety. To-day this mountain race takes five or six hours, which shows the degree of fitness necessary for this gruelling sport, probably the greatest test of muscle and stamina in ski-ing.

MOUNTAIN SKI-ING

Real mountain ski-ing is in rather a different category from racing however, especially in the Alps where great glaciers and dangerous crevasses pose their own problems. Having sampled all kinds of ski-ing, I would rate mountaineering on skis as being the most adventurous sport of the lot and one of the cheapest, because in the mountains one has to live simply, carrying one's own food and cooking it in the simple huts provided by the Alpine Club.

A TOUR IN THE MOUNTAINS

Let me tell you of a tour four of us did in the springtime, in April, when the high mountains are safer for ski-ing than in winter because the weather is more settled. Our plan was to use the highest railway in the world to the Jungfraujoch at over 11,000 feet, and launch ourselves with ten days' food on to the greatest ice-stream in Europe, the Aletsch Glacier.

The great glacier falls steeply in a bulge at first, then for seven kilometres flows evenly to join up with three other streams of ice at a region known as Konkordia. Here on skis we knew we were in one of the remotest situations in Europe with fierce peaks on every side of us glittering under the frosty sky. That night we slept in the eerie silence, which seems to be of death in this world of ice where no rivers run. Although we had skied over 14 kilometres that day and climbed 2,000 feet we were too wide awake to let ourselves sleep properly, for we knew we should be up long before dawn.

You have to be up early in the high alps, otherwise climbing and ski-ing become unsafe as the heat of the day thaws the steep slopes and causes avalanches. We were up in the dark, therefore, threading a way carefully past a crevasse system with its caves of icicles, while the high peaks were tinged with the pink of the rising sun. Noting carefully the best way down, we made for a narrow snow saddle, deposited our skis, and climbed to a narrow summit using the ice-axe and rope. Balanced on an edge of snow-cornice above blue valleys

thousands of feet deep, we looked out to the great peaks of the Matterhorn, Dent Blanche, Weisshorn, Mont Blanc and a host of other fierce-looking mountains.

Then came the thrill of the day when we returned to our skis, brewed coffee, and fastened on our skis for the long dive downwards. The snow was safe and fast, and we each chose our own line of descent, swinging back and forth or schussing like arrows until too much speed warned us to curve into another series of turns.

But the best climb of all was ascent of the Finsteraarhorn, over 14,000 feet and the highest peak in the Oberland. The snow was ice-hard and our breaths smoked as we left the hut before dawn, watching for the first rays of the sun touching the tops of the mountains with fire, which is one of the wonders of an Alpine sunrise. Suddenly above the pale folds of ice the spires of the peaks glowed like red-hot pokers, becoming lemon-tinted, then dazzling white as the flood of light spread down the peaks and engulfed us with warmth.

But now we had to be more careful with the coming of the sun, for ahead of us were blue caverns denoting the rifts in the ice known as crevasses. A crevasse when you can see it is not dangerous, but when it is hidden by a thin lid of snow it is a menace, because suddenly you can fall through and lose your life. So we put on the rope and tested with our ski-sticks before trusting the weight of our skis on any indentation that looked like the lip of a crevasse.

UP TO THE SUMMIT

The danger area passed, we were soon climbing steadily to a huge spine of rock soaring up to the pointed summit. Below us the clouds were drifting in from Italy, telling us of a change in weather, for until that day the clouds had been above us, not below us. But we had no intention of giving up just yet, so out came our ice-axes and rope. We left the skis, and soon were scrambling upwards, cutting steps or edging up the red granite, knowing that whatever happened we would need to turn back at 3 p.m. otherwise we should be caught on the mountainside in darkness on the descent. We were getting anxious as this great ridge went on and on, one pinnacle after another, then suddenly there

A crevasse on the Finsteraarhorn. Crevasses constitute a danger to spring-time mountain-eering in the High Alps, but the danger is greater if they are hidden by a thin lid of snow.

Ski-ing in Scotland is becoming more and more popular and facilities are increasing and improving each season. Here two experienced skiers execute Christiania turns.

The finest day the author has ever spent on a Scottish mountain top. Taken in Inverness-shire after a storm, the photograph shows the view from Carn Laith towards Loch Laggan.

were no more pinnacles, just a sugary dome like icing on a cake, and that was the summit.

Unfortunately we could not linger on that exciting place, because of the lateness of the hour and the clouds which were racing steadily below us, filling up the valleys. Perhaps it was already snowing down there. But our skis saved the day. Once we had climbed rapidly down the rocks and slipped them on we shot down the slopes, reaching the hut none too soon for a real storm was starting with lightning flashing and a blizzard, such a blizzard in fact that we were pinned down in that remote hut in the Alps for the next three days. Five feet of snow fell outside, smothering everything and making us anxious about the escape route back over the mountains.

HUNTING, THEN EXPLORATION AND SPORT

Our escape was an example of the use of skis for a journey that could not have been accomplished on foot, for a walker would have been up to the waist in snow at every step. Even on skis it was hard work breaking a trail, with the skis disappearing out of sight at each thrust. But we crossed the high pass and found our way back up the Aletsch glacier, using the long boards as a means of transport,

just as Stone Age man did to hunt the elk in Scandinavia under similar conditions.

Skis have conquered the ends of the earth, and are used at the North and South Poles, as well as in the Himalaya, where they have been taken to over 20,000 feet on the highest mountains in the world. The great Norwegian explorer, Fridjof Nansen, made history in 1888 when he took skis to Greenland and skied over 300 miles across the ice-cap. That was a great journey which did much to stimulate an interest in the use of skis for exploration.

Man learned to use long planks of wood in order to hunt and travel over the deep winter snow, but it took him twenty-five centuries before he used skis for sport. Ski-ing became fashionable and was regarded as the sport of the rich for a time, but now it is once more something which can be enjoyed by everyone. It is a truly democratic sport. You can judge some men by the size of their cars or their yachts, but skis are the same whether they stand outside a luxury hotel or a hut in the Highlands. The rewards of ski-ing are so tremendous that no one should miss them, especially when you are young, and have no fear of falling. Like fighter pilots, ski-racers are old at thirty, so now is the time for you to begin.

THE THRILL OF
UNDERWATER FISHING

SOME years ago in the warmer climates of the world, and especially in the sunny Mediterranean area, a new form of sport came into being and quickly gained popularity wherever conditions were suitable. It was fishing—but with an exciting difference. It was fishing *under* water!

The warmth and the clarity of the sea off the south coast of France, for instance, made it a particularly suitable region in which to enjoy the sport. There also, regardless of the fact that underwater fishermen wear no extra protective clothing, it is possible to dive to much greater depths than would be possible in colder waters.

Nevertheless, enthusiasm for underwater fishing soon spread to cooler climates, and to the British Isles. Especially off the southerly Cornish coast, it was found that during the summer months the new style of catching a fish could be practised quite comfortably, and one of the first clubs of underwater fishermen to be formed in this country was the Looe (Cornwall) Underwater Fishing Club which was formed in 1953. Prospective members of this Club (nicknamed locally "The Sea Creepers") must be good swimmers, and before they can become fully-elected members must have speared underwater a fish of not less than 1 lb. in weight.

THE "SEA CREEPERS" IN ACTION

If you should see some underwater fishermen off for an hour or two's sport, you would probably not recognise them from their appearance as fishermen at all. For they carry not waders but towels and swimming trunks, and their equipment is not rod and line but an assortment of odd-looking apparatus.

Later on, clad in their special masks and flippers, and grasping spear or trident, they will resemble a film version of men from Mars as they enter the water. The one great advantage they will have over ordinary fishermen is that they will not only be able to see the fish they are trying to catch but, more important, whether there is in fact anything worth catching.

Many rod and line anglers do not wholly approve of the idea of spearing a fish underwater. Even these, however, usually take a keen interest if an underwater fisherman should come along and offer to look round beneath the surface. He may be able to tell the angler that the bait he is using is not the best for the type of bottom. He may even be able to recommend a move to a more suitable spot if the fish should happen to be feeding elsewhere that day!

HOW TO DRESS FOR UNDERWATER FISHING

The necessary equipment for underwater fishing costs on an average in the region of £3, exact prices of individual pieces varying from maker to maker. It consists of a mask, breathing tube or snort, and a pair of flippers.

The mask, which enables its wearer to see clearly under water, is generally an oval-shaped piece of glass set in a rubber frame which encloses the eyes and nose and straps tightly around the head.

The snort is a plastic or metal tube of about two feet in length. The diver grips one end of this between his teeth and an outer rubber shield keeps the water from entering his lips as he sucks down air from the upper end of the tube which protrudes above the surface. The most efficient type of snort has a valve which closes automatically to stop water entering the upper end of the tube as it becomes submerged. This type is well worth the extra small cost—without a valve it is possible to receive a nasty mouthful of water if the diver happens accidentally to suck in air as he plunges downwards!

Most people are familiar with the flippers, which are of the kind made famous by the exploits of wartime "frogmen." Wearing these on his feet, the diver is able to propel himself through the water without using his arms, so leaving his hands free for whatever weapons he may be using to catch his fish.

UNDERWATER WEAPONS

This weapon, which is the only other necessary piece of equipment, is usually a trident or

Two ways of loading a spring gun on land.

of underwater fishing—or rather, fish-hunting—are the shallow method and the deep. In shallow fishing the swimmer cruises along just under the surface of the water. On spotting a fish, he immediately dives to the kill, the valve in his breathing tube automatically closing as he does so. Mainly flat-fish are sought in this manner, and often all that can be seen of these surprisingly agile fish, as they lie at the bottom, are their eyes protruding from the mud or sand, so perfectly are they camouflaged.

Unfortunately, there is a marked disadvantage in fishing by the shallow method. The swimmer's flippers are inclined to make a commotion by breaking the surface, and so frighten off any fish which may be lurking near.

In deep fishing, there is certainly no risk of this sort of nuisance. As the fishermen dive far beneath the surface, they make no more disturbance in the water than do the fish themselves. Indeed, these seem to regard them almost as though they were fish too,

a spear. Often it may be a home-made double-pronged spear which can be fashioned fairly easily and cheaply from a pair of straightened-out shark hooks which are attached to a length of copper pipe.

A very much more effective weapon, but much more expensive is the harpoon gun. Made mainly from aluminium tubing, the approximately 2ft.-long gun weighs only about 3 lb. It is powered by hefty rubber strands, and possesses a pistol-type handgrip. In use, the gun is carried in front of the swimmer and is fired at arm's length, having sights similar to those on a rifle.

The striking range of this powerful and deadly weapon is ruled by the length of nylon cord by which the harpoon is attached to the gun. With an average gun at a range of 12 feet, the harpoon will strike at a pressure of 33 lb. to the square inch.

Even though it has a safety catch the harpoon gun is treated very gently by the sensible underwater fisherman, for it can be a perilous instrument in careless hands.

STALKING A FISHY PREY

The two principal methods

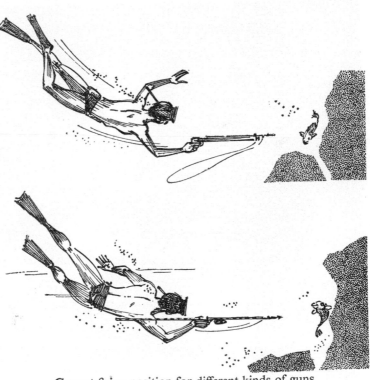

Correct firing position for different kinds of guns.

The photographer's flashlight momentarily illuminates a shoal of mackerel. You might be able to take such a photograph yourself off the coast of Britain.

A John Dory gliding past a rock façade keeps a watchful, and, it seems, a rather supercilious eye on the photographer. This fish is also to be found off the coasts of Britain.

allowing them to approach often as close as 5 or 6 feet before taking any real notice.

Once a fish is chosen as " target," the chase is really on! If the underwater sportsman is to claim his quarry, he will have to exert much patience and skill at stalking, before he will be in a position to use his spear or gun. A cool head and sound ability as a hunter will claim many more prizes than will a super-efficient weapon.

Without breathing apparatus, the diver can sometimes reach a depth of from 30 to 40 feet, but at this depth a nasty pressure at the temples and a tendency of the mask to flatten against his face will probably warn him to return nearer the surface. Few submarine fishermen make a practice of diving as deeply as this, however, and there is much fine sport to be obtained in shallower waters.

The length of time for which a diver can stay beneath the surface depends on just how long he is able to hold his breath without discomfort. Most swimmers who are seriously interested in the sport of underwater fishing hope that some day they will have the opportunity of using oxygen or compressed-air equipment which will enable them to make really deep dives of much longer duration.

The position for the overhead attack.

TAKING "SNAPS" BELOW THE SURFACE

An underwater (pressurized) camera costing £100-£125 is usually another pet ambition of anyone who has ever seen the beauties of the underwater world—fantastic rock formations, sands, shells and weeds of wonderous shape.

Weeds beneath the surface are not weeds as most people think of them. Some are weird tree-like plants, which are unfortunately as dangerous as they are lovely, that is, to the ordinary swimmer, to whom the risk is great

of becoming entangled in their waving branches. They give little trouble to the properly equipped underwater swimmer, however. Being able to see clearly in the depths, it is a simple matter for him to avoid the weeds, or to pick his way safely through the strange channels and tunnels which they form.

A fish-holder of strong wire for the catch.

Visibility beneath the surface is normally about 25 feet, but in rough weather the sea-bed or river-bed often becomes so disturbed that visibility is cut to nothing, so making submarine exploration impossible.

Summer is, of course, the best time of all to practise the sport around British coasts, when the temperature of the air is warm, and the winds mild. In winter, although the water itself is not unduly cold, the icy bite of the air usually deters even the hardiest of swimmers. Underwater fishing has its dangers, as have most truly exciting sports. To a careful swimmer, however, and one who is using the correct equipment, the dangers are few indeed, and are far outweighed by the pleasures and thrills to be obtained from this thoroughly healthy sport.

A plastic case for use underwater. It can be made to house any suitable camera.

SEAWEEDS AND THEIR USES

IN Victorian times collecting seaweeds was as popular as collecting stamps or autographs is to-day. Long before this, however, seaweeds were collected in great quantities to use as manure, and they were also burned in pits on the open beach to extract iodine, which we now get mostly from coal tar. A few seaweeds in this country are used as food but not on as big a scale as they are in China and Japan, where for centuries seaweeds of many kinds have been the main breakfast dish, like bacon and eggs in our own country.

But in July, 1952, there was held at Edinburgh a great meeting, called the First International Seaweed Symposium, ˙and it may fairly be said to have put seaweeds " on the map." For this meeting was attended by famous chemists and manufacturers from over twenty countries, and they met to give their reports on all the wonderful things they had been making from seaweeds and the great benefits mankind might hope to enjoy from seaweeds in the near future.

SOME PRODUCTS OF SEAWEED

Here are just a few of the things now being made from seaweeds. Chemicals and medicines of almost every kind and pure jellies in which doctors can breed " cultures " of germs, and so get to know more about how to treat all kinds of illness. Seaweeds are being used more and more in the manufacture of both human and cattle foods, in the making of the hundred and one things called " plastics " (anything from mackintoshes to toast racks) and in " slimming agents " for people who are growing inconveniently fat. Surgeons use powders made from seaweed which will check too profuse bleeding; dentists use a special soluble wool for the same purpose. Other products include dusting powders, penicillin salts, surgical gauzes, a wax essential to successful operations on the skull, and a new first aid dressing. Seaweeds are providing us with tooth brushes, chicken foods, tasty syrups, wonderful plant fertilisers and even fire-proof curtains. It is no wonder that we are now studying very carefully the seasons at which seaweeds multiply best, the animals that tend to destroy them, and the most suitable times of year to harvest these precious sea crops.

SOME BRITISH SEAWEEDS

In the picture you will see that the seaweeds shown (they are all British) have been arranged in a sort of pattern, or procession, beginning with small short kinds growing in fairly shallow water, and as the procession winds its way slowly downwards, it ends up with quite enormous weeds growing at a considerable depth, about sixty fathoms or 360 feet. Below this there is not enough light to support plant life. Now the weeds were not arranged like this only to make a pleasant picture. If you take a walk on the beach at extreme low tide, i.e., a " spring tide," such as that which falls at the new and full moon, and you gradually work your way to the water's edge, half a mile or more from shore you will make an interesting discovery. And this is that the seaweeds are all more or less arranged in the order in which we have drawn them. Moreover you will find this holds good, in a rough and ready way (there is sure to be a good deal of overlapping) on whatever part of the coast you may be. There is of course a reason, as there is for everything in nature. Just as on land you will find that plants are arranged in belts or zones, according to the height at which they grow, and the nature of the soil, so, in the sea, plants grow in a certain order for one of two main reasons. First of all the depth at which they grow is dictated by the amount of light each requires and secondly the length of time each can withstand exposure to sun and air when the tide leaves them stranded. There are between seven and eight hundred kinds of seaweeds found round our coasts and many are never found between tide marks. To collect them we must hook them up from the seafloor, or wait for a storm to cast them ashore.

Besides the plants shown there are thousands of kinds of minute floating plants that can be seen in detail only with the microscope, though they may be so abundant as to discolour the water over a great area. Many kinds also form thin sheets or films over the rocks below and just above the water line, some

Seaweeds shown in the order in which they generally occur between tide marks: 1. the floating Gulf weed or sargassum. 2. sea lettuce. 3. laver. 4. channelled wrack. 5. flat wrack. 6. bladder wrack. 7. knotted wrack or sea whistles. 8. red weed. 9. Irish moss, or Carragheen moss. 10. coral weed. 11. peacock weed. 12. serrated wrack. 13. sea ribbons. 14. cow tail, sea tangles or kelp. 15. bulbous-rooted kelp. 16. sea thongs or bootlace weed.

Collecting seaweed from the seashore for use as a fertiliser and in the manufacture of cattle food; two of the many uses of seaweed.

even bore into the rocks, and some are reinforced with lime so that they look more like corals than plants. The largest plant in the world is a seaweed growing off the southern parts of South America. It has fronds two hundred yards long and " floats " as big as football bladders.

Seaweeds were probably the first of all plants to appear on our planet and how some gradually made their way into fresh water and then invaded the land, must have been a very long process. One plant, the eel grass has reversed this. It is a fresh water plant that has harked back to the sea, and has fibrous roots and small flowers, things possessed by no true seaweed. Eel-grass makes a useful sound-proofing material for the walls of flats and broadcasting studios. When dried it looks and feels like wood-shavings, and is also used for packing valuable china and glassware. A seaweed has only a sort of sucker base, or hold fast, and it multiplies by casting adrift countless millions of minute structures, known as spores, each of which will in time give rise to a new plant.

HOW TO PRESS SEAWEED

Only a few common kinds of seaweeds have popular names. All the rest are known only by scientific names. It is only possible to press and keep the smaller and finer weeds, mostly red kinds, and to name them you must look them up in Prof. L. Newton's handbook on British seaweeds. First wash the weeds well in fresh water to remove the salt, then float a piece of weed in a basin of water and gently slide a piece of stiff card or plywood beneath it and lift out. The weed will lie flat on the card and it must then be dried by putting sheets of blotting paper on top and pressing with heavy weights. After a few weeks it will be quite dry, and can be gummed by its stem into a book with blank pages. Kept in the dark its colours will fade very little. Looking up its name can be exciting and will teach you a lot about these " sea gardens."

ON DRAWING DOGS
Advice from an Artist

IN ORDER to draw a dog successfully, in action or at rest, you must first study its anatomy, that is to say its bony frame-work, the muscles covering it and the hairy coat which encloses it. Take note of where bones come near the surface of the skin causing bulges that catch the high-lights; muscles also play an important part in forming lights and shades.

To begin with it is better to draw the dog sitting or lying down. Use straight lines wherever you can and curves only where absolutely necessary. Draw them in as quickly as possible before your model moves. It is quite a good rule to start with the head, a few triangular lines indicating nose, eyes and ears, then continue with a straight line or two on the back, legs and paws. If he has not moved, put a touch of shadow under the body. If he moves, at once begin another drawing. In this way you may have three or four studies going at the same time. Often the dog will revert to one or other of his earlier positions, in which case quickly add a line or two to the necessary drawing.

TRAINING YOUR VISUAL MEMORY

At first you will have difficulty in remembering the details of what you see, but with practice, you will learn to memorise more every time you try. Look at the shape of neck, body, legs and tail. Note the direction in which the hair grows on both long and short-coated dogs. Try to draw a few of the above details from memory; you will be surprised at how little you can remember. When you next draw your subject, concentrate on those forgotten details and, with practice, you will find your visual memory is sharpened and, as a result, your sketches will soon show a marked improvement.

Shading is a great help in making your drawing come " alive." Watch for the highest light and the deepest dark on your subject. Draw shadows in a mass rather than broken up. The minor lights and shades can be suggested with one or two lines. Unless your model is asleep, or has his head turned away,

try to make his eyes the most attractive feature of your drawing. The high-lights in the eyes and on the nose should be the brightest things in the picture, the dark pupils and the black shadows of the nose helping to create the effect. Whatever light there is usually falls on the upper parts of the dog, therefore the undersides should have the deepest shadows. Treat these shadows with strong, thick strokes and they will give strength and character to your drawing.

EFFECTIVE " SNAPSHOT " STUDIES

The rough sketch of the head of a Yorkshire terrier on the following page illustrates this rule. You will notice that the dog's bright, dark eyes focus the attention in spite of the massed shadow under the jaw. Look, too, at the study of a cairn's head. Here it is the shaded hair on the jaws that gives character to the sketch, but does not detract from his bright eyes. Drawn front face, you will see his eyes are set in a triangle of shadow; the black nose and the ears also form triangles.

The wire-haired fox-terrier was done mostly in straight lines and angles drawn in roughly before he moved. The study of a sheepdog in action was taken at a sheepdog trial and is, of necessity, very roughly done. In the somewhat conventional study of a Peke, the group formations of hair are clearly shown.

In drawing a smooth-haired dog like the Labrador, you have to focus on the shadows caused by bone and muscle formations rather than those made by hair grouping, but, as always, keep the eyes as the chief point of interest.

On the next page you will also see more highly-finished sketches of cocker spaniels, and various other well-known breeds. The depths of shading give roundness and character to the dog, whilst the shadows on the ground help the perspective and give the whole drawing solidity.

Remember to reward your model with a biscuit after he has been " sitting " for you, for the prospect of a reward will hold his interest and perhaps also his " pose."

These rough sketches show how effective a few simple lines can be when drawing dogs. Copy these sketches first, and then, when you understand how to achieve an effect simply, try drawing from life. Your model may not sit or lie still for long so draw in your outline quickly, and then if he moves start another sketch.

Here you have some more highly-finished studies of dogs. You will see how in each case the high-lights in the eyes and on the nose are the brightest things in the drawing. The way the hair grows has been skilfully shown in each sketch and the differences in the coats of the various breeds can be readily seen.

HOW TO DRAW PORTRAITS

YOU may enjoy drawing and be good at it, but you have probably found that faces are rather difficult to draw. Our artist gives you, therefore, some advice which will be of great use to you if you follow it carefully.

First of all think before you draw, and look about you in school, in buses, in the street and at home. You will quickly realise that although the component parts of all faces are the same, the differences from face to face are very noticeable.

THE GENERAL OUTLINE

Your first model should be yourself, for you will have more patience than anyone else. Sit in front of a mirror, or, if possible, three mirrors, of the type you find on some dressing-tables, for with these you can see both your full face and profile. First indicate lightly the shape of the head, which you should note is *not* completely round; it is more the shape of an egg, flattened at the sides where the ears are. Having sketched in the general shape of the head, draw a guide line running down the face from the forehead to the chin to indicate the position of the nose. It is a help when drawing the nose to think of it as being made up of planes, as if it were carved from wood. You will see when you look at your model that the nostrils vary as much as the shape of the nose, and that the under side of the nose follows the curve of the upper lip.

THE EYES

The eyes, which are the feature which gives " life " to any portrait, are set half-way up the head and a horizontal line drawn at this point will help to position them. As you no doubt know, the eyes are round balls set into the skull with only a small section of them showing. The lens is slightly rounded and this swelling on the eyeball alters the shape of the lids when the eyes are turned. Notice the thickness of the lids as they slide over the eye; it is more noticeable in profile. People's eyes vary in their setting, size and distance apart, as well as in colour, so study them carefully. It is helpful to know that, as a general rule, the distance between the eyes is equal to the width of one of them. Practise drawing the eyes from every angle. As one usually notices the eyes first in a portrait, when they are badly drawn it is very obvious.

CHECKING THE PROPORTIONS

The distance between the chin, the bottom of the nose, the eyebrows and the hair line is generally equal and here is the way to check these important proportions: hold a pencil at arm's length between the first finger and the thumb, so that the point of the pencil comes between your eyes and a point on the sitter's face—say the bottom of the nose. Now by moving your thumb down the pencil to the point where it is level with the bottom of the chin, you have a measurement to check with the other features on the face, and also in relation to the width of the face. This use of pencil and thumb is a good way of checking the proportion of your drawing.

THE EARS

When you have established the relative positions of eyebrows and mouth, draw in guide lines across the face. You can then position the ears from these guide lines, for the top of the ears is generally in line with the brow, and the bottom of the ears in line with the base of the nose. Ears are as distinctive as any feature, and you will seldom find two people with ears of the same shape. Watch the twists and folds and the shape of the lobe and notice the angle the ears are set in the head, whether vertically or sloping backwards.

THE MOUTH

When drawing the mouth, remember that it is on a curve and that both lips are not constructed in the same way. The upper lip is divided into two sections, like the bows of a ship, and the lower is generally fuller and does not slope back quite so abruptly as the upper lip. You will notice that the nostrils widen slightly and change shape when the mouth smiles. Watch the corners of the mouth and the lines running from the sides of the nose.

If you have to draw teeth, treat them as one continuous curved shape, and then lightly indicate the divisions between them. Remember that it is impossible to smile continuously

From the rough outline to the finished product. Our artist has shown you how to get the correct proportions for the head and how to draw and shade the features.

for any length of time, as the face muscles begin to ache, so make sure that the expression on your model's face is one that can be held for at least ten minutes at a time.

THE HAIR

The hair is only drawn in when the shape of the head has been determined. Be careful to look for the main mass of hair, and, having indicated it lightly, you can then emphasise the characteristic sweeps and waves. The drawing of the hair should not be too indefinite and shapeless, but you must guard against attempting to draw each hair separately.

SHADING

Lighting plays an important part in helping you to convey the features of your sitter. In a good light you will notice that the shading on the face is darkest where the planes change their direction, and if you half-close your eyes the complicated half-tones tend to disappear and are reduced to simple planes of light and dark. You will see what I mean if your sitter is near to a light surface, such as a wall, and the reflected light on the face can be a little confusing. You will also notice a reflected light under the chin from a white collar. The main contours on the face generally show up as the darkest in the shaded parts.

Of course portrait drawing involves more than just the face. The neck and the tilt of the shoulders have to be considered as well as clothes. Care must be taken in drawing these too, so that the overall effect is not spoilt.

GENERAL INSTRUCTIONS

Now for a few more tips:

(a) If you are using pencil, buy only a good make and a B and 4B are all you need.

(b) Try to use your rubber only to " clean up " at the end, because constant rubbing out makes the drawing " smudgy."

(c) The type of paper you use will affect the finished appearance of your drawing and you can experiment with various kinds, from an ordinary writing pad—avoid the shiny surfaces—to the rough-finish hand-made papers. You can buy drawing paper in sheets or in blocks, but your local artists' materials shop will help you to choose the kind you need.

(d) If you buy paper in sheets you will need a firm support when drawing. A piece of

The effect of the hair has been given without drawing each hair separately.

builders' Essex board about ½ in. thick and about 16 in. by 14 in. makes a very useful light drawing-board. Hardboard is also very good for the purpose, but it is very difficult to stick drawing pins into it, and your sheet should be fixed to the support or it will slip down when you tilt your drawing-board.

(e) Never have your drawing-board flat on the table, or wherever you are working; you will find it easier if you rest the drawing-board on your knees and hold the top with one hand while you draw with the other.

(f) Your finished drawing will look much better if the head is well placed on the paper. For instance if you draw the head too near the bottom of the paper, it will look as if the model is slowly slipping out of sight, and if you place the head looking to left or right, do not draw it with the nose almost touching one edge of the paper. To help you to decide on a good position in advance, cut out from a piece of stout paper a rectangle equal to the proportions of the sheet you intend to draw on and hold this frame in front of the model from where you are sitting. You can move it about until you arrive at an arrangement that you find the most interesting.

Finally don't be in too much of a hurry. Practice will not teach you much unless you are working on the right lines. Make haste slowly and then every sketch will teach you something interesting and increase not only your skill, but your pleasure.

SOME AMUSING SEA SHELLS

ALMOST everybody loves shells and it is strange to think how their wonderful shapes and often gorgeous colours have been beautifying the sea bed, for hundreds of millions of years before there was one human being to admire and make use of them.

For shells have been put to innumerable uses since the dawn of human history. Great kitchen middens, or scrap heaps, outside cave dwellings are evidence of how our remote ancestors valued as food the soft succulent animals that made the shells. To-day hundreds of kinds of shell fish are popular as food and their shells are used as money, in the making of every kind of ornament, as knives, fish hooks, and even ground down to make fine porcelain.

On that part of Australia which is fringed by the Great Barrier Reef, over a thousand miles of coral, one of the commonest objects for collecting rainwater, and even used as a baby's bath, is the shell of the giant clam which may measure four feet in length. Just as with our own oyster and mussel, there are always two of these shells, joined firmly together by a leathery hinge, and two powerful muscles. People have been caught by the ankle, as the result of carelessly putting one foot in a giant clam as it lay half open and partly buried in coral at low tide. To be caught in such a terrible man-trap would mean being held until the tide came in, and of course drowning. For this reason men working on the Barrier Reef at low tide are warned always to carry a crowbar with them; then, if they do get caught they can free themselves by cutting the great muscles that open and shut the two huge " valves " of the shell. A giant clam can make a good meal for four men.

TINY SHELL BORES THROUGH ROCK

In tropic seas there are whelk shells over two feet in length, and in home waters there lives a sea snail with a shell thinner than any egg-shell and so fragile the snail never comes ashore. It spends its life bobbing about on the waves, and eating jelly-fish. One common shell, the angels' wings, or piddock, shown in our picture, is almost as fragile, yet it tunnels into the hardest limestone, and does much damage to harbour walls. The shell is covered with fine sharp ridges, and the animal that lives in it, sets up a rocking movement, so that the shell acts like a file or drill and so drives a tunnel through stone. Another shell, much smaller, belongs to the ship worm, and this pest tunnels into timber. The ship worm, which is really a kind of clam, is said to have sunk more wooden ships than ever came to grief through storms, or the guns of the enemy.

One shell we all know well, the scallop, can fly through the sea by quickly opening and shutting. It escapes in this way from its chief foe, the starfish, by what is really a sort of jet propulsion. The scallop is a genuine flying saucer.

There is therefore a use in the very shape of a shell. The colours which chiefly excite our admiration are mostly just for camouflage, that is to conceal the shell's owner from its many foes. For even in our seas there are fish with teeth so strong they can crack up the strongest shells. Just as dangerous to clams and scallops is the rock whelk you can find by thousands on any rocky shore at low tide. It drills neat holes through a clam, and then sucks out the owner a bit at a time. Such drilled shells you may pick up at any low tide.

HOW SHELLS ARE MADE

Yes, we all know shells, but how do they come about, these hard strong portable homes that protect soft pulpy animals? If you open an oyster, or take a boiled whelk or winkle out of its shell, you will see that the animal is enclosed in a sort of bag of thin skin, like a cape or cloak. It is called the mantle, and it is this which forms the shell.

In some wonderful way which we still do not perfectly understand, it extracts carbonate of lime from the sea water and plasters this in a thin slice along the lip or outer margin of the shell. It is like building up a wall layer by layer. At the same time special glands pour out into the cement those wonderfully blended colours we admire so much. Cement and colours quickly harden on exposure to the water. Though this work never entirely ceases, it slows down in cold weather, and then the layer thickens to form a ridge, called a " winter

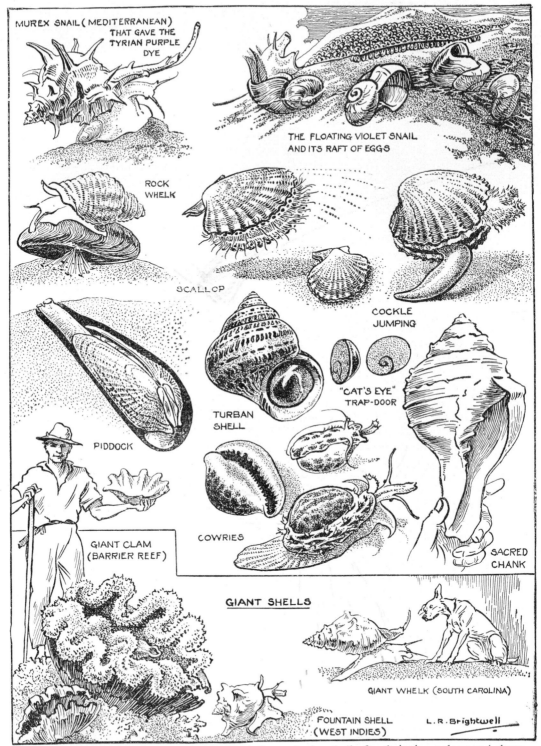

MUREX SNAIL (MEDITERRANEAN) THAT GAVE THE TYRIAN PURPLE DYE

THE FLOATING VIOLET SNAIL AND ITS RAFT OF EGGS

ROCK WHELK

SCALLOP

COCKLE JUMPING

TURBAN SHELL

"CAT'S EYE" TRAP-DOOR

PIDDOCK

GIANT CLAM (BARRIER REEF)

COWRIES

SACRED CHANK

GIANT SHELLS

GIANT WHELK (SOUTH CAROLINA)

FOUNTAIN SHELL (WEST INDIES)

L.R.Brightwell

When at the seaside young and old alike enjoy gathering shells, for their size, colour and shape vary so, and almost all are beautiful. These drawings show some of the curious and amazing shells described in this chapter. The giant clam is the most dangerous one.

ring." So by counting these winter rings on a shell you can get a rough idea of its age.

Since sea water is richer in lime than fresh water, sea shells are much stouter than those of pond snails. Sometimes the horny trap door, such as that of a winkle, is reinforced with carbonate of lime, and when this is coloured we get a beautiful " Cat's Eye " stone, still prized for brooches and bracelet ornaments.

Some shells have made human history. It was the murex of the Mediterranean that supplied the Tyrian purple used for the robes of kings, and purple is still regarded as a royal colour. But perhaps the most famous shell in the world is the sacred chank (a kind of whelk) found in the Indian Ocean. This shell is associated with such great and powerful Indian deities as Vishnu and Krishna, and the shell has been famous as a religious emblem throughout the length and breadth of India since perhaps 2000 B.C. There are large factories turning the shell into all kinds of ornaments, especially bangles, and it is even worn on the foreheads of draught oxen, much as horse brasses used to be employed in this country as safeguards against witchcraft and the evil eye.

What a world of romance there is in shells. The shells of the scallop, so prized as food, were once, you may remember, worn in the hats of pilgrims to show they had made the long and dangerous journey in order to worship in the Holy Land.

THE SAGE'S PIGTAIL

There lived a sage in days of yore,
And he a handsome pigtail wore;
But wondered much and sorrowed more
   Because it hung behind him.

He mused upon this curious case,
And swore he'd change the pigtail's place,
And have it hanging at his face,
   Not dangling there behind him.

Says he, " The mystery I've found;
I'll turn me round "—he turned him round;
   But still it hung behind him.

Then round and round, and out and in,
All day the puzzled sage did spin;
In vain—it mattered not a pin—
   The pigtail hung behind him.

And right and left, and round about,
And up and down, and in and out,
He turned; but still the pigtail stout
   Hung steadily behind him.

And though his efforts never slack,
And though he twist and twirl and tack,
Alas! still faithful to his back,
   The pigtail hangs behind him.
                W. M. Thackeray

FAMILIAR SEA ANIMALS WHEN VERY YOUNG

Some familiar sea animals are not easily recognisable when they are very young, but here you can see them in their young and fully grown states. The numbers refer to the same animal on each page and the actual sizes are given in all cases—on this page in fractions of an inch. The

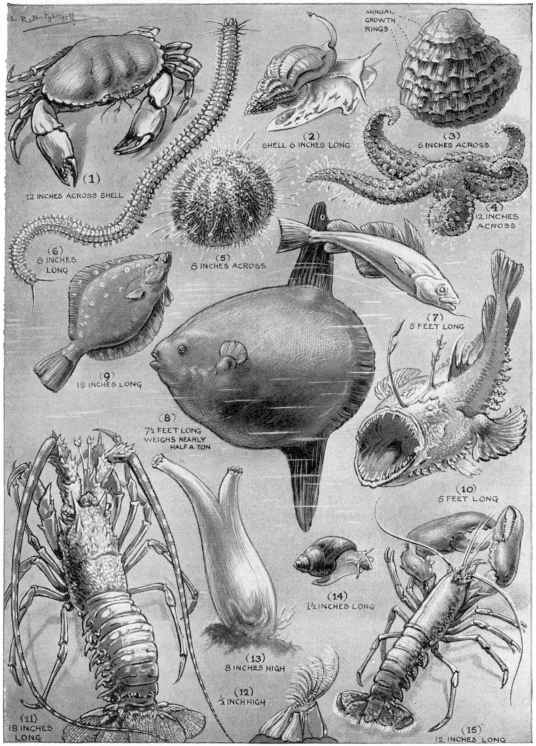

L. R. Brightwell

ANNUAL
GROWTH
RINGS

(1)
12 INCHES ACROSS SHELL

(2)
SHELL 6 INCHES LONG

(3)
6 INCHES ACROSS

(4)
12 INCHES
ACROSS

(5)
8 INCHES ACROSS

(6)
8 INCHES
LONG

(7)
5 FEET LONG

(8)
7½ FEET LONG
WEIGHS NEARLY
HALF A TON

(9)
15 INCHES LONG

(10)
5 FEET LONG

(11)
18 INCHES
LONG

(12)
½ INCH HIGH

(13)
8 INCHES HIGH

(14)
1½ INCHES LONG

(15)
12 INCHES LONG

animals shown are as follows: 1. edible crab. 2. whelk. 3. oyster. 4. starfish. 5. sea-urchin.
6. ragworm. 7. cod. 8. sunfish. 9. plaice. 10. angler fish (this fish is sold as rock salmon
in fish shops). 11. crawfish. 12. acorn barnacle. 13. sea-squirt. 14. periwinkle. 15. lobster.

SOME VERY PECULIAR ANIMALS

EVERYBODY knows what a specialist is. It is a person who is able to do one thing better than anybody else; for the specialist spends all his time studying and practising just one subject, whether it be Latin or Greek, medicine, law, or even playing cricket. And it is much the same with animals. A dog is a good all-round animal; it can do a little of everything, running, jumping, swimming, even a clumsy sort of climbing. And, of course, there is almost nothing it will not eat.

But there are other animals who for hundreds of thousands, perhaps millions of years, have settled down to just one way of life, and this specialisation has made them very peculiar both in habits and appearance. At the top of the picture are some creatures that do nothing but make war on the white ant or termite. Termites abound in most hot countries, living underground and throwing up enormous earth-works, often as big as houses. But their food is wood; nothing made of wood is safe from them and it is this which makes them so troublesome to man. In Africa and South America tables are placed with their legs in basins of water for the termites will not cross the water. Since they live underground it is hard to deal with them by means of the many poisons we can use against insects at home.

CREATURES WITH VERY LONG TONGUES

Man would be very helpless against the termite were it not for a race of strange creatures called ant-eaters. They are all very powerful creatures, with arms like those of blacksmiths or prize-fighters as a result of tearing down the termites' earthworks. Once a nest is opened they lick up the insects with tongues so long that they are anchored to the ant-eaters' breast-bones, not like ours in our mouths. One lick, and a hundred termites stick to the whip-like tongue for the ant-eaters' saliva is as sticky as rubber solution.

The African aardvark, or earth-hog, lives underground, and can burrow so fast that it can race two strong men armed with picks and shovels. The American ant-eater sleeps in the open but though it has no teeth, its arms and claws are so powerful that even the jaguar is afraid of it. It has been known to hug a man to death.

Malaya is the home of such numbers of every kind of insect, great and small, that unless there were animals that specialised in eating them, man would have a very bad time indeed. One of the champion insect eaters is the tarsier, a tiny member of the great lemur family, many members of which, such as the gentle, ring-tailed lemur, you may see in any good Zoo.

AN AGILE INSECT EATER

The tarsier is no bigger than one's fist when bunched up at rest. But though next of kin to the monkey, it is built very like the tree-frog. It has very long hind limbs, and each finger and toe ends in a round sucker pad which enables it to hold firmly to slippery bamboo stems, wet tree branches and big leaves. Like the tree-frog it can take enormous leaps, the long tail serving as a balancing pole, like the staff or umbrella carried by a slack-wire artiste.

This power to jump enables it to catch insects on the wing; and the mouth like that of the bat, another insect-eating beast, is so wide that it really does stretch from ear to ear. It can take in quite large insects and when eating a grasshopper, the tarsier screws up its large, night-piercing eyes for they must be kept safe from the wildly-kicking legs.

HOW THE AYE-AYE CATCHES ITS DINNER

From Madagascar comes another strange lemur, the aye-aye, which is also a specialist. It lives mostly on fat beetle grubs, similar to those of our native stag-beetle, which tunnel deep into trees. The aye-aye's dinner is a sort of drill, in four movements. First, with its big eyes the aye-aye spies where a beetle grub has hidden. Secondly, the great ears are put close to the hole, and if the aye-aye hears a noise of chewing timber, it knows the hole is occupied and is not an old " worked out " burrow. Thirdly, the huge rabbit-like front teeth then clear away the old wood until the grub is

Our artist has drawn for you some of the animals described in the article. They are most of them benefactors to man, the ant-eaters consuming termites which wreak such destruction in the tropics, the aye-aye winkling out the wood-destroying beetle, and the tarsiers eating insects.

revealed, and then finally, the long middle finger, thin as a piece of wire, is pushed into the hole and the fat grub winkled out.

As with all the lemurs, strange superstitions centre round these harmless beasts. If, for instance, a dead aye-aye is found the natives give it quite a state funeral. They might do worse, for the aye-aye is a real benefactor, destroying wood-spoiling insects.

THE BRUSH TURKEY BUILDS A MOUND WEIGHING FIVE TONS

Last of our peculiar animals is a bird, the brush turkey or mound-builder of Australia. Birds are very closely related to reptiles; they have horny beaks and scaly legs, they lay eggs, and feathers are only scales split up. Most reptiles lay their eggs in sand, or heaps of vegetable rubbish, scraped together and then left for the heat of the rotting rubbish and the warmth of the sun to hatch the eggs. The brush turkey behaves in just this reptilian manner, and it is the cock turkey that does all the work. Walking backwards and in a steadily widening circle, he kicks out behind him until a mound of leaves and sticks and dead flowers grows and grows to an enormous size.

At Whipsnade Zoo in Bedfordshire, the old nest of the brush turkey is taken to pieces at the end of the season and weighed and it always weighs about five tons—the work of one bird rather smaller than a farmyard turkey. When all is ready the hens, half a dozen perhaps, lay their eggs in the mound. Sometimes several cock turkeys combine and between them build a mound as large as an average bungalow. The temperature of this incubator is taken by each bird pushing his long bare neck deep into it. More rubbish is added, or removed just as the father turkeys deem fit.

At last the eggs hatch and the chicks scramble out into the open and search for their own food, and even fly, from the beginning. There is just one catch in this wonderful way of bringing up a family. Big lizards called monitors also lay their eggs in the mound and the baby monitors, great egg eaters, hatch more quickly than do the turkey chicks. You can guess what happens. But that is Nature's way, and were it not for the lizards there would be far too many brush turkeys.

WELCOME TO DAY

Pack, clouds, away, and welcome day,
  With night we banish sorrow;
Sweet air, blow soft, mount larks, aloft
  To give my Love good-morrow!
Wings from the wind to please her mind
  Notes from the lark I'll borrow;
Bird, prune thy wing, nightingale, sing
  To give my Love good-morrow;
    To give my Love good-morrow
    Notes from them both I'll borrow

Wake from thy nest, Robin-red-breast,
  Sing, birds, in every furrow!
And from each hill, let music shrill
  Give my fair Love good-morrow!
Blackbird and thrush in every bush,
  Stare, linnet, and cock-sparrow!
You pretty elves, amongst yourselves
  Sing my fair Love good-morrow;
    ᾿ To give my Love good-morrow
    Sing, birds, in every furrow!
                        Thomas Heywood

ANIMAL ARMAMENTS

EVER since the dawn of the human race, about a million years ago, mankind has been inventing weapons. At first they were used for hunting, but later for warfare, and since this meant one set of humans matching their wits and strength against other humans, their weapons became more and more ingenious. The cave-man used crude bows and arrows, slings for throwing stones, and various kinds of swords, spears and axes. For protection he used shields and stout coats made from the tough skins of animals such as the wild pig and elephant.

Fairly early in human history metal was used in place of stone, and this led to the invention of armour. But during the Middle Ages gunpowder was thought of and then armour became quite useless. Each succeeding war brought into being more and more ingenious and deadly weapons. World War I saw the birth of fighter aircraft, more or less modern mines, both on land and under water, the tank and poison gas. Steel ships having taken the place of wooden ones, much more violent explosives than gunpowder had to be devised in order to send the ships to the bottom of the sea. To-day we are beginning to realise that the hydrogen bomb is surely not to be the last of man's inventions for killing his fellow man.

All this, one must admit is very terrible, but still we must try to see things in their true perspective, and then we shall not be dismayed by panic-stricken folk who cast up their hands in horror, and tell us that we are living in "the sunset of the human race." We are not doing anything of the sort, and shall one day see the foolishness of the armament race, and live at peace with one another.

Man is an animal, remember that. Also he is the youngest of the animals. The horse, dog, elephant and many other familiar beasts were well established on our planet at least twenty millions years before there was any creature that you or I could have recognised as a human being.

THE FIGHT FOR SURVIVAL

The armament race, which all sensible people realise is a sad waste of time and energy so far as civilised human beings are concerned, began at least 520 million years ago, for in that period were laid down the oldest rocks containing fossil remains, the stone imprints of long-vanished plants and animals, once as full of life as the plants and animals we see around us to-day.

In the far-off period of 520,000,000 B.C. were creatures called Trilobites with hard shells, and hard shells are just Nature's armour against foes. These foes were mostly creatures something like the modern octopus, with parrot-like beaks, able to bite and tear, and these same creatures covered their movements by squirting out clouds of ink; an idea which is now copied by the Army and Navy when a smoke screen is employed.

About this time came into being the sea anemones and jelly fishes we all know. When a sea anemone touches a prawn or fish, the creature touched becomes paralysed and is easily pulled down into the anemone's stomach. The picture shows you how an anemone carries in its tentacles myriads of stinging cells and the microscope shows that each one of these is a miniature of the harpoon used by whalers. To you and me a few score of these tiny harpoons may only cause a slight rash, but they mean death to a small fish.

In the days when our coal mines were living trees, about 250 million years ago, the insects became a power in the land, and some of their weapons were wonderfully up to date. Insects soon developed all manner of devices for cutting, tearing and stabbing. The wasps were probably the first to use the poisoned dagger, which is what the wasp's sting amounts to. Insects have given our camouflage experts plenty of ideas, and many insects rely upon frightening the foe by striking strange attitudes and making terrifying noises. The bearskins once worn in battle and the paint which savages daub upon their faces, are very ancient " frightening " tricks, and devices like them were used by the insects millions of years before the dawn of man.

FISH WITH POISONOUS TEETH

Fish and reptiles developed poisonous teeth and spines, and the non-poisonous spines

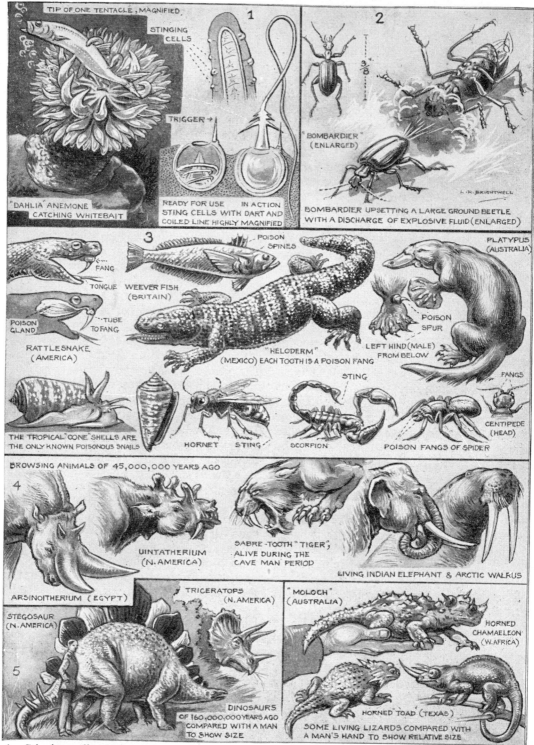

1. Stinging cells, perhaps the earliest weapons. 2. Bombadier beetle, the only creature—apart from man—to use explosives. 3. Poison fangs, spines and " hypodermic syringe " stings. 4. Horns, teeth and claws. 5. Defensive armour of long ago and to-day.

of many lizards serve at once as protection and camouflage. It is a mistake to think that the now extinct dinosaurs were more fantastic than any living creatures. As you see in the picture, some modern lizards though small have quite equalled the dinosaurs in defensive weapons.

The more we study natural history, the more surprised will we be at the manner in which all kinds of quite unrelated animals have developed very similar tools or weapons just because they happen to serve the same useful purposes. When the warm-blooded hairy mammals, i.e. creatures first reared on milk (you and I are mammals), at last appeared, warfare became more and more a war of wits, but still weapons were used on a very large scale. There were even rats and armadillos with horns, and some of the earlier kinds of deer and antelope wore far more fantastic horns than do their modern successors.

Just as the medieval knight's armour became at last so cumbersome that it was more of a danger than a protection to its wearer, so the weapons worn by many beasts attained such huge proportions that they were no help at all. Smaller beasts with better brains gained the mastery and the monsters that seemed so unconquerable at last became extinct.

Modern warfare becomes more and more terrible with each new weapon that ingenious man invents. But the human brain is such that in the very act of devising some new engine of destruction, it can also see the wickedness and foolishness of such inventions. And so in time the human race may indeed give up warfare as a means of settling disputes which leaves the victor almost as crippled as the vanquished. But when we remember that man is still a very young animal, measured in geological time, the outlook is not so black as the timid or unimaginative have painted it.

TWO PUZZLES

HOW MANY MADAMS?

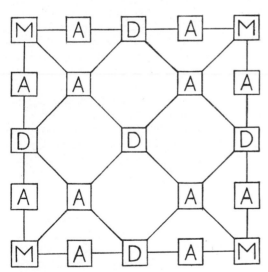

How many times can you spell out the word 'Madam' going from one letter to the next backwards or forwards, up or down?

DRAWING PROBLEM

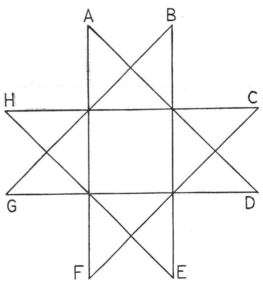

What is the least number of strokes needed to draw this design, and how would you do it without lifting pencil from paper?

Solutions on page 345

LIGHTS THAT LIVE

Some Animals that Shine at Night

ONLY a hundred years ago animals that shone in the dark were thought to be servants of witches, and in various ways connected with black magic. It was of course nonsense, and did not explain anything. But still the mystery remains. *Why* do some animals shine at night? The reason why some do is known, but others still provide problems for the patient seeker after truth.

You can see some of these animals in your own garden or in the nearest country lane. Often on a dark night we find, even in town gardens, what looks like a miniature electric train, only an inch or so long, slowly making its way over the paths and flower-beds. Pick up the train and you find you have caught a very small and thin centipede. Some of its light will have come off on your fingers, and there will be a glowing track on the ground where the creature just passed. In Southern France these centipedes gather together so that large patches of earth glow like molten gold, but why we still do not know. The light comes from some substance on the surface of the animal. The centipede should never be hurt, as it lives on harmful grubs and is one of the gardener's friends.

In deep country lanes during very wet weather we are sure to find the glow-worm. The glow-worm is really a beetle, but only the male looks like a beetle. The female glow-worm and all the children look rather like broad flat caterpillars.

THE GLOW-WORM'S " COME HITHER " SIGNAL

The female glows much more brightly than the male, and there is no doubt it is a " come hither " light, so that the male may be attracted, and in time some eggs laid, and more glow-worms light up the lane. Even in the egg the glow-worm shines. In wet weather they can be seen searching for slugs and snails to eat. These, as you know, are covered with slime, so a good meal leaves the glow-worm in rather a mess, but the glow-worm gives itself a wipe down after a feed.

From the tail end it shoots out a bunch of tiny whips and these dust and scrub it until it is quite clean, then suddenly disappear.

In some tropical countries some near relatives of the glow-worm reach quite a large size, two inches or more and have even been used by man as night-lights. In Vera Cruz at one time these beetles were collected on a large scale and sold to ladies who wished to cause a sensation at balls and parties. The insects were threaded on wires and twined over the already beautiful evening dress. It sounds rather cruel and certainly unpleasant, though it is doubtful if a beetle can feel pain. In Mexico a very large firefly, or fire beetle is still used as a lantern, just as it was in the days of the vanished Aztecs five hundred years ago. The Aztecs even sewed and painted by beetle light, and when going on a night journey tied the beetles to their wrists and ankles, and so passed through the darkness like living torches.

But to see luminous animals at any time of the year and in our own country we must go down to the sea. Stand at the end of a long pier on a dark night in early spring or autumn and you will see this light at its brightest. Gaze overside at where the water joins the pier's piles and there the water seems to run in streams of flashing, blue green sparks. Better still is it to go out in a boat, fishing by night, or if you are on a steamer walk to the stern and look down at the wake, the long line of disturbed and tumbled water, churned up by the propeller. There you see the same sort of sparks, coming and going, whirling and swirling in a fairy dance. And every one of those sparks is *alive*.

THE WANDERERS OF THE SEA

The sea is full of plankton (Greek for " the wanderers ") made up of minute plants and animals, and many animals which will later become quite large creatures living on the sea floor, or swimming about the sea anywhere between the sea-bed and the surface.

Just why all this life is lit up we do not know. Much of the living fire that lights the sea at

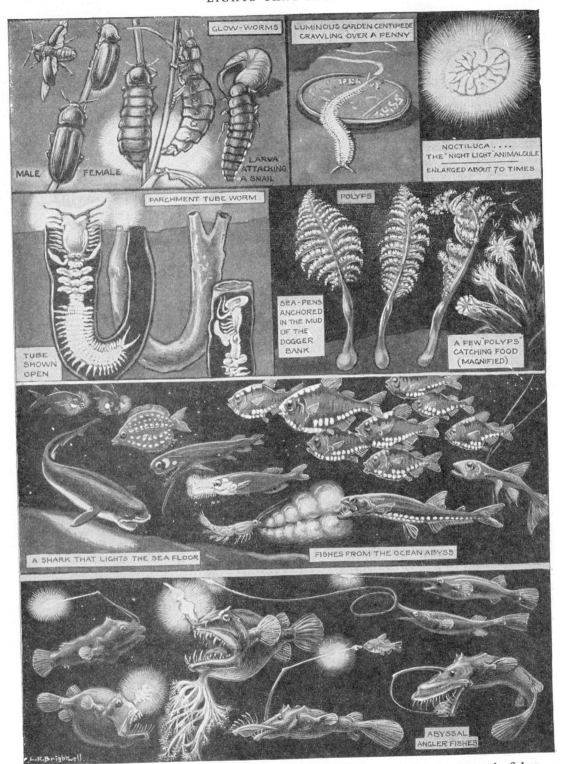

Some of the animals that shine at night are shown here. Though you might never see the fishes from the ocean abyss, you might well see a glow-worm or a garden centipede.

night is provided by a tiny one-celled creature called Noctiluca or the " night light," and it must be an easy mark for millions of creatures eager for a meal.

Still more mysterious is the light made by a worm that lives in a tough parchment-like tube the size and shape of a horseshoe. This worm can be dredged on most parts of our coast where the sea floor is sandy and even be found stranded at low tide in some of the Scottish firths. The worm is a strange-looking creature, and a bucketful will provide light strong enough to read by. So far from being any use to the worm it seems only to be a source of danger, for wandering eels, seeing the light, put their long narrow snouts down the tube and bite off the worm's head.

To-day we all know that the depths of the ocean, though very black, are still lit up by myriads of lights, blue, green and red which come very often from fairly large animals, though few deep-sea fishes grow to a great size, owing to the great pressure, intense cold, and poor food supply. But the American scientist Doctor William Beebe has been down to great depths in a steel ball called the Bathysphere and described how shoals of fishes went by so lit up that they looked like a moving town.

FISH WITH HEADLIGHTS

Some carry great luminous organs in front of them like the headlights of a car, or bear them in rows on their sides like the portholes of a ship. Many of the deep-sea angler fishes bear lighted bulbs on the ends of their living fishing rods, and one species, which lives mostly on shrimps even has a long line with a hook at the end, attached to a jointed rod with a light bulb fixed near the hook. One might think no shrimp would have much chance against such a very complete angler, but Nature, like ourselves, finds an answer to each new weapon as soon as it is invented. Many deep-sea shrimps cover their retreat by squirting out clouds of blinding blue-green phosphorescent ink, and when the angler closes his many-toothed jaws, the shrimp is far away.

Although the sea covers about three-quarters of the area of the world, the advance of technical knowledge has only recently enabled the scientist to explore the ocean depths and study the movements and habits of the myriad creatures who inhabit the sea.

DO YOU KNOW?

Can a ship climb a hill?

We know that the surface of water always lies level. How, then, can a ship go uphill or downhill on level water? This was a problem that had to be solved when men wished to make canals.

There are many important canals in our country. You may travel by water, on a barge, all the way from Leeds to Liverpool or straight through Scotland from the Clyde to the Forth. There are many other important waterways like these in our land.

But the country through which these canals are built is not level. How then could canals, with water, be made? The answer is that the canal goes along for a time until the ground begins to rise. Then a lock is built. A lock has two sets of strong gates, thus making a kind of box in the canal, with gates at each end. The canal at the other side of the lock is higher. If you see a lock on a canal, look carefully at it. You will see that on one side of the gates the water is much higher than at the other.

If a boat wishes to go to the higher stretch of canal it first enters the lock. Then the gate is shut behind it and water from the other gate is allowed to flow into the lock. The boat is lifted up as the water rises, and then, when the water in the lock is level with the higher water outside, the gates are opened and the boat sails out. Thus, by the use of many locks, ships, barges and boats are able to sail uphill.

What is the sunniest part of the British Isles?

The island of Guernsey is the sunniest place in the British Isles. It has nearly 1,900 hours of sunshine each year. London, under its cloud of smoke, gets about 1,250 hours of sunshine, but there are places quite near to the capital with as much as 1,550 hours.

Ben Nevis, in Scotland, is the coldest part of the British Isles. It has only 1,000 hours of sunshine in the year.

Members of a riding-school off for a canter. Horse-riding not only provides splendid exercise but also opens up a whole world of friendship, both human and equine.

THE ROMANCE OF RIDING

FROM the most remote ages riding has been the accomplishment and pleasure of man. There is no doubt that horses existed in the very earliest times. Geologists have discovered the fossil remains of them in all the continents of Europe, Asia, Africa, and America, mingled with the bones of such ancient creatures as the mastodon, long since vanished from the earth; and man must soon have found a way to tame and use these wild, roving animals as his servants and his friends.

In olden days riding was a necessity, the quickest and easiest means to move from place to place. The knight had his destrier, or great horse, for battle, his palfry for pleasure or the chase. His choice of mount was usually a stallion, his rank and valour scorning the gentler mare and more tractable gelding, which were left for churchmen and women to ride. Frequently with a merchant or farmer, his wife would ride pillion, perched on a special seat behind, clasping her goodman's waist and clutching her skirts as they jogged along muddy lanes and splashed through fords on a trip to market or a visit to friends.

But in these days the motor car and omnibus have claimed the roads. King Petrol holds his sway. Only an occasional tradesman delivers his goods by pony cart. A brewer's dray appears at local shows, gay with its brass-decorated harness and usually drawn by a pair of well-matched, splendid greys. Yet still the love of horses stays with us, shared by the highest and the lowest in the land, the sport of queens, the trade of tinkers, the heritage of all, the pleasure of the many—and what better way is there to know and enjoy a horse than to ride it?

But riding is more than a matter of mounting and managing to stay up in a saddle. It is an understanding, a sympathy in mood and movement between rider and mount, conveyed in signals the rider gives plainly and the horse has been schooled to understand and obey.

The horse is not a machine. It is a live and sensitive animal that likes firm yet kindly treatment and resents rough, cruel handling. Its behaviour may be influenced by breed, temperament, condition and conformation, but the rider on the top must always be the dominant factor in its performance. No horse will respond to an uncouth, heavy-handed and ill-balanced rider. Only to a patient, firm and knowledgeable horseman will it give of its best.

BOTH HORSE AND RIDER MUST BE TRAINED

The duty of a well-schooled horse is to receive and obey instructions. The task of a well-trained rider is to give them as plainly as he can. Both have to learn. Study an expert rider on a schooled horse. His application of these signals called " the aids " is effortless and almost unseen, yet the horse responds smoothly and obediently because it is being spoken to in movements it understands.

A fretting, resentful performance means either a badly-trained mount or a rider at fault. The horse must be controlled in a language he understands, the signals of hands and legs and voice, consistently and clearly given. Too often one sees muddled and contradictory commands—heels kicking on, hands pulling back; the body jerking forward with each backward movement of the arms; or falling back with every quickening in pace, the so-called rider dragging at the reins, and also the horse's mouth, to keep himself in balance —a confusion of movement that cannot possibly mean anything to the animal, yet for which he is blamed and often, alas, abused and punished for not understanding.

The first essential for riding is a good seat. This means the ability to remain secure and well balanced in the saddle at whatever pace and throughout whatever movements the horse may perform. A good seat depends partly on balance and partly on grip exercised by the buttock muscles, the thighs, the knees, and upper part of the calf upon the saddle. There must be no stiffening of the body, the arms, or the legs.

Without a good seat it is impossible to have good hands, that is to be able to maintain a light but sufficient tension on the reins, allowing the freedom of movement which the horse requires whilst still keeping him in control, to the happiness of both mount and rider. Both seat and hands can only be acquired by correct tuition and practice.

Certain qualities of character are also needed for successful horsemanship. These are perseverance, determination, self-control, patience, unselfishness and courage. A rider must never lose his, or her, temper with a horse. Quiet determination and persistence is a better way than punishment, but if deemed necessary, this must be immediate and just. So must reward, the praising rub, the rewarding carrot or apple, but the moment of award must be correctly timed and the tit-bit merited. The nervous rider or beginner is often too ready to pat a horse after a poor performance or even misbehaviour, possibly out of relief that the awkward moment has passed.

GETTING TO KNOW YOUR HORSE

A good rider thinks first of his horse, finding out all he can about its welfare, considering its comfort before his own. He is swift to praise and slow to blame. If his mount misbehaves he looks first for the flaw in himself.

Horse and rider are keen to go.

He tries to see and understand from the view-point of a horse, remembering that although so large and strong the horse is by nature nervous, shy of strangers, and easily frightened by sounds and sights it does not understand, sometimes very silly things, it seems, as harmless as a shred of torn paper waving in a hedge, or a sack thrown down upon the ground. In such circumstances the natural impulse of the animal is flight. Boisterous movements also alarm a horse. One should never be approached from behind, but always from the side or the front. The speaking voice should be quiet, and all actions unhurried and deliberate.

Another point to be remembered is the range and limitation of a horse's eyesight. Of course, he cannot possibly see behind him, and the position of his eyes on either side of his head give him a wide range of vision sideways, but also a blind spot in front. That is why a horse will often toss his head if anyone stands immediately in front of him and tries to stroke

his nose, and also why he will advance upon some object apparently indifferent to it, then suddenly sight the thing and shy away. The best way to approach a horse is always from the side, failing that the front, but never, never for safety's sake, startle him by word or touch standing behind his heels!

Also the horseman must never forget that a horse can be uncomfortable or ill. A badly-fitting bridle may upset a normally responsive and well-mannered animal. An ill-fitting saddle will pinch or rub. Too slack a girth can gall the flesh raw. An essential of good riding is to know the correct position and adjustment of the horse's saddlery or "tack."

Again a horse that suddenly refuses or gives an unusually poor performance may be ill. They can suffer but they cannot speak, so it is the duty of the rider to find out and remedy what is wrong.

No rider must ever be too sure or too conceited to learn, not only how to stay on top,

Going over the top is one of the greatest thrills of horse-riding, demanding perfect co-ordination between horse and rider, as well as much patient training.

but how to saddle, unsaddle, groom, and tend a horse.

Riders fall roughly into the two classes of owner-riders and those who hire their mounts. The first are luckier in that they alone handle the horse they own, riding, schooling, and becoming thoroughly accustomed to its temperament and ways. But theirs, also, is the

improve every horse he rides. He must keep a keen eye on the ground over which he travels, neither risking a broken leg in rabbit-holes nor strained tendons by travelling too fast over steep downhill slopes. And never must he return to the stables with a sweated, exhausted mount.

Bad habits once acquired in horsemanship

A well-groomed pony is a credit to its owner. It is well worth while spending time and trouble on the care and well-being of your mount.

full responsibility for stabling, feeding, and exercising the animal themselves or arranging and paying for this to be done. The rider of the hired horse has nothing of this. If the mount he books falls lame or sick, another is provided for his pleasure. The problems and cost of stabling, fodder, farriery and wages are not for him. He rides carefree and for his own enjoyment.

THE WELFARE OF THE HORSE

But he, as much as anyone, owes a duty to his horse. While it is in his care he must consider himself responsible for its welfare. He must use it carefully, and handle it as skilfully as he is able, trying by good horsemanship to

are hard to lose, and for that reason early tuition should be the very best available, under a riding master, not a farmer or a groom. Riding, like every art, has its theory, and for true proficiency this must be learnt. In this the would-be rider who lives in a town is as fortunate as his country cousin, since even in the heart of such great cities as London and Birmingham excellent instruction can be had, while a riding school or stable hiring horses can usually be found on the fringe of most large towns.

The first mount for a child or a beginner must be good-natured and kind. All good riding schools have an old favourite, a generous, kind-hearted mount that has taught many a learner to ride. In the case of a would-be owner-rider buying a pony, it is best to go to a good dealer or consult a wise friend, with further advice from a veterinary surgeon. In every case the best purchase is a horse the buyer has known and ridden.

A new horse usually means new tack, or good second-hand, which is sometimes preferable to new, if it has been well kept and is in good condition. The same advice applies to this. Go to a reputable saddler, or ask the opinion of an experienced person before you buy. Saddlery must be reliable and sound for the sake of safety. It must be carefully watched and thoroughly cleaned, especially the undersides of all straps and under buckles.

DRESSING THE PART

The dress of a rider must be neat and workmanlike. Jewellery, flowing hair, big bows, or other ornaments are not allowed. A head-covering should always be worn, preferably a velvet hunting cap or bowler, with the hair kept tidy under it.

Good manners in riding should never be forgotten. Anyone who helps the rider must be thanked, from the little boy who opens a gate to the car driver who slows down to let the horse pass. A horseman must be careful of the land over which he rides, never trampling growing crops, and taking care to leave gates as he finds them, unless they have been left open by some other person's carelessness. The strongest rule in riding is that every rider must be ready to help another one in trouble, no matter how exciting the ride or whether his own pleasure will be spoiled.

The riding of horses is more than a sport or a hobby. It is a splendid exercise, training for character, and the key to a whole world of friendship, human and equine. The fellowship of horsemen is world-wide. The rider of horses need never be friendless or lonely. Riding schools, riding clubs, branches of the Pony Club exist all over the British Isles, offering membership and company. Hunting, horse shows, gymkhanas, point-to-point races are organised for the rider to share and enjoy. But the greatest pleasure of a horseman will always be the thrill of a good horse under him, and the green stretch of turf ahead, the speed of a gallop, the stride of a walk, the smell of a friendly stable, and an eager whinny to welcome him! Saddle up!

There is a happy fellowship to be found in riding schools and Pony Clubs, where members share a common pleasure in the enjoyment of their hobby.

A section of your stamp album could be devoted to stamps depicting different sports.

SPORTS ON STAMPS

MORE than fifty different sports have been illustrated on postage stamps, in fact, nearly every outdoor sport you can think of. The most notable exception (would you believe it?) is cricket! Other exceptions are Polo, Lacrosse and Golf.

To collect all stamps depicting sports would be a formidable task, but you could make a wonderful collection by choosing, say, just the sports which you yourself enjoy.

Alternatively, you could collect Water Sports —Swimming, Diving, Rowing, Sailing, Canoeing, Water Polo, Water Ski-ing, etc.

Another interesting section on sport for your album could be compiled from stamps commemorating World Championships. The country in which the event takes place often issues a special stamp or stamps in honour of the occasion. For instance, Austria has produced a stamp commemorating the Ski-ing Championship; Japan, Wrestling; Poland, Cycle-Racing; Portugal, Hockey on Roller-skates (incidentally, Portugal is the only country which has produced a stamp depicting this game), and Luxembourg, Fencing. This last stamp shows the épée, a heavy weapon similar to the old duelling sword, the foil, a practice weapon with a straight steel blade tipped with a round button, and the sabre, together with the mask and glove. Modern fencing first became known in England in the seventeenth century.

SPECIAL STAMPS FOR THE OLYMPIC GAMES

Many stamps have appeared in honour of the International Olympic Games. The first country to issue such stamps was Greece which produced eight in 1896 to celebrate the first modern revival of the Games. Special issues of stamps, made by the country where the Games have been held, have raised a great deal of money for Olympic Tournaments.

No stamps were produced by the countries which held the 2nd, 3rd, 4th and 5th Olympic Games. The 6th were prevented by World War I but the 7th were held in Belgium in 1920, and a stamp was issued for the occasion. The 8th Olympiad was held in Paris in 1924, the 9th in the Netherlands in 1928, the 10th in Los Angeles in 1932 and the 11th in Berlin in 1936. All these were honoured by stamps.

The 12th Olympiad, due to take place in Tokyo in 1940 was, of course, cancelled owing to World War II as was the 13th. The 14th, in 1948, was held in Great Britain and we issued 4 designs to celebrate the event. Finland also produced 4 designs when the 15th Olympiad was held there in 1952.

Stamps have also been issued for the Winter Olympic Games.

Stamps have appeared for the Balkan Games, Central American and Caribbean Games and Spartacist Games. Poland issued two sets of stamps in July 1954 to commemorate the Spartacist Games.

The 1st Asian Games were held in New Delhi in 1951, and India issued a design for the occasion. The Philippine Islands issued 3 designs in honour of the 2nd Asian Games held in Manila in 1954.

There have been several British Empire Games meetings since the first were held in Canada in 1930 but so far no stamps have appeared for these events.

SPORTS STADIUMS ON STAMPS

There are many beautiful sports stadiums to be seen on stamps, notably the first important stadium to be erected in modern times, the one in Athens which was built in 1896 for the first revival of the Olympic Games. The entrance to this stadium appears on a Greek stamp. Other stamps showing stadiums have been issued by Finland, Hungary, Nicaragua and Portugal. Playing fields are depicted on a stamp produced by Salvador.

STAMPS SHOWING SPORT IN ANCIENT TIMES

The following countries have issued stamps showing sport in ancient times.

Greece: Hunting Wild Boar, Gladiators and Chariot Driving.
China: A Winter Hunt (around the fourth or fifth centuries A.D.)
Belgium: A Chariot Race.
Mexico: An Aztec Athlete.

FOOTBALL AND NETBALL STAMPS

If you are a boy you probably play football. This game can be well represented in your stamp album. If you collected all the stamps showing the various aspects of football you would have a complete record of how the game is played.

Hungary issued a stamp in 1953 to commemorate the victory over England at football.

This was the first time that England had been beaten by a Continental team (Hungary beat England by 6 goals to 3 at Wembley on 25th November, 1953).

If you are a girl you may have played netball. This game (basket-ball) is the only important sport which originated entirely in America. The first basket-ball was a "soccer" ball and the first baskets used were two peach baskets! The game has changed considerably since those early days; the baskets now, of course, are nets. Many countries have stamps showing this game.

WOMEN AND SPORT

An interesting collection could be made of women on sporting stamps.

Czechoslovakia shows a woman discus-thrower, Germany a horsewoman, Japan, Germany and Poland, a woman skater, Yugoslavia a girl hurdler, Russia a girl gymnast and Sweden a woman skier. There are, of course, many more examples.

CHILDREN ON SPORTING STAMPS

The Netherlands have an attractive set of stamps showing children and sport. One shows a girl swimming and others show boys skating, canoeing and tobogganing. Perhaps you can find some more.

FISHING STAMPS

Fishing has been depicted many times on stamps but it is usually shown as an occupation rather than a sport, fish being a necessity of life.

There is a Japanese stamp showing a man fishing with cormorants, Oceanic Settlements feature " Spearing Fish " and on a stamp of Nauru you can see a man netting fish. Nauruans depend for their livelihood on food from the sea, so this can hardly be included in a collection of sporting stamps. A British Guiana stamp shows an Indian shooting fish with a bow and arrow. Whether a necessity or not, this is probably considered a very fine sport!

SPECIAL SPORTING STAMPS

Sometimes a set of stamps is issued concerning one particular sport. For instance, Turkey has four stamps showing the four holds in wrestling while Austria has four ski-ing stamps

Only the reigning monarch may be depicted on British stamps, but special stamps are designed for important occasions such as Coronations and Jubilees. Here you can see three of the four stamps commissioned in honour of the International Olympic Games, held in Britain in 1948.

depicting the Climb, the Start, the Race and the Ski-jump.

SPORTING STAMPS FROM DIFFERENT COUNTRIES

The following list, though by no means complete, gives an idea of the vast field of

Canoeing: Czechoslovakia; France; Russia.

Cycle Racing: Bolivia; Bulgaria; Czechoslovakia; France; Germany; Guatemala; Italy; Japan; Luxembourg; Monaco; Nicaragua; Poland; Romania; Russia; San Marino; Trieste.

Discus Throwing: Bulgaria; Colombia; Costa Rica; Dominican Republic; France; Greece; Japan; Monaco; Panama; Peru; Romania; Russia; Salvador; San Marino; Turkey; U.S.A.

A feeling of high-speed action is conveyed in these stamps depicting different types of sport.

sport covered by various countries on their postage stamps.

Archery: Belgium; Lithuania.
Athletics: Albania; Belgium; Colombia; Czechoslovakia; France; Romania; Russia.
Baseball: Colombia; Japan; Nicaragua; Panama; Philippine Islands; U.S.A.; Venezuela.
Basket-ball: Bolivia; Bulgaria; Hungary; Lithuania; Monaco; Nicaragua; Panama; Peru; Philippine Islands; Trieste.
Bob-sleighing: Germany.
Boxing: Bolivia; Luxembourg; Netherlands; Nicaragua; Panama; Philippine Islands; Poland; San Marino.

Diving: Bolivia; Bulgaria; Finland; France; Germany; Guatemala; Japan; Lithuania; Monaco; Nicaragua; Romania; Russia; Slovakia.
Fencing: Bolivia; Bulgaria; France; Germany; Hungary; Luxembourg; Monaco; Netherlands; San Marino.
Football: Bolivia; Bulgaria; Colombia; Costa Rica; Czechoslovakia; Fiji; Finland; France; Germany; Guatemala; Hungary; Italian Colonies; Italy; Japan; Liechtenstein; Luxembourg; Monaco; Netherlands; Nicaragua; Panama; Poland; Romania; Russia; San Marino; Slovakia; Switzerland; Trieste; Uruguay.
Gymnastics: Bulgaria; China; Czechoslovakia; Hungary; Japan; Monaco; Russia; San Marino; Sweden; Yugoslavia.

Hockey: Japan. Hockey on Roller-skates: Portugal.

Horse Jumping: Bolivia; France; Japan.

Hunting: Belgian Congo; China; Germany; Romania; Spanish Morocco.

Hurdling: Belgium; Bolivia; Colombia; Cuba; Japan; Luxembourg; Monaco; Romania; Turkey; Yugoslavia.

Hurling: Ireland.

Ice-Hockey: Czechoslovakia; Poland; Romania; Russia; Sweden; Switzerland.

Ice-Skating: Germany; Hungary; Japan; Norway; Poland; Romania; Russia.

Javelin Throwing: Belgium; Bolivia; Finland; Germany; Greece; Hungary; Japan; Lithuania; Mexico; Romania; San Marino.

Jumping: Greece; Japan; Poland; Romania; Russia.

Judo: Japan.

Motor Car Racing: Bolivia; Germany; San Marino; Yugoslavia.

Motor Cycle Racing: Hungary; Russia; San Marino; Yugoslavia.

Motor Cycle and Sidecar Racing: Yugoslavia.

Mountaineering: Hungary; Japan; Romania; Russia.

Pelota: Bolivia.

Pole-Vaulting: Belgium; Bulgaria; Guatemala; Japan; Nicaragua; Turkey; Yugoslavia.

Putting the Shot: Bulgaria; Hungary; Japan; Netherlands; Switzerland; Yugoslavia.

Rifle Shooting: Switzerland.

Roller-skating: San Marino.

Rowing: France; Germany; Monaco; Netherlands; Romania; Trieste.

Rugby Football: Japan; Romania.

Running: Belgium; Bolivia; Bulgaria; Czechoslovakia; Finland; France; Germany; Greece; Guatemala; Hungary; Israel; Lithuania; Monaco; Netherlands; Poland; Romania; Russia; Salvador; San Marino; Slovakia; Turkey; Yugoslavia.

Sailing: Bahamas; Monaco; Netherlands, New Zealand; Nicaragua; Poland; Russia; Trieste.

Shooting: Russia; San Marino.

Ski-ing: Austria; Bolivia; Finland; Germany; Hungary; Japan; Lebanon; Monaco; Poland; Romania; Russia; San Marino; Slovakia; Sweden; Switzerland; U.S.A.

Ski-jumping: Austria; Finland; France; Germany; Japan; Norway; Romania; Russia; Sweden; Yugoslavia.

Sling-ball: Sweden.

Soft-ball: Nicaragua.

Speedboat Racing: Russia.

Sprinting: Belgium; Japan; Romania; Russia; Switzerland; U.S.A.

Steeplechasing: Germany; Romania.

Swimming: Colombia; Czechoslovakia; France; Hungary; Japan; Panama; Poland; Romania; Russia; Trieste.

Table-Tennis: Nicaragua; Romania.

Tennis: Bolivia; Colombia; Guatemala; Monaco; Nicaragua; Philippine Islands; Russia; San Marino.

Tobogganing: Germany; Romania.

Vaulting: Finland; Hungary.

Volley-Ball: Bulgaria; Hungary; Japan.

Water-Polo: Luxembourg.

Water-Ski-ing: Bahamas.

Weight Lifting: Bulgaria.

Wrestling: Finland; Greece; Japan; San Marino; Sweden; Switzerland; Turkey.

RING OUT, WILD BELLS

Ring out, wild bells, to the wild sky,
　The flying cloud, the frosty light:
　The year is dying in the night;
Ring out, wild bells, and let him die.

Ring out the old, ring in the new,
　Ring, happy bells, across the snow:
　The year is going, let him go;
Ring out the false, ring in the true.

Ring out the grief that saps the mind,
　For those that here we see no more;
　Ring out the feud of rich and poor,
Ring in redress to all mankind.

Ring out a slowly dying cause,
　And ancient forms of party strife;
　Ring in the nobler modes of life,
With sweeter manners, purer laws.

Ring out the want, the care, the sin,
　The faithless coldness of the times;
　Ring out, ring out my mournful rhymes,
But ring the fuller minstrel in.

Ring out false pride in place and blood,
　The civic slander and the spite;
　Ring in the love of truth and right,
Ring in the common love of good.

Ring out old shapes of foul disease;
　Ring out the narrowing lust of gold;
　Ring out the thousand wars of old,
Ring in the thousand years of peace.

Ring in the valiant man and free,
　The larger heart, the kindlier hand;
　Ring out the darkness of the land,
Ring in the Christ that is to be.

Lord Tennyson

ANIMALS ON STAMPS

A Fascinating Hobby

NEARLY every animal you can think of has been depicted on a postage stamp, from a hedgehog to a tree-climbing kangaroo. Animal stamps alone would make a very fine and formidable collection.

Over a hundred different beasts can be found on stamps and nearly every country in the world has, at some time or other, produced a stamp portraying an animal.

The first animal ever to appear on a stamp was the bear, and this is shown on one of the earliest stamps known. In about 1846 the Postmaster of St. Louis, Missouri, arranged for a stamp to be issued for the convenience of himself and the local inhabitants. On this stamp the Arms of Missouri were supported on either side by a bear. The stamps are nicknamed " St. Louis Bears."

These early stamps, of course, are now extremely valuable. Many of them would have been destroyed had it not been for a Negro porter who worked at the Court House at Louisville, Kentucky. One day in 1895 he had been told to tidy out the cellars and burn a great pile of old papers.

As he was shovelling the bundles into the furnace some of the papers fell out and he noticed that they bore unusual stamps. He stopped burning the papers and looked through them for more stamps. He found 137 of them —all " St. Louis Bears." He gave them to two caretakers in the building who, in exchange for the stamps, treated the Negro to a drink.

Later the caretakers sold many of those " St. Louis Bears " for 20,000 dollars (about £7,000) each!

Fine drawings of wild animals of Asia and Africa shown on postage stamps.

A person who wanted to send a letter at that time, however, had no need to buy these stamps unless he wished. He could pay the money over the post office counter and just have the letter marked with a postmark, or he could buy a stamp and stick it on his letter.

Moldavia was the first principality ever to issue stamps, and the chief feature of their design was another animal, a bull's head with a posthorn hanging from its mouth. These appeared in 1858 and are known to collectors as " Bulls."

ANIMALS FROM ALL OVER THE WORLD

Canada, when it was a colony in 1851, issued a stamp showing a beaver. This animal is now regarded heraldically in Canada, in much the same way as the lion is regarded in England.

As there were very few of these early stamps issued, they were very expensive and quite impossible for all but the wealthy to collect. However, the Moldavia " Bull " was reproduced by Romania in 1932 to commemorate the seventy-fifth anniversary of the first issue. Also, the Canadian Beaver stamp can be found depicted in miniature on a stamp issued in 1951 to celebrate the centenary of the first Canadian postage stamp.

All kinds of animals, wild and domestic, have been portrayed on stamps (not to mention birds, fishes, insects and reptiles). The animal depicted usually inhabits the country of issue, although this is not always the case (e.g. lion and lioness shown on

German—Russian Zone—stamp to mark the seventy-fifth anniversary of the Leipzig Zoo).

Even confining yourself to wild animals alone, you could make a very large collection of stamps, and new ones, of course, are continually being issued. It would also be interesting to collect stamps showing animals to be found in the National Parks of the world.

Air-mail stamps, as you would expect, often show birds of all kinds, symbolising flight and power. You would probably guess that air-mail animal stamps show an aeroplane flying over wild animals, but you would be wrong. Strangely enough, most of the stamps display an aeroplane and a domestic animal. Only one, a French Guiana stamp, issued in 1947, shows a wild animal—a peccary. (This is a kind of wild pig.)

LEARNING GEOGRAPHY FROM STAMPS

If you are a horse-lover you could find many stamps showing horses, and people

The animals on these stamps are remarkable for their perfect likeness to the real thing.

riding them. San Marino has a stamp depicting a mail-coach drawn by horses (an air-mail stamp, strangely enough!); Ecuador has a man jumping a gate on horseback; French Morocco has a magnificent picture of Moorish tribesmen on horseback (a Flood Relief Aid Stamp); Spanish Morocco has an Arab Postman riding a horse; Uruguay has a Gaucho on horseback, and Canada has a Royal Canadian Mounted Policeman. In 1935 Australia issued a stamp celebrating the Silver Jubilee of King George V, showing the King mounted on a horse called Anzac, given to him by the Australian Commonwealth.

Australia has many interesting animal stamps, apart from the inevitable kangaroo. Among the most attractive is the one showing the Koala Bear, which is a living Teddy-bear! The Merino Ram shown on the stamps issued to mark the Captain John McArthur centenary has great importance for Australia. Until 1834 it was supposed that sheep-farming in Australia could never be successful. McArthur, however, set to work to breed a kind of sheep that could adapt itself to the climate, and now there are seventeen times as many sheep as there are people in Australia, and they supply a quarter of the world's wool.

The following list of animals featured on stamps and the countries which issued them is comprehensive but by no means complete. See how many more you can find. (There are nearly eighty names of animals on the list and the collective words, such as cattle and sheep, cover many different species. (The Moldavian "Bull," for instance, is included under "Cattle.")

Alphabetical List of Animals showing the Countries which have depicted them on Stamps

Alligator	French West Africa.
Ant-eater	French Guiana; Sarawak.
Antelope	Angola; Bahawalpur; Belgian Congo; Liberia; Mozambique Company; Somalia; Togo; S. Rhodesia.
Armadillo	B. Honduras.
Badger	Liechtenstein.
Bear (Brown)	Finland; Russia.
Bear (Polar)	Canada; Greenland.
Beaver	Canada.
Boar (Wild)	Hungary; N. Borneo.
Bongo:	Liberia.
Bruang	N. Borneo.
Buffalo	Abyssinia; Angola; Liberia; N. Borneo.

Camel	Aden; Bahawalpur; Eritrea; French Levant; French Somali Coast; Ifni; India; Italian Colonies; Lebanon; Mauritania; Mongolia; Port. Nyasaland; Tripolitania; Tunis; Sudan; Spanish Morocco; Western Sahara.
Caribou	Newfoundland.
Cattle	Argentine; Australia; Bahawalpur; Bechuanaland; Bolivia; Belgian Congo; Brazil; Bulgaria; Cameroons; Canada; Chile; Colombia; Costa Rica; Cuba; Dominican Rep.; Ecuador; Egypt; Eritrea; France; Honduras; India; Kedah; Moldavia; Mozambique Co.; Netherland Indies; Nicaragua; Nigeria; Panama; Paraguay; Poland; Romania; Russia; Salvador; S. Africa; Thailand; Uruguay; Venezuela.
Chamois	Andorra; Liechtenstein; Slovakia.
Cheetah	Somalia.
Chevrotain (Water)	Liberia.
Chimpanzee	Belgian Congo.
Chinchilla	Bolivia.
Civet (Palm)	Liberia.
Crocodile	Angola; Basutoland; Belgian Congo; Liberia; Mozambique Co.; N. Borneo.
Deer	Mauritius; Liechtenstein; Hungary; Israel; New Caledonia; N. Borneo.
Dog	Greenland; Newfoundland; Japan; St. Pierre and Miquelon.
Donkey	Costa Rica; French West Africa.
Eland	Angola; S.W. Africa.
Elephant	Abyssinia; Angola; Belgian Congo; Burma; Cameroons; Ceylon; Eritrea; Gambia; Indo-China; Liberia; Malay States; Perak; Selangor; Sierra Leone; Sirmoor; Somalia; S. Rhodesia; Togo.
Elk	Canada; Finland.
Fox	Hungary.
Gazelle	Abyssinia; Angola; Italian East Africa; Spain; Tripolitania.
Giraffe	Abyssinia; Angola; Mozambique Co.; Port. Nyasaland; S. Rhodesia; Tanganyika; Sudan.
Gnu	Angola; Orange River Colony; S. Africa.
Hare	Hungary; Liechtenstein.
Hedgehog	Hungary
Hippopotamus	Angola; French West Africa; Liberia; Mozambique Co.; Somalia.
Horse	Australia; Austria; Belgium; Bolivia; Bulgaria; Cameroons; Canada; Cyrenaica; Ecuador; Germany; Gold Coast; Greenland; Guatemala; Iceland; India; Japan; Jugoslavia; Mexico; Mongolia; Netherlands; Nicaragua; Poland; Romania; Russia; Saar; San Marino; Spanish Morocco; Switzerland; Syria.
Ibex	Sudan.
Impala	Angola.
Jaguar	Bolivia.
Kangaroo	Australia; New South Wales.
Kangaroo (Tree-climbing)	Papua.
Kob	Liberia; West Africa.
Koala	Australia.
Lechwe (Nile)	Sudan.
Lemur	Madagascar.
Leopard	Abyssinia; French Congo; Liberia;

No wonder young collectors try to make a stamp zoo, when such beautifully designed animal stamps are available. Why not begin to collect now?

Leopard	Middle Congo; Mozambique Co.; Tripolitania.
Lion	Abyssinia; Angola; Belgian Congo; Germany; Kenya, Tanganyika and Uganda; Mozambique Co.; Nyasaland; S. Rhodesia; Tripolitania.
Lizard	Ecuador; New Zealand.
Llama	Bolivia; Peru.
Marmot:	Liechtenstein.
Marten	Hungary.
Moose	Canada.
Okapi	Belgian Congo.
Orang-Outang	N. Borneo.
Otter	Hungary.
Platypus	Australia.
Reindeer	Norway; Tannou-Touva.
Rhinoceros	Abyssinia; Angola; French Equatorial Africa; Mozambique Co.
Seal	Greenland; Newfoundland.
Seal (Elephant)	Tristan da Cunha.
Sea Lion	Falkland Isles.
Sheep	Argentine; Australia; Bulgaria; Canada; Chile; Falkland Isles; Italy; Mongolia; New Zealand; Russia; Spanish Morocco; Somaliland; S. Africa; Tannou-Touva.
Springbok	S. Africa.
Squirrel	Andorra; Finland.
Tarzier	Sarawak; Seychelles.
Tapir	Nicaragua; N. Borneo.
Tiger	Malay States; Negri Sembilan; Pehang; Perak; Selangor.
Tortoise	Ecuador.
Turtle	Cayman Islands.
Vicuna	Bolivia.
Walrus	Canada.
Warthog	Angola.
Waterbuck	Angola.
Whale	Falkland Isles.
Wildebeest	S.W. Africa.
Wolf	Russia.
Zebu	Cameroons.
Zebra	Mozambique Co.; Port. Nyasaland; S.W. Africa.
Zebra (Mountain)	Angola.

NICKNAMES FOR STAMPS

Apart from " Bulls " and " Bears " there are other stamps which have animal nicknames. The issue for Afghanistan (1870) are known as " Afghan Tigers "; for Sudan (1898) " Camels "; for Federated Malay States (1900) " Tigers "; for Brazil (1843)

Camel and aircraft: the old and the new.

" Bull's Eyes "; for Brazil (1850-66) " Cat's Eyes "; for Brazil (1844) " Goat's Eyes." All these nicknames have arisen from the general appearance of the designs.

ERRORS OF DESIGN ON ANIMAL STAMPS

On the Tripolitanian stamp of 1930 there are antelopes, but unfortunately the designer has taken the wrong reference and the antelopes depicted are the Blackbucks found in India, and not the African species!

The ant-eater on the Sarawak ten-cent stamp was drawn without a tail. As fully half of its body consists of tail, the design has now been discarded and a map has taken its place. Incidentally, the inscription on the Tarzier stamp of the same set should read " The Tarzier " instead of " The Tarzius," but this has, so far, not been corrected.

On the Portuguese Nyasaland stamp of 1901, showing a giraffe, the centre was accidentally inverted so that the giraffe is standing on its head—quite a feat, I should think, with a neck as long as that!

When a stamp is printed with an error of design it usually becomes extremely valuable owing to its rarity.

SIZES OF ANIMALS ON STAMPS

It is difficult to gauge the size of an animal from its picture on a stamp, unless it is shown against some recognisable background which is near enough to the animal to be seen in the same proportion.

For example, the walrus on the 1954 Canadian issue, when fully grown, is fifteen feet in length and weighs more than a ton! On the other hand, the beaver issued at the same time is not more than three feet in length.

The largest animal to appear on a stamp is the Stegodon Ganesa (India, 1951), but this is a prehistoric animal which lived in the Himalayan foothills, possibly millions of years ago! This was the predecessor of the elephant and became extinct with the coming of the Ice Age. Its tusks were over nine feet long and can be seen, together with a skull, in the Natural History Museum at South Kensington in London.

So, if you feel like getting a zoo or a farm (or both) together in the pages of your stamp album, why not start now?

WILD LIFE OF THE AMERICAS

A handsome ocelot, native of Mexico, keeps an alert watch for any sign of danger.

THE American Continent is extremely rich in the variety and diversity of its plant and animal life. Within its 16½ million square miles every variation of climate is to be found, with the result that there are conditions to suit the needs of almost every species of animal and bird.

In the following pages we have included as many different animals as possible, although naturally, we have been unable to do more than feature a representative selection. You will see many animals that are already familiar to you, and perhaps some which will be unfamiliar. There are pictures of the formidable brown bear of North America, beautiful mountain lions in the remote fastness of their den amidst the rugged grandeur of the Grand Canyon, the prickly little porcupine, the sleek and powerful jaguar, and many others.

The racoon inhabits North America.

Capybaras, largest of the rodent family.

This fine elk, surprised while drinking, casts a wary eye on the photographer.

The solitary moose is found in the virgin forest lands of North America.

A timber wolf halts in his tracks, suspicious of any unknown sight or sound.

Bears, being curious, must always investigate anything that arouses their interest.

Resting, but never completely off guard, this silver fox is a native of North America.

A look at the lithe body of this beautiful creature makes it easy to understand why the jaguar is often used as a symbol of speed and power. The jaguar's range extends from Texas in the north to as far south as Patagonia. It is a carnivorous animal.

Not so very long ago, vast herds of bison roamed the plains in Canada and America, then, with the influx of settlers, came the professional buffalo hunter, whose unrestricted slaughter of the animals for their hides almost wiped out the herds. To-day, through Government intervention, the herds are controlled and protected.

This handsome bird with the crest of glossy
black feathers is a currasow.

The sharp quills of the porcupine enable him
to fend off his enemies.

A mountain lion and his mate rest outside their home amidst the grandeur of the Grand Canyon,
famous American National Park. So perfectly do they blend with their surroundings that from
a little distance they are almost invisible.

Swans are devoted parents and take turns at guarding the nest of eggs.

The coyote is not a favourite with cattlemen because he attacks their cattle.

The two-toed sloth spends his life in this upside-down position.

This sad-faced little fellow, the woolly monkey, is a native of South America.

A brown capuchin monkey from Guiana.

A weeper capuchin from South America.

The hyacinth macaw, so called because of its vivid blue plumage, inhabits Central Brazil.

An American king vulture, carrion-eating bird of prey with a brightly-coloured head.

This strange creature, found in tropical America, is the great ant-eater. As his name suggests, his basic diet is ants. His strong claws break open the ant-hill and then he extracts the ants with his long sticky tongue.

Angry clouds over the sea in the evening with a rainstorm in the distance.

HOW TO READ THE CLOUDS

WHEN I was a schoolboy I first became interested in the weather through watching anxiously for any signs that gave promise of the weekly half-holiday being fine. Sometimes I would be tempted by a rising barometer to plan a week-end on the road, and then find an hour or two after we had set off that a steady downpour had set in for the rest of the day.

But there are ways of foretelling coming weather other than by the barometer or the usual newspaper and B.B.C forecasts. The weather in this country is so local that it may be raining in one place and quite fine a few miles away. That is why many country dwellers and fishermen are able to tell much better the coming weather in their own districts.

When you are out of doors you have plenty of opportunity to study the sky. When you see some of those lovely colours in the sky at sunset, do you just admire them as something beautiful, or do you ever think what they may mean? Really, each colour is telling you the story of what sort of weather to expect.

LEARNING FROM THE SUNSET

Let us look at some of these sunsets, and see what we can learn. When you see the sun sinking in a round, red ball, and a reddish glow spreads all across the western sky until it melts into that delicate blue right overhead, you may be sure of a fine morrow. But you must not confuse this sort of red sunset with the angry, dull red, low clouds that scud across the sky in the evening before a storm. These fine weather sunsets bring us heat in summer and frost in winter.

Then there is the colour that fishermen and sailors fear more than any other, and that is yellow. When you see the sky quite clear of clouds over the west at sunset, but in place of the comfortable red glow the sky is all yellowish, you will know that not only rain—but heavy gales—will be raging within the next thirty-six hours.

Sometimes there seems to be no colour at

all in the sunset, even though the sky is quite cloudless. It is neither red nor yellow, but a sort of dirty, ash-grey. When you see this, it means that you will awake to one of those dull, rainy mornings.

In April you will often see the sky green between the clouds instead of blue. This denotes showery weather, with plenty of sunny intervals. But you must not let the sunshine tempt you out without your mac, because as long as there is any green about, you must be prepared for sudden, squally showers that spring up without any warning.

You are all familiar with those copper-tinted clouds, with bright silvery edges, which bring us widespread thunderstorms in summer and hailstorms in winter. Then there are those low, puffy clouds that are so often seen in the winter months, tinted with a violet hue. They bring us several days of dull, sunless weather with east winds, but without frost.

Lastly, there is blue, which you know best of all. You will say that a blue sky, of course, means fine weather, but it is not always so. It depends what *shade* of blue. If it is a *light* blue, into which the clouds seem to melt away with soft edges, you can count on its being fine, but if the sky is a *dark* blue, against which the clouds are outlined with sharp edges, then stormy weather is on the way.

So just make a note of these colours—two kinds of red, two kinds of blue, yellow, green, copper and violet. Then watch the sky, and you will soon be able to tell your friends what sort of weather to expect from day to day.

FORECASTING FROM THE CLOUDS

You will also find it worth while to study the cloud *formations* as well as their colours. These are often of very different types, some associated with fine weather, and some preceding a period of rain. Probably a kind of sky most familiar to you is what you will have heard people call a " mackerel sky."

When you see those small, dappled clouds in groups high in the sky, during a fine spell, you may be sure there is a change for the worse coming, but there is one consolation: it will bring one of those unsettled days that is not very wet for long, nor very fine for long. In other words, it will be one of those showery types of day.

During the squally periods that we now and then experience in the summer, you will at times notice a kind of festoon cloud spreading up from the north or north-west. It has tiny clouds on its lower surface, suspended like folds of drapery hung in festoons which give the cloud its name. This always means there will be sharp squalls with torrential rain, and they will come up very suddenly.

The type of sky you should most dislike to see is the leaden sheet of cloud, which accompanies steady rain. It is called the " nimbus " cloud. This is the second lowest cloud in altitude, of dark and threatening appearance, and it is worth watching its formation, because that will enable you to get some idea of how long the rain is likely to last. If you see some high thin clouds forming above this cloud, as it approaches, which shoot out in different directions and are very numerous, then the rain will be heavy and lasting; if there are only very few of these upper shoots of cloud, then the rain will be less heavy and soon over.

MARE'S-TAILS IN THE SKY

Cirrus clouds form the highest layer of the

This is a good example of a mackerel sky which is almost always the forerunner of unsettled, showery weather. The correct name for these clouds is cirrocumulus.

cloud family, and are often called " mare's-tails." In appearance they are quite thin, and stretch in streaks across the sky in all directions. When you see these it means that a change in the weather is coming. If you watch these fibres, you will see them extend horizontally or vertically. If they develop into sheets and fall lower towards the earth, rainy weather can be expected. The wind will veer in the direction in which the streaks of cirrus run across the sky. Also, if these fibres look as if they are brushed backwards at one end, and the direction is opposite to that of the prevailing wind, then it will change to that direction. If that is S.E. or S.W., heavy rain and high winds will follow.

If the fibres are pointing *upwards*, it means that the clouds are coming lower, and rain is approaching, but if they point *downwards* the opposite holds good.

The next in the cloud family is known as the " cumulus," the most familiar cloud of all, which is associated with both fine and showery weather, for there is both a " fair-weather " and a " shower " cumulus. You will see the former has banks of soft white clouds drifting leisurely across the sky on a summer day and melting away at sunset. The " shower " cumulus, however, rises like gigantic puffs of smoke from a long base-line, and sometimes may reach up to one and a half miles high. These clouds, unlike the " fair-weather " cumulus, are inclined to grow denser towards sunset, till they gradually cover the greater part of the sky.

Another branch of the cloud family is the stratus, which is the lowest type of all clouds, and will sometimes come down to within a few hundred feet of ground level. When these clouds form at the top of a hill it is usually a forerunner of rain. You may have noticed the atmosphere below a sheet of stratus is often very clear, and distant objects like ships at sea ten or twelve miles away look quite near at hand.

There are some types of cloud that are most often seen in certain parts of England. If you live in the southern counties, especially along the Kent or Sussex coast, you may have heard people speak of " Folkestone pillars." They are a series of towering conical cloudbanks rising up from a dense base, frequently seen over the eastern English Channel, during

Cumulus cloud reflected in the river on a fine summer's day. The weather is likely to remain good for some time.

showery weather with sunny intervals, and are of the cumulus cloud family.

In Cornwall you will often see yet another kind of cumulus cloud, locally known as scud. It is a low mass of thin cloud that seems to fly at a great rate across the sky—sometimes throughout the whole day—and clear away completely at sunset, without bringing any rain.

WHEN THE SKY IS WHITE

Many of you may have noticed that when the blue sky of a summer morning begins to whiten over about midday, making the sun look somewhat watery, it is not a good weather sign. On most occasions when this happens the whitening of the sky presently turns into a more leaden hue, and rain sets in about tea-time. You need to watch this change very carefully, however, because this early whitening over of a blue sky does not always mean rain. It depends very much from which direction this gradual cloud layer is spreading.

If it is coming in from the west, south or south-east, then you may expect rain in a few

The sky at sunset can often give an indication of the weather to be expected on the morrow, and the colours of the sky are always a joy to behold.

hours, but if it is spreading in from a northerly or north-easterly quarter, it will probably drift vaguely across the sky most of the afternoon, and then break up into thin films of cloud and clear away at sunset.

The direction from which the clouds approach is therefore very important. Another thing to watch is whether a cloud seems to be growing denser. It is always quite easy to see this, because the sun will look more and more watery.

You should also notice whether there seems to be any fall in the altitude of the clouds. That is shown when they begin to look more of a smoky colour than their earlier filmy whiteness, which is due to the rain-type formation developing.

WATCH FOR THE DAWN

The morning sky will sometimes add to your weather knowledge. A dawn flecked with angry red patches of cloud is a forerunner of a stormy day, especially if this spreads right across from the eastern to the western sky.

Also you must not be too much encouraged by a very brilliant early morning, free of the soft dawn-haze that accompanies fine weather. A day that starts with that hard clear brilliance will often develop into steady rain before the middle of the morning, whereas a leaden grey sky will frequently break into a day of brilliant sunshine soon after breakfast. It is always wise in these cases to study the sky in conjunction with a falling or rising barometer.

If you study clouds on these lines you will find that it becomes more and more fascinating, and you will soon gain a reputation among your school friends as a weather-forecaster.

When I was at school and made out my own local forecast, I found it useful to tabulate at the end of each day the barometer readings, the type of sunset, and the cloud changes I had observed during the day, and then enter in the opposite column the following day's weather. This is very good practice for you to become a competent amateur weather-prophet, and also forms a useful check on the accuracy of the forecasts in your own district.

JET PROPULSION IN
THE ANIMAL KINGDOM

THAT rather overworked phrase, "there's nothing new under the sun," can, like all such phrases be overdone. Even jet propulsion, however, is not new, it was in general use by animals long before man applied the principle to aircraft. But the animals have used it always under water, for, of course, as all who have played with a water pistol know, a jet of water can be a very forceful thing. Some of us have had the nozzle of a garden hose suddenly twist the wrong way; and the fire hose is still used not only to put out fires, but to persuade disorderly crowds and rioters to disperse.

Jet propulsion was the principle means of locomotion with the squids and similar animals, hundreds of millions of years ago, when these creatures were even more numerous than they are to-day. It is the simplest of jet propulsion methods for it consists simply in breathing. Next time you go to a marine aquarium, watch the cuttlefish, squid, or octopus carefully and you will see at once what happens. Just underneath the animal's head is a wide-mouthed pipe leading into the animal's bag-like body. The body is always heaving or pulsing, like the bellows of a bag-pipe, as its owner sucks in and blows out water, forty times to the minute perhaps. The water when drawn in flows over the creature's gills, which take the place of our lungs. These extract the life-giving oxygen, just as our lungs extract it from the air, and the stale water breathed by the squid or octopus is blown out through the siphon pipe.

So long as the animal rests quietly on the aquarium floor it will stay put. But the moment it breathes really hard, it is forced backwards, sometimes at a great pace. In fact in order to sit down comfortably the octopus must hold on to something with all the sucking discs on the undersides of its arms, and there are about two hundred suckers to each arm.

THE OCTOPUS'S SMOKE SCREEN

The siphon pipe can be put to other uses besides breathing. The female octopus uses it to blow sea water over her many bundles of eggs to keep them fresh and vigorous, and all the octopus and squid tribes use the siphon pipe to squirt out a cloud of dark-brown ink or sepia to baffle pursuers. Perhaps this first gave the Navy the idea of using smoke screens to hide ships from the enemy. In the depths of the ocean where all is inky blackness, of course this sepia, which is used as an artist's colour, would make little difference. So deep-sea squids have developed a luminous ink, which dazzles the foe with a cloud of bright misty blue. It is shot forth as the animal jerks backwards; so here jet propulsion serves a double purpose, a swift retreat and a temporary blinding of the enemy.

A FRESH-WATER AQUARIUM

A fresh-water aquarium is much easier to keep than a marine one, and in spring and summer anyone may watch jet propulsion as practised by that well-known pond animal, the grub or nymph of the dragon-fly. Like most pond insects it is a rather blood-thirsty beast and must be fed on tadpoles or small worms.

Sometimes the dragon-fly nymph stalks its prey warily, like a cat creeping within reach of a bird. But sometimes it makes a rush, by jet propulsion. Along each side of its body is a row of holes called spiracles. Through these a complicated pumping machinery draws in water to bring oxygen, without which no animal can live, to the creature's blood. The stale water from which the oxygen has been removed is not breathed out through the mouth, but through an opening at the tail end.

So, like the octopus and its cousins, the dragon-fly nymph brings into use jet propulsion simply by breathing hurriedly. The "mask," shown in the picture, is a wonderful extra limb, with a hinged joint in the middle and a pair of nippers or forceps at the free end. With it the nymph can seize victims at a distance. It is like the "catch pole" used by police very many years ago to catch runaway thieves.

Also in your fresh-water tank you may see another sort of jet propulsion, as used by the little fresh-water lobster or crayfish, common

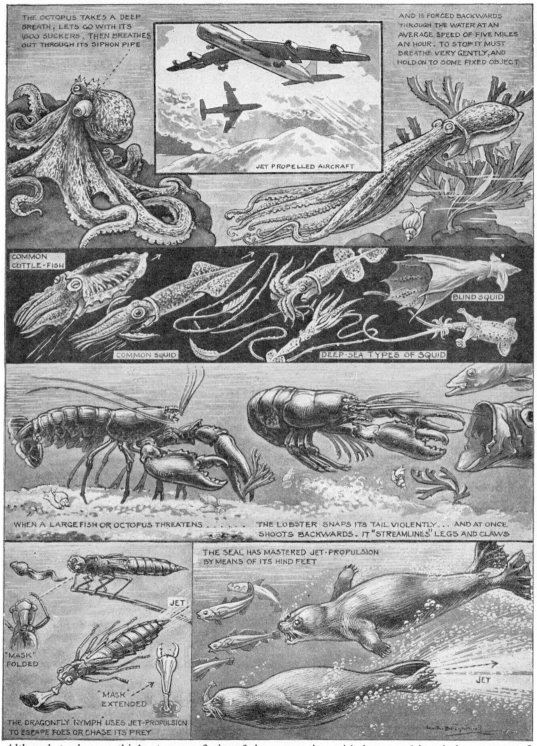

THE OCTOPUS TAKES A DEEP BREATH, LETS GO WITH ITS 1800 SUCKERS, THEN BREATHES OUT THROUGH ITS SIPHON PIPE

AND IS FORCED BACKWARDS THROUGH THE WATER AT AN AVERAGE SPEED OF FIVE MILES AN HOUR. TO STOP IT MUST BREATHE VERY GENTLY, AND HOLD ON TO SOME FIXED OBJECT

JET PROPELLED AIRCRAFT

COMMON CUTTLE·FISH

COMMON SQUID

BLIND SQUID

DEEP·SEA TYPES OF SQUID

WHEN A LARGE FISH OR OCTOPUS THREATENS . . . . . . THE LOBSTER SNAPS ITS TAIL VIOLENTLY . . . AND AT ONCE SHOOTS BACKWARDS. IT "STREAMLINES" LEGS AND CLAWS

"MASK" FOLDED

JET

"MASK" EXTENDED

THE DRAGONFLY NYMPH USES JET·PROPULSION TO ESCAPE FOES OR CHASE ITS PREY

THE SEAL HAS MASTERED JET·PROPULSION BY MEANS OF ITS HIND FEET

JET

Although to-day we think at once of aircraft in connection with jet propulsion, it is a means of propulsion which has been used in its simplest form from time immemorial by a wide variety of animals. Its effectiveness can be clearly seen in these drawings in many of our rivers, and often for sale in the aquarium shops.

HOW THE LOBSTER REVERSES

All the members of the lobster clan, shrimps, prawns and crawfish use the same kind of jet propulsion employed by the crayfish. It is very simple. The creature when alarmed simply folds its tail beneath it so violently that the jet of water forced forwards, drives the animal backwards, much like the hurried breathing of the octopus. Thanks to these lobster-like animals having their eyes mounted on long movable stalks, they can direct their backward movement with some accuracy. Otherwise this continual " driving in reverse " would be very risky.

In Madeira a lobster-like creature called the langouste is hunted by chasing it under water. The boys trained to this queer fishing are champion swimmers but they often have a hard chase before they bring the clumsy-looking, but really nimble, langouste to the surface.

Only one warm-blooded group of animals, the seals, have mastered jet propulsion, and by quite a different method from that of the octopus, lobster or dragon-fly. The seal's front legs are of use only for steering it round corners and scrambling over rocks. To swim forward it uses only the enormous, webbed hind feet. These are first spread to their full extent, then cupped, as one can cup the hands, and finally brought together flat. The result is a jet of water sending the buoyant seal forward at a surprising pace. Its cousin, the sea-lion, swims mostly with its huge front flippers, though the hind limbs may, like the seal's, drive it forward by that force, which you and I have come to look upon as one of the latest wonders of this enterprising age.

TWO PUZZLES

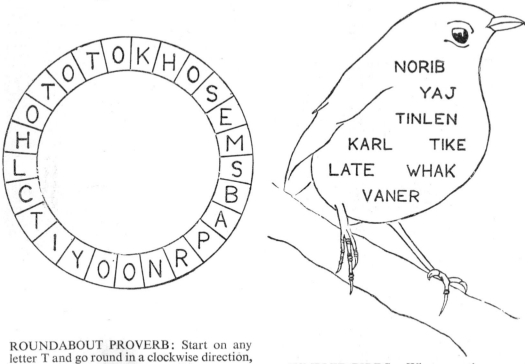

ROUNDABOUT PROVERB: Start on any letter T and go round in a clockwise direction, picking out letters to form a well-known proverb to do with food. The number of letters in each word is 3, 4, 5, 5, 3, 5.

JUMBLED BIRDS: What are the correct names of the birds which have got jumbled in the picture above ?

Solutions on page 345.

PHOTOGRAPHING
THE MOON AND STARS

EVERYONE admires the moon and stars, but when it comes to taking photographs of them many of us conjure up visions of special cameras, worked by expert astronomers, coupled on to giant telescopes which automatically follow their subjects across the sky. Yet it is possible to take very interesting photos of the moon and certain stars with your own simple camera, and without ever leaving your garden or even your window. You will get a lot of fun out of this (it is a grand excuse for staying up late), and in the process learn more about the stars and their two great fascinations—the vast size of them, and their huge distances from the Earth.

As an example of size, the bright star at the head of Orion (Betelgeuse) is big enough to contain the sun and ourselves twice over, and as an example of distance, a star's light travels at 186,000 miles a *second*, yet the light of some of them takes thirty thousand years to reach us.

What can our home-taken star pictures show? By "star" I mean the moon and planets too. The great astronomical photographs, of course, show immense detail, and many new stars have been discovered from them. At home, we shall have mainly to confine ourselves to showing their apparent movement across the sky, though with a little ingenuity we may be able to show some interesting detail of the moon, and try some other experiments as well.

TECHNICAL POINTS

Before getting down to details, here are a few technical hints that apply to *all* star photos:

(a) Use your widest stop (f 4.5, 3.6, or whatever your lens will give you). This is, of course, to allow as much light to enter as possible.

(b) Focus the camera at " Infinity."

(c) Avoid setting up the camera near any artificial light, such as a street-lamp or lighted window. This would ruin a long exposure.

(d) Steadiness is essential, so if you can fit a " cable-release " to your camera, do so.

(e) Develop your film or plate for longer than usual, unless the photo is of a very bright moon. If a shop does your developing, be sure to tell them what to expect.

PHOTOGRAPHS WITHOUT A TELESCOPE

A stand for your camera is desirable but not essential, as blocks of wood can be used to tilt it instead. You *must* have an absolutely firm table or flat wall. Here are details of four interesting pictures you can take.

(a) *Moon's Track*. Choose a cloudless, moonlight night. Fix camera facing moon, so that it appears in the *right*-hand side of the view-finder (this means it will start on the left of the picture). Open the shutter, and leave it open for about an hour and a half, taking care nothing crosses in front of the lens during that time. At the end, don't forget to close the shutter before picking up the camera.

Result: the moon's track shows as a silver bar across the black print. By measuring its width and length, you can tell how long the moon takes to move its own width.

(b) *Separate Moons*. As for (a), but take an exposure of 1 second every 5 minutes.

Result: a string of moons equally spaced out. The atmosphere will diffuse the light and cause a silvery mist around them (Plate 1). This can be cut out if an enlargement is made (Plate 2).

(c) *Planet and Star-Tracks*. Choose a bright planet: Jupiter, Venus or Saturn. Venus is often hard to get in real darkness, as it is always near the Sun. You can tell a planet, because it doesn't twinkle like a star.

Wait till a time when an extra-bright

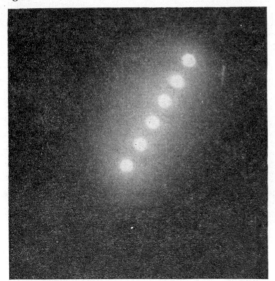

Plate 1. The Moon, taken with a small camera at 5-minute intervals. Exposure 1 sec.

star will show on the same print as the planet, then take 2 exposures as in (*a*), each of 30 minutes, about a fortnight apart. These will show how the two bodies have changed their relative positions, and you will also see the tracks of several fainter stars.

(*d*) *Circumpolar Stars*. Point the camera at the Pole Star, and leave the shutter open for a couple of hours. The result will look something like the drawing opposite. The Pole Star is not, actually, right at the Pole, so it describes a tiny curve itself, with the rest showing concentric curves around it. This is an excellent way of showing the Earth's rotation. When taken through a big astronomical telescope the result is astounding: like a Catherine Wheel on Coronation Night!

PHOTOGRAPHS THROUGH A TELESCOPE

These are not as difficult as you might think. Quite a small telescope, say ×15, will give interesting results, but here

some form of stand is essential, and it must be a really steady one. A flimsy, folding tripod may not be stable enough to carry camera, telescope *and* the board on which they must be mounted. A stout tripod such as photographers use for School Groups might be obtainable second-hand, while a very good substitute, is an old rifle-stand such as is used to teach musketry to recruits; your local Territorial Hall may have a cast-off one—otherwise a shop that sells surplus Government stores. The photograph on the opposite page shows a simple method of arrangement using a rifle-stand; the camera is held in place by long metal bolts, with or without wooden blocks according to its size. The telescope rests on two hollowed-out wooden blocks, and is clamped down by curved metal strips, bolts and wing-nuts.

Most of these fittings can be picked up at an ironmonger's, while if you have a Meccano set you will find some of the strips and angle-pieces useful.

THE MOON

By far the best subject is the Moon; when photographed through a telescope, particularly when not quite full, it shows clearly as a

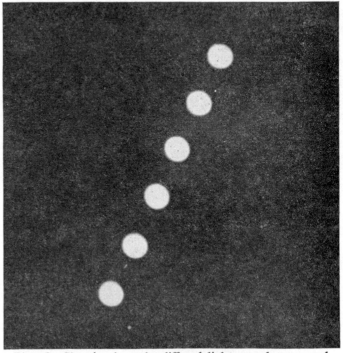

Plate 2. Showing how the diffused light may be removed.

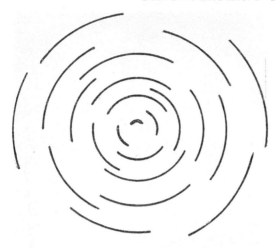

The concentric curves described by the circumpolar stars, showing the Earth's rotation.

ball in the sky, and not as a disc—which is what it looks like to the naked eye. Here is the correct procedure.

(a) Aim the telescope, on its stand, at the moon, and focus it.

(b) Slip the camera, at its widest stop and focused for Infinity, behind the telescope.

(c) Check the sighting, either by looking along the top of the telescope, or else over sights previously fixed to the side of the board.

(d) Hold a piece of dark cardboard just in front of the telescope, open the camera-shutter (cable-release desirable) and wait at least 20 seconds, to allow all vibration to die down. This is the only way to ensure steadiness at time of exposure.

(e) Whip away the cardboard for about $\frac{3}{4}$ second, replace, and close shutter.

All this has to be done very quickly and smoothly, owing to the surprising speed with which the moon moves " out of the telescope." So don't be discouraged if you have a few failures at first. The main difficulty is in getting the moon properly in focus *on the film or plate* (as opposed to your eye). By far the easiest way to ensure this is to beg or borrow a small " reflex " camera, for that will show the image of the moon properly focused on the "ground-glass" at the moment the exposure is made. With an ordinary plate camera, you focus the moon on the ground-glass, then remove it

An old rifle-stand converted to hold the author's telescope and camera. In the second picture the author's Indian servant shows how the telescope is held.

and substitute the plate—not quite so simple but straightforward enough.

With a plain film-camera, the safest way is to make three exposures—one as described, then one with the telescope shortened by ⅛ inch, then lengthened by ¼ inch. One of these three should be " sharp."

Your first really clear picture of the moon taken through a telescope will give you great satisfaction, and it is well worth while getting an enlargement made. This will look quite professional enough to illustrate any astronomy book, as it will clearly show all the largest craters and " seas," as they are called. These show up well on Plate 3.

OTHER POSSIBILITIES THROUGH A TELESCOPE

Lunar Eclipses. If you get a next-year's diary each Christmas, look up when eclipses of the moon take place and note the dates. More details will appear in the daily papers just before the eclipse. A successful series of pictures showing the Earth's shadow advancing, then retreating, would make a fascinating record—and your local paper or even a high-class magazine might jump at the pictures and pay you good money for them! But *don't forget* to lengthen the exposure as the bright area decreases.

Double Stars. A star is not worth photographing through a small telescope, as your print would show nothing but a bright dot. There are, however, a number of well-known " double " stars, which are really two separate ones which revolve round one another. It would be an interesting experiment to try some of these. Look through your telescope at the middle star of the Great Bear's tail (Mizar).

Plate 3. The craters Copernicus and Tycho can be seen in this close-up of the Moon.

You will see that it is not only a "double" but has a fainter star (Alcor) very close to it as well. This would be a good group to try for a start; choose a *moonless* night and allow at least 2 minutes' exposure.

AN EXCELLENT STAR-BOOK

If you would like to know more of the stars, there is a very good little book about them called *A Guide to the Sky*, by Ernest Agar Beet, published by the Cambridge University Press. This will help you to identify many constellations, and it contains much exciting information as well. My acknowledgments are due to it.

SUMMARY

Here are the main points I have mentioned, summarised for easy reference:

- (*a*) There is no need for a special camera, or special film.
- (*b*) Develop for longer than usual, especially star-track negatives. *Warn* the developing shop what to expect.
- (*c*) Use a cable-release if your camera will take one.
- (*d*) Use the widest stop; focus at " Infinity."
- (*e*) Avoid being anywhere near an artificial light.
- (*f*) Absolute steadiness is essential.

Good luck, and don't be discouraged by a few failures, you will find it great fun.

The double star of the Great Bear formation.

THE PERILS A DIVER DREADS

Some of the perils which a diver dreads. 1. The giant clam of the Barrier Reef, Australia. 2. The giant spider crab of Japan. 3. Sharks. 4. Portuguese man-o'-war, a jelly-fish with a terrible sting. 5. The giant octopus of the Pacific.

THE MARINELAND OF THE PACIFIC OCEANARIUM

The Pacific Oceanarium at Palos Verdes, California, is full of fish which must be fed by hand to prevent them living on each other. Here one of the divers feeds a manta ray.

A porpoise snatching a ball from a diver. These fish are very playful and full of fun

Two 350 lb. porpoises sweep down to get their daily meal of fish from the diver.

One of the divers slowly swims over an eagle ray, whose tail has a lethal sting in it.

The diver is here seen pushing a mackerel into the mouth of a great blue shark. He wears wire mesh gloves in case the shark mistakes his hands for a mackerel.

London—fifty million years ago. In the background is the sea in which the great London clay bed was deposited. The animals in the centre are coryphodons (a prehistoric hippopotamus), those, left, are hydracotherium, ancestor of the horse and the size of a fox.

The Evolution of the World
THE AGE OF MAMMALS

THE dinosaurs, biggest land monsters of all time, ruled the Earth for something like 100 million years. Then, quite suddenly as far as geological time is concerned, they died out. They vanished so quickly that the rapidity of their disappearance is one of the great mysteries of evolution.

Then, equally suddenly, traces of the first mammals appear in the record of the rocks. Mammal is the general name given to animals with bodies of even temperature, which give birth to their young as babies and not eggs, and feed them with milk whilst small.

This does not mean that mammals did not exist in the reptilian age; primitive mammals have been traced back 165 million years! But they seem to have been comparatively tiny creatures, probably about the size of mice. Certainly there were no mammals big or strong enough to attack a dinosaur. We believe this to be so because the rocks which have retained secrets of the dinosaurs have yet to reveal a single complete skeleton of a mammal during this period.

Mammals reached supremacy on the Earth about 75 million years ago. This period is called the Cainozoic era and, of all the geological ages, it is perhaps the most interesting because

it introduces into the panorama of life the kind of creature from which we have descended. It is also of interest because the end of the era cannot yet be described—it lies in the unpredictable future.

STRANGE CREATURES OF THE PAST

The Cainozoic period may be subdivided into seven epochs, starting with the Palæocene and coming down to the Recent, the one in which we are now living. At the beginning of the Palæocene epoch the Earth must have been a pretty desolate place. Except for a few turtles, alligators and boa constrictors, most of the mighty dynasty of reptiles had vanished, and the rare mammals that had existed alongside them were small both in size and numbers.

But, with the disappearance of the dinosaurs, life stirred once again, to make rapid strides forward. Those mammals which had previously lived in trees out of the reach of dinosaurs descended to evolve on and explore the ground. The first mammal of importance is the prodiacodon, a creature resembling a primitive hedgehog and living on insects. Its importance in the evolutionary story is that from it evolved all the modern animals with which we are familiar to-day. After it came a wide variety

236

of creatures, including mioclaenus, a strange horse-headed but cat-bodied animal from which hoofed animals have evolved. Geological and climatic conditions were ideal and at the close of the 15-million-year period the Earth once more teemed with life.

THE MAIN EVOLUTIONARY LINES

The next epoch lasted 20 million years. Called the Eocene, this period saw the appearance of tetonius, small monkey-like creatures, important because they were the first animals to have close-set eyes. For the first time distance could be conceived stereoscopically, an aptitude which to-day we find convenient in a hundred different ways.

From the Eocene epoch we pass to the Oligocene, which covers the period from 40 to 30 million years ago. These years saw the passing away of many primitive mammals and the emergence of a more modern style of animal life. The monster of the day was the brontops, a ponderous, hoofed and horned beast about 14 feet long, feeding on plants; subhyracodon also appeared, the prototype rhinoceros, together with archaeotherium, an ugly pig. By the time this epoch came to an end

the main evolutionary lines were well established, with the ancestors of the modern animal kingdom in existence in considerable numbers.

The next period, from 30 to 10 million years ago, is called the Miocene. This epoch witnessed a major event in the panorama of life, a spectacular spreading of grass. Through the ages this has evolved into the forage plants now the basic food supply of beast and man alike. Life was, perhaps, as plentiful as at any period of all time.

Following the Miocene came the Pliocene epoch, lasting until one million years ago. This was a period of steady evolution, during which mammals continued to increase in size. Well established were the elephant-like mastodons which, originating in Egypt in the Miocene period, had emigrated in one of the greatest mass movements in the history of the world. Travelling across southern Asia, up through what is now China, across a land-bridge then linking Asia to America, they had entered the New World and flourished alongside its other teeming life.

THE ICE AGE

But, great changes were in store. The Earth,

Discovered in a glacier in Siberia in 1903, this mammoth was perfectly preserved. Grass in its mouth was as fresh as it was when, feeding peacefully thousands of years ago, death struck quickly and apparently without warning.

An Ice Age relic. This great boulder, weighing several tons, was carried to its present position by glaciers, which, during the Great Ice Age, covered Britain to the Thames.

for reasons not yet fully understood, began to grow colder. To the north and south great ice caps began to form. Little by little the winters grew colder and winds sharper. Year by year, mile by mile, the ice advanced and the sub-tropical forests retreated towards the Equator. Thus was the Pleistocene epoch ushered in—the only age we can study at first hand—the age in which we live.

For 100,000 years the ice sheets extended southward, until one-third of the earth's surface was engulfed. The land now called Canada was one big sheet of ice, huge glaciers penetrated the central plains of the United States; even Britain was engulfed down to the Thames. Then, unaccountably, the ice sheet gradually receded.

Soon, however, the cold climate returned and once again the huge continental glaciers ground down from the North. Four times the ice came and four times it withdrew. The last great

retreat began only 10,000 years ago and is still perceptibly continuing to-day.

As can be imagined these ice ages played havoc with both land and life. As the glaciers crunched back and forth, whole mountains were eroded, new valleys and river-beds carved. Animals grew to sizes never equalled before or since, the most famous of which were the sabre-toothed tigers and the giant mastodons and woolly mammoths. The sabre-toothed tiger was larger, heavier and more ferocious than any other tiger of to-day. The name derives from two six-inch fangs growing from the upper jaw, with which it stabbed its quarry to death. This tiger knew no fear and, armed with his fiercesome teeth, attacked even the mastodons.

The mastodons and mammoths were the biggest of all the Pleistocene mammals. The latter, resembling an elephant with outsize tusks, ruled the great American plains, more than a match for all other creatures.

The sabre-toothed tiger was very much larger, heavier and more ferocious than the tigers of to-day. It had two fangs, each six inches long, with which it stabbed its prey to death.

THE MAMMOTHS DIE OUT

Then, when the Sun returned to mark the beginning of the end of the last ice age, the past presents us with another mystery almost the equal of the disappearance of the great reptiles.

This full-size statue of an elk shows the size of these great animals that once roamed the face of the earth.

For, swiftly again as far as geological time is concerned, the big mammals died out. The mastodons and mammoths died among the glaciers in such vast numbers that to-day half the world's ivory has come from their great imperishable tusks.

Along with the mammoths, the sabre-toothed tigers and sloths also abruptly vanished. It was indeed a period of great change. As in the case of the reptiles 100 million years earlier, animals by the hundred thousand, whole families, whole species, died out. The finest range of animal life the world had ever seen was reduced to a mere shadow of its former glory. Only Central Africa and Asia seemed immune from the wholesale extinctions.

And, as in the case of the dinosaurs, we wonder what caused this mystery. Plague? Climate changes? Competition? We do not know.

But with the great ice sheets there appeared in the panorama of life an animal which had hitherto been absent, *Homo sapiens*—that is, Thinking Man. There appeared for the first time small, two-legged, hairless, shivering and unarmoured creatures whose priceless advantage was a big brain giving them a unique capacity for reason—human beings.

THE EVOLUTION OF MAN

The Story of our Ancestors

THE colour plate on the following two pages is designed to show the probable pattern of the Evolution of Man. The figures are arranged to give the appearance of a continuous evolution, but it must be clearly understood that it is not a factual family tree. It would be quite untrue to say that each was the ancestor of the type immediately following. The men appeared in widely separated places on the continents of Europe, Asia and Africa and cannot, therefore, be considered a direct line of descent.

The whole story of known types is very complicated; strains have died out, others have interbred, and so on, and there are still many gaps to be filled in the history of man's rise to his present position, and much research remains to be done, before a fully-documented family tree can be compiled.

The earliest Australopithecus, known as Makapan Man (on account of the place where his fossil remains were discovered), is shown handling rough stone which he may have used for throwing. He lived 700,000 and more years ago. More brutish in appearance is the later Australopithecus of some 600,000 years ago, the Swartkrans Man. He had huge jaw muscles like the gorilla, attached to a similar bony crest running laterally along the top of his skull. Neither of these creatures was at all massive; standing erect, as they certainly did, they were five feet, or less, in height.

Three Australopithecines are seen, in the middle distance, on the left of the picture, gathered at one of their " squatting-places."

Heidelberg Man lived among the marshy wastes and forests of Europe some 400,000 years ago. Nothing is known of his method of living, which must have been very primitive, or of his weapons and tools.

In the centre of the picture a pair of Heidelberg Men are trying to capture an ibex.

Peking Man lived in Asia, as his name is intended to suggest. He had choppers of flint and sharp scrapers, with which to cut up and flay the carcasses of the animals he killed. He obtained control and knowledge of fire. In spite of his advances he was an uncouth person and a cannibal to boot. He had his day more than 300,000 years ago.

A little later as the centuries go in our vast time-scale, the later, or classic, Java Man appeared in Asia, somewhat less than 300,000 years before our modern age. He may have used rude spears of sharpened wood.

Much later comes the Neanderthal Man, user of flint and fire and wearing skins to protect himself from the bitter winters of the Inter-glacial Period in Europe, more than 100,000 years ago. He was brutish in appearance, though large-brained. He walked with a slouch and a stoop. He had great bony brow-ridges, a receding chin, small thumbs and large toes. His big toe was splayed out, according to actual footprints found deep in caves where he hunted the huge sleepy cave-bear.

Cro-Magnon Man followed hard upon the heels of our simple Neanderthaler. So close in fact that it is suggested that this tall newcomer was partly responsible for the disappearance of his primitive neighbour. The Cro-Magnons were true men. Tall, big-boned and possessed of a fine physique that may have been very like some of the larger inhabitants of Northern Europe to-day, he was a fine artist and crafts-man, working in flint, bone and ivory. His was the hand that painted the wonderful animal pictures on the walls of caves . He had barbed fishing spears of ivory, and may have used the bow, according to objects, possible " arrow straighteners," which have been found in his dwelling-caves.

Chancelade Man was another fine worker in ivory, bone and flint. He lived in the cold times of the last Ice Age in Europe. According to the quality of his bone needles, he must have been a good tailor, using animal skins to fashion clothes very like those of the modern Eskimo.

Cro-Magnon and Chancelade Man each given a haircut, a shave and a new suit of clothes, would not warrant a second glance if they ventured down your own High Street, though the former would possibly be admired for his fine bearing and rugged good looks. It has not been necessary, therefore, to include " Modern " man in the drawing.

THE EVOLUTION OF MAN: The probable pattern of Man's evolution is shown here, but it is impossible to give a definitive family tree. The key numbers refer to the following: 1. Makapan Man (South Africa) 1,000,000-700,000 years ago. 2. Swartkrans Man (South Africa) 600,000

years ago. 3. Heidelberg Man (Europe) 400,000 years ago. 4. Peking Man (Asia) 350,000 years ago. 5. Java Man (Asia) 250,000 years ago. 6. Neanderthal Man (Europe) 150,000-50,000 years ago. 7. Cro-Magnon Man (Europe) 40,000 years ago. 8. Chancelade Man (Europe) 30,000 years ago.

Stonehenge—the remains of a temple erected by ancient Britons 4,000 years ago. It stands on Salisbury Plain and is thought to have been connected with Sun-worship.

The Evolution of the World

THE END OF THE WORLD

OUR story of the evolution of the World started with the birth of the stars 5,000 million years ago. From then, down the slow ages of time, we have traced the cooling of the Earth, the formation of the seas, and the dramatic appearance of living matter. In the panorama of life we have traced evolution from the first tiny one-celled creatures, through the ages of fish, plants and the mighty reptiles. We have given an insight into the teeming animal life of a million years ago and the great Ice Ages in which the fierce sabre-toothed tigers and the big mastodons and woolly mammoths flourished.

And now, at last, we come to the Age of Man. Many readers will be surprised to learn that our appearance is, comparatively speaking, so recent.

Our youth, as far as the long life of the Earth is concerned, is dramatically revealed in an analogy given by the great scientist Sir James Jeans. " Imagine," he explained, " Cleopatra's Needle (a monument on the Victoria Embankment in London, and about 70 feet high) and

on top of this place a penny and on top of that place a postage stamp. Then, if the column represents the age of the World, the penny represents the whole period of man's existence and the thickness of the postage stamp the length of time during which we have been slightly civilised." So, if the panorama of life is likened to an eight-hour play, then we have not yet been on the stage a second!

OUR ORIGIN

The origin of our ancestors is still something of a mystery. The popular belief is that we have " descended " from some man-like ape such as the chimpanzee or gorilla, or from a predecessor of these animals. If one puts the skeleton of a gorilla alongside that of a man the similarity is startling, making it easy to explain the slight differences evident as due to a general process of refinement. However, any real scientific study of the problem is made extremely difficult by the scarcity of fossilised remains of early men in the record of the rocks. Human skeletons are scarce for the same reason as are those of animals living during the great age of reptiles. Prehistoric man lived and died in the open, the bodies being consumed by decay with the passing of time. The little sure knowledge we have is derived from rare traces found in caves. The discovery of really old human bones is thus an event of great importance.

The earliest evidence we have of some creature either human, or at least more man-like than any ape now living on Earth, are flints and stones that have the appearance of having been chipped to form crude tools or weapons. These rough, and perhaps natural, stones have been found in rocks laid down four or five hundred thousand years ago. In Java, in rocks laid down during this age, some scattered bones have been found of a creature who might well have made these early tools. The skulls had a brain about half-way in size between that of a chimpanzee and man. But the creature was not a man, nor was it a tree-climbing ape like the chimpanzee. It was a walking ape and has been named the Pithe-canthropus Erectus—the earliest known ancestor of man!

EARLY FOSSIL REMAINS

The remains of a skull unearthed at Kanjera,

The Thames Valley as it appeared 100,000 years ago. Known as the Early Stone Age, the primitive men of the time hunted big game, including elephants and rhinoceros, both of which can be seen in this picture, with crude flint missiles.

during the Oligocene epoch, that is, about 30 million years ago. No remains of the creature that might have worked these stones have been found. But if he existed at all he must have been a member of the mammal line of Hominidae, that is, the great family of animals walking on two legs as we do to-day. It may be only coincidence that the preceding epoch saw the appearance of the monkey-like tetonius creatures, having close-set, human-like eyes!

Similar early implements, much more certainly artificial, called " Eoliths " have been found that date from the Pliocene epoch, or well before the First Glacial Age. But here again no bone fossils have been found in the record of the rocks to match them.

For the first remains of true primitive men we have to wait until well into the First Ice Age, East Africa, provide further proof that true man existed as early as 300,000 B.C.; perhaps as far back as 650,000 B.C. Another precious relic of around the same age was found in a sand-pit near Heidelberg, some eighty feet from the surface. The relic is only a jawbone, not of modern man although the teeth are human, nor is it the jawbone of an ape; it is the jawbone of one of our ancestors.

For the next two hundred thousand years the only evidence to come to light of early human life is a succession of flint implements, of steadily improving quality. By the time the Fourth Ice Age reached its maximum, some 50,000 years ago, Man was well established in caves and leaving recognisable remains. These were the Neanderthal Men. They existed as a race for over 100,000 years.

Australian Aborigines. Isolated from the outside world for thousands of years, these inhabitants of the northern areas of Australia still live much as our ancestors did in the Stone Ages.

Then, between 25,000 and 40,000 years ago, as the Fourth Glacial Age was beginning to wane, different men arrived upon the scene. These were the Cro-Magnon Men. Far above the Neanderthal level of achievement and intelligence, they seem to have soon exterminated their predecessors.

The human race was well and truly established.

From then on it is but a short time—short that is, by the standards which we have been discussing—to the appearance of culture and civilisation and then an even shorter time up to the present.

Sir James Jean's analogy of the postage stamp is, thus, an excellent indication of the shortness of our existence on Earth. From the earliest possible traces we have existed less than one seventy-fifth of the time during which the Trilobites dominated life on Earth, or less than one-hundredth of the time of the Dinosaurs.

The period during which life will be possible corresponds to an extension of the "monument" mentioned earlier by many hundreds of yards, perhaps miles. We cannot foretell what the future holds for us. We may annihilate ourselves with atomic bombs, or the human race may disappear in the mists of time as did the trilobites, giant reptiles and mammals before us.

THE EARTH'S FUTURE

Of the future of Earth herself, however, scientists are more sure. It seems pretty certain that the Earth will exist as long as the Sun— and the Sun is young as stars go. Its supply of hydrogen fuel will last for, perhaps, 50,000 million years. The Earth, however, will not be habitable for the whole of this period.

At one time it was thought that as time went by the Sun would gradually burn itself out like some gigantic bonfire and, as it cooled, life would disappear from the Earth as first the oceans and then the atmosphere froze. Now,

Devoid of all air, and with all traces of life long since perished, the earth in its final days
will be a dead world just as the Moon is to-day.

however, we know more about the processes that keep stars alight and quite a different end is predicted.

In about 10,000 million years' time the Sun will have used up about one-third of its hydrogen fuel and, contrary to what one might expect, it will then start to get hotter and hotter. The processes causing this are very complicated but, slowly, the Sun will grow brighter and brighter—and hotter. As it gets hotter the temperature of the Earth will rise. The tropical regions will be the first to become uninhabitable.

For a period, the Polar regions will flourish like the tropics do to-day, until they likewise become too hot. Then, as the temperature continues to rise, even the oceans will boil away and life will perish from the Earth.

Then for many thousands of millions of years the scorched remains will continue to circle round the Sun. After further æons of time the Sun may expand to become what astronomers call a " red giant," so huge that its monstrous swollen body might well extend to the orbit of the Earth and, perhaps, even Mars and Jupiter.

DEATH OF THE SUN

Finally, in its dying stages, the Sun may explode as a nova, that is, disintegrate in a series of explosions each of which will increase its brightness 10,000 times. The Earth will not outlive the day of the first of these. As the explosions take place the Earth will be exposed to the dreadful white heat of the Sun's interior.

Within minutes the very surface will melt, engulfing the planet in an inferno of flame and fury. The Earth may even disintegrate. At best it will be a scorched cinder circling the remains of the shattered Sun until it flickers out and all is dark and cold. The remains will then voyage through space until the end of time itself.

Let us hope that before this final catastrophe, descendants of the human race will have found themselves a new planet around a more hospitable Sun.

DO YOU KNOW?

Do fish go to sleep in the winter?

Many animals go to sleep during the cold weather and do not wake up until spring has come. This is called hibernating.

It is not often, however, that we hear of fish going to sleep. But in the cold north lands, where the great rivers are frozen over during the winter, many fish are caught in the ice.

When they are caught in this icy prison they go to sleep and lie inert till the frost has gone and the waters begin to thaw. The fish then revive and come to life, swimming away in search of a meal after their long sleep.

Nature has thus given another proof of her great wisdom in preserving these small creatures who would otherwise have lost their lives.

What is ermine?

Ermine is a beautiful white fur used for ladies' fur coats and capes. It is also used for trimming the gowns worn by Royalty, by peers of the realm, by judges and other important people.

Small black tails of fur are generally fixed at intervals on the white fur.

This lovely fur comes from a small animal that lives in our own country as well as in Europe and America. This animal is the stoat.

It is a member of the weasel family. In summer the stoat is reddish-brown in colour, but the tip of its tail is black.

When snow comes and the woods and hillsides where the stoat lives are all white, the stoat also turns white. This is Nature's trick to protect the stoat from its enemies. It cannot be seen when moving about in the snow. The tip of the tail, however, still remains black. The tip of the tail is used to decorate the white fur when used for capes or borders of gowns.

Why is the post office so called?

In the olden days when travel had to be done on horseback or in coaches, there were special places along the main roads where fresh horses were kept.

These were called *posts*. In a long journey, as from London to York, horses would require changing a number of times.

So when a quick journey had to be performed, it was called a " post-haste " journey, and the rapid coaches were called " Post-Chaises."

When the postal system came into being the offices and collecting-boxes were called post-offices and post-boxes. The men who collected and delivered the letters were known as postmen.

WILD LIFE OF AFRICA
"Nature Red in Tooth and Claw"

OF all five continents, Africa is the most prodigal of wild life and has an especial interest from the fact that it has existed as land from a very remote geological epoch.

In southern Africa were found the remains of an extensive group of extinct reptiles of exceptional interest, because they include types bordering on the primitive salamanders, and others representing the ancestral stock from which mammals have originated.

At the period when these reptiles flourished, Africa appears to have been connected with India by way of Madagascar and the Seychelle Islands, and it is almost certain that on this great continent the evolution of reptiles to mammals took place.

It is probable that this change took place in the central or southern portion. This transition was of supreme importance in the life-history of the world, for it was the beginning of the chain of evolution which eventually evolved man himself.

The wild life of Africa differs very greatly between the northern and southern portion, in keeping with the marked difference between the native races of that continent.

The animals of North Africa approximate largely to those of southern Europe and western and north-western Asia. The great sterile area of the Sahara, with a breadth in some parts of more than a thousand miles, is the main barrier between the wild life of the north and south.

The only true North African monkey is the Barbary ape, which differs from its Asiatic cousin by the complete absence of a tail. It is a native of the north-western corner of Africa, and those members found on the rock of Gibraltar may have originally crossed over by a land bridge or been subsequently introduced.

Their size is that of the average dog and their fur a light, yellowish brown. Associating in troops, they feed on pineapples, chestnuts, figs, melons and nuts. In captivity these apes

These lordly lions, taking their siesta in the jungle, look very placid and peaceful. But see them when they are roused! A lion's roar, in the still of an African night, is one of the most sinister sounds in nature, and an angry lion is a very terrifying adversary.

will take care of smaller animals belonging to quite different groups, and when young are lively, active and clever, but grow surly and vicious with age.

PIGMY ANIMALS WHICH WERE EMBALMED

In Egypt the pigmy muskshrew should be noted as being one of the smallest of non-flying mammals, being only 1½ inches, with a tail just under an inch. The bodies of these little creatures were carefully embalmed by the ancient Egyptians.

Hedgehogs also inhabit these northern regions, showing the link with Europe, and in Egypt there is a small species with long ears that is also found in Cyprus.

An exclusively African family of jumping shrews is found in Algeria. About the size of a rat, this little creature hops on its hind-legs like a miniature kangaroo, and has a nose like a tiny elephant's trunk. It is consequently often referred to as the elephant-shrew.

Although to be found in many parts of Africa and in some parts of south-western Asia, the North African lion should be noted because of its large size and long and very full mane, which grows as far as the middle of its back, and even on the under side of its body. The lioness of this area has the inner side of the forelegs white. Hidden by the tuft of hair on the tip of the lion's tail is often a small horny spur, the use of which is still unknown.

Extending southwards as far as Swaziland and the borders of northern Transvaal, they formerly abounded in such areas as the Kala-hari Desert and the uplands of Mashonaland, before the white farmers settled in the latter country.

Night is the lions' hunting time and, except-ing in the great reserves, they are seldom seen in the day, when they take their rest either in high grass or among thickets. These great cats also have a tendency to avoid moonlight nights to some extent and are markedly more active in stormy or overcast weather.

Unlike the lesser cats, they have a habit of roaring loudly and frequently when on the prowl. A roar is not necessarily a warning of danger, as lions often roar to their fellows, but they will give vent to a low coughing grunt when about to attack.

The sound of a " pride " or troop of lions calling to others in the still of an African night is without doubt one of the most impressive sounds in nature. And a fight between rival lions for the possession of prey can be truly terrifying. The most dangerous lion to man is the old lion that, unable to chase other animals, will take toll of the slower human beings.

Lions will hunt alone or in pairs, but in southern Africa four, five or more are quite frequent. Their principal prey comprises antelopes, giraffes, zebras and buffaloes, according to the areas in which they live. Though they will on occasion attack a rhinoceros, it is a formidable foe they prefer to avoid.

LIONS CANNOT CLIMB TREES

Though lions can leap considerable dis-tances, they are unable to climb trees, and this fact has often saved a native's life, and on one occasion at least that of a white game-ranger. This man was attacked at nightfall quite suddenly by two male lions who were actually after the horse he was riding. As the first lion leaped on the horse's hind-quarters, the horse reared up, throwing the ranger on to the second lion, that immediately seized the man by his right shoulder and began dragging him into the bush. Fortunately the ranger had retained his hunting knife and his presence of mind, and, despite great agony, managed to stab the lion mortally as he was dragged along.

The great cat then dropped him, and the ranger was just able to crawl a few feet into the fork of a neighbouring acacia tree before the second lion, having lost the horse and scenting the trail of blood, came to the base of the tree. The ranger just managed to retain his hold until his native " boys " rescued him at break of day.

Attacking, the lion lays back its ears and rushes at its prey with its body close to the ground. Nature provides perfect camouflage for all its wild creatures, and the lion's tawny hide blends with most of its surroundings. In particular, when crouching, its colour and shape bear a close resemblance to the many ant-hills that abound throughout Africa, and they have often been confused at quite close quarters with these great heaps of earth.

A curious fact that only those travellers

Grace and power are the characteristics of these lionesses on the prowl along a track in the Kruger National Park. They are always alert and watchful, ready to confront any danger.

Even leopards have their lighter moments, and this pair at Belle Vue, Manchester (far away from their native haunts) are having a friendly and frivolous frolic together.

who have seen it will believe is that lions, when fully fed and no longer hungry, will pass through herds of antelope and zebra without attempting to molest them, and the herd in question will continue quietly browsing as if aware that they are not in any present danger.

A fine specimen of the African lion, such as may be encountered in the large game reserves, will measure as much as ten feet from its head to its tail and weigh nearly 600 lb.

As a rule, the manes of lions in captivity are fuller and finer than those encountered in their natural haunts. But the finest of all are now found in the reserves, where immunity from the hunter and plentiful game, coupled with freedom, produces the healthiest animals.

THE LEOPARD'S SPOTS

Next in point of size and frequently fiercer is the leopard, whose range extends over the whole continent. In the mountainous area of Morocco and, in some cases, in East Africa, there is a large spotted species similar to the Asiatic animal, whereas the average African leopard has fur with much smaller black spots. Along the Red Sea coast and in Abyssinia the ground colour of the leopard's coat is greyish and in some cases nearly black along the spine.

This cheetah is one of a privately owned pack, which has been trained for hunting. Cheetahs can outpace greyhounds and maintain a speed of over 60 m.p.h. over short distances.

There is a tendency in Abyssinia and East Africa for the leopard's markings to take the form of large rosettes like those of Persian and Indian leopards, and it is among leopards of these markings that the wholly black leopard is sometimes found. This black species has the reputation of being the most ferocious of all. In Somaliland both lions and leopards are much smaller than in other areas of Africa.

The leopard is without doubt the most dangerous and troublesome to man. Lions will seldom attack man or his domestic animals without provocation, but leopards will often do so.

They are, moreover, expert climbers, very silent and quick in their movements and curiously difficult to see until quite close at hand. They will stealthily enter buildings which a lion would never do and, if cornered, will attack at sight.

Equally cunning is the leopard when being hunted, and it will usually see the hunter first, retreating at once if unobserved, so that its presence may never have been realised.

The lion, despite its probable origin in desert regions, has usually a partiality for water; but leopards—in Africa at any rate— are frequently found in rocky, desolate regions devoid of water, though they are excellent swimmers when water is encountered.

The cry of the leopard, so seldom heard, is something between a grunt and a cough, which is repeated three or four times. Even the cubs of leopards are intractable and not easily tamed.

THE LEOPARD'S LARDER UP A TREE

In Africa the leopard is accustomed to put the remains of its " kill " up a tree, probably to protect the meat from prowling hyenas. The remains of so large an antelope as a kudu have been found in the fork of a tree some feet from the ground, this place evidently being the larder of some leopard. The baboon appears to be a very favourite food of leopards, and the almost human cry of this animal when caught is one of the most startling and eerie sounds in the silence of the African jungle.

Known as the hunting leopard, the cheetah is without doubt the fastest mammal of the wild. It can also be one of the tamest, despite the black patch of fur from eye to muzzle

The caracal, a red lynx with pointed and tufted ears, is a member of the cat family but far removed from the domestic cat. Here it is enjoying a chicken meal, feathers and all. It will fight tooth and nail when cornered.

which gives it, at first sight, such a formidable expression.

"Cheetah" is the English pronunciation of the Indian "chita," meaning "spotted," and it will be noted that, unlike its cousin the leopard, this large cat has solid black spots, not arranged in rosettes, besides the black line of fur between the muzzle and the eye, and the eye and the ear. About the size of the leopard, it is of lighter build, having a smaller head and ears, and longer and more slender legs. The eyes are round and as beautiful as those of the gazelle.

This large cat is one of the few wild beasts found both in Africa and Asia. It is not found in forest country, for its method of hunting is only suitable for the open, and so it usually lives in districts where bushes and rocks abound, inclining to desert country and does not ascend high mountains.

Its method of hunting its prey is, however, like that of the domestic cat. It begins by stalking its intended victim, but does not rely on a short rush at the end, as it can chase the fleetest animal for some distance and capture it by sheer speed. This speed is greater than that of a greyhound and can be maintained for as far as a quarter of a mile.

The cheetah will seldom attack domestic animals, and has never been known to attack men, but it can master other wild life much larger than itself such as the bull kudu, which a pair have been known to pull down. When pleased it will purr exactly like the domestic cat. Smaller members of the cat tribe that are found in Africa are the serval, caracal and the wild cat. The serval ranges over the greater part of the continent from the Cape to the Mediterranean, and has the build of a smaller type of cheetah, except that its ears are larger and its tail shorter. About three and a half feet in length with a tail of about sixteen inches, it is a spotted animal with black markings leading from the eyes to the tall ears, that are shaped rather like those of a lynx. Some specimens have nearly black fur. The fur on the large ears of all is black with a white spot.

The caracal is a red lynx with black ears and a direct link with its European cousin. It frequents the more arid areas of the continent and ranges across Syria and Persia as far as the plains of India.

THE ANCESTOR OF THE KITCHEN CAT

The wild cat has closer fur than its European counterpart, and the typical Egyptian species is believed to be the original ancestor of our domesticated cat. The early Egyptians held their cats in great veneration, and vast numbers of mummified specimens, carefully embalmed, have been discovered at various times; and they appear to have been trained to assist fowlers in catching birds.

Hyenas are almost always looked upon as cowardly. But the African spotted species is far less so than its striped cousin of the northern part of the continent and of India, and is a larger and more graceful creature. The hind-legs of the striped hyena are so much shorter than its forelegs that it results in an ugly lurching movement when on the move. The spotted is a more normal and more venturesome animal, even being liable to attack human beings.

With their reputation as scavengers and their weird uncanny cries, they are heartily disliked both by Europeans and natives. In fact, many of the native peoples associate them with the powers of darkness, and believe that witches take their form at night and prowl round the kraal. The horrid cackling laugh of the hyena would certainly encourage such a belief in primitive minds. The spotted hyena may be as much as six feet in length, but lacks the mane that is so characteristic of the striped variety.

Passing on to the dog tribe, it is to be noted that Africa has no wolves, but their place is taken by jackals, which abound throughout the continent. The largest of these is the Egyptian species and the handsomest the black-backed jackal ranging southwards. This animal is rather larger than the average fox, and near Cape Town it is usually referred to by that name. Like the hyena, jackals have a wailing laugh, though not so loud and long, and utter a cackling sound when attacked.

Africa has its foxes, the Algerian race being very similar to the European kind. A very distinct type found in the region of the Sahara is known as the fennex. It is only fifteen inches in length with a tail of about seven. It is reddish fawn above and white beneath with a black tip to its tail. The long wide ears are reddish brown.

A PACK OF HUNTING-DOGS

The African hunting-dog has a peculiar colouring of tawny orange, white and black in its coat which, with its build, has a distinct

This five-months-old lion cub is devouring his prey—a freshly-killed ground-hog.

This is a black-backed jackal, a fox-like animal with a wailing laugh.

A herd of buffalo keeping their heads above water as they swim across a flooded river.

resemblance to the spotted hyena. This unique animal stands about two feet and is about five feet in length, including the tail. Its range extends from the Cape through East Africa to Somaliland.

These hunting-dogs derive their name from the habit of living in large packs which run down and can kill the largest antelopes. As the leading dogs become exhausted in the chase, those in the rear, having husbanded their strength, come to the front until their prey is spent, and either resigns itself to its end or stands at bay. The leader of the pack will then attack and the rest soon pull down their quarry. These packs are a great menace to the herds of farmers and natives, and also have the greatest contempt for domestic dogs, which they will attack at sight.

Africa has its weasels and polecats—also that interesting little animal, the ratel. Better known as the honey-badger, the species is also represented in India. Ratels feed on honey when it can be obtained and are reputed to follow the birds known as " honey-guides " in their search for that luxury. If they cannot get honey they turn flesh-eaters, feeding in addition on insects and fruit.

Grey above and black beneath, the South African ratel ranges over the greater part of Africa south of Nubia and the Gabun. In the Congo forest there is a completely black

The South African ratel, or honey-badger.

species. The most striking feature of the South African honey-badger is its colouring —light above and dark beneath, reversing the usual type of colouring among mammals.

THE BUFFALO'S HORNS

One of the largest families of African animals is that of the hollow-horned ruminants, consisting very largely of that group commonly known as antelopes. The ox tribe is represented by various forms of buffaloes. The typical Cape buffalo is a huge black beast; the great spreading black horns of the old bulls meet in the middle line of the forehead, forming an enormous helmet-like mass.

Buffaloes more or less resembling this type extend some distance north of the Orange River; but in Uganda and the Lake Albert district the horns become flatter and thinner. The Abyssinian buffalo is tawny or blackish brown in colour, and similar types extend as far north as the valley of the Nile.

On the north side of the Congo Valley there is a small animal, red or yellow in colour, and measuring only forty-two inches in height. Being, unlike other members of the species, a forest animal, spreading horns would be a disadvantage, so Nature has provided this little buffalo with small horns which curve up and out and back to save its being caught in overhanging boughs.

It is believed to be the one animal clever enough to recognise the tread of man by hearing alone.

The great Cape buffalo has always been considered one of the most dangerous big-game animals of Africa, accounting for many a hunter and not a few lions, the latter generally avoiding a direct encounter. The sight of one of these great beasts at close quarters certainly suggests that it must be a formidable foe.

The buffalo, a member of the ox tribe, is a huge black beast with spreading horns.

WILD LIFE OF AFRICA

Nature's Amazing Variety in Animal Life

GIRAFFES are with their cousin, the okapi, the only remaining representatives of a once large family. There are two kinds—the Southern Cape giraffe and the Northern Nubian species.

The two species are quite distinct in colour. The Nubian has white lines on a chestnut ground with the lower part of the legs white, and carries a horn in its forehead; while the Southern has chocolate blotches on a buff ground with tawny legs spotted to the fetlocks and no third horn.

These are broad definitions, because there are several local varieties whose colouring varies with the district—obviously another brilliant example of Nature's camouflage. For instance, the Somali giraffe harmonises with the bush jungle which forms its background, the Southern giraffe becomes almost invisible in the chequered shade of its favourite mimosa trees, and even blends with the actual trunks. The paler colouring of the Northern giraffe makes it little more than a shadow against the sandy tint and white shimmer of the Nubian desert; while the Baringo race harmonises with the darker and fuller colouring of a tropical East African forest.

Giraffes depend mainly upon sight and hearing to warn them of danger, and their great height enables them to overlook a wide extent of country.

"ONE WHO WALKS SWIFTLY"

When running, the giraffe moves the fore and hind leg on the same side together, which gives it a rolling motion like a ship at sea; while the long neck sways from side to side and the tapering, tufted tail is carried bent forwards over its back. Walking, the giraffe is one of the most graceful animals, and its name actually means " one who walks swiftly."

The animal's only means of defence appears to be kicking with the forelegs; although in captivity it will sometimes deliver a swinging blow with its horns, which, although blunt and short, are formidable weapons with the weight of the long neck behind them. Possibly this method is a throw-back to their far distant ancestors when giraffes actually had antlers like the stag.

Although this animal can go without water, at any rate for a very long time, it does occasionally drink but very awkwardly, as to reach sufficiently low down it has to straddle its legs and stretch its head forward. This ability to live without water for long periods has doubtless preserved the giraffe on many occasions from man and its only real enemy among other animals—the lion.

In any case it would usually require more

The giraffe is the tallest of all living animals. His markings render him almost invisible among the trees.

than one lion to pull down a giraffe, whose average height, in the case of the bull, is eighteen feet, while the female's growth is fifteen to sixteen. The babies are very small at birth and are complete miniatures of the parent, being able to trot with their mother three days after birth.

The tender leaves on the crown of trees are the favourite food of the giraffe, and it gathers these with its long, black, almost finger-like tongue, which it uses much as the elephant uses the tip of its trunk.

Until recent times naturalists believed the giraffe was an entirely silent animal and that it never lay down. But they were wrong. Although seldom heard, it is true, the giraffe sometimes voices a low bleating call, and it will lie down quite frequently, stretching out its long neck along the ground to rest it. Despite the great length of this neck, it is a curious fact that it has exactly the same number of bones as the average animal.

Giraffes were formerly killed in large numbers by African hunters not for their flesh, which is very unpleasant, but for their hides, which served to make shields, and for the hair of their tails.

THE MINIATURE MOUSE DEER

The only deer found in Africa is a small race of the red-deer called Barbary deer, akin to the Corsican stag and, as one would suppose, haunting the strip of forest country between the Mediterranean coast on the frontiers of Algeria and Tunis down to the Sahara.

For the rest of the continent, the miniature mouse deer alone represents this family. Commonly called the water-chevrotain, its range extends across the forest zone from the west coast to the Ituri forest in the east, where it is represented by a separate race.

It is only thirteen or fourteen inches high at the shoulder and is olive grey in colour, spotted and streaked with white or yellow, the throat and chest having a number of broad white streaks extending from side to side with a dart of the same colour on the cheek and nose.

A procession of giraffes in Kenya in the Ngong hills. The giraffe is such a mild-mannered beast that it is generally safe to approach it. Should it wish to defend itself, however, it kicks out with the most tremendous force inflicting crippling blows to its attacker.

They live on the banks of rivers in Equatorial Africa and are great swimmers and divers. Like the okapi, this little animal comes of a very ancient family and its only other relatives live in Asia.

RIVER HOGS

The river hogs are a widely scattered group. There are some in Ethiopian Africa, and a smaller variety in Madagascar. Long tufts of hair grow from the tips of the ears, and the animal has a wide range with several local races differing a good deal in colour. A special characteristic is the great development of the ridges on the skull of full-grown boars, the upper pair projecting as crests above the line of the face. The southern or Cape race is greyish yellow in colour; but in the Lake Mweru district and Nyasaland there is a reddish race. The boars stand about thirty inches at the shoulder.

The most remarkable member of the race is the red river hog of West Africa. It is generally considered the dandy of the family, having greatly developed ear tufts and being bright reddish brown in colour with a black face and white spectacle-like rings round the eyes. These brightly-coloured swine associate in large groups throughout well-wooded districts on the banks of rivers.

One of Nature's nightmares is the forest hog of the Equatorial forests of Mount Kenya and the Nandi district near Lake Victoria. It is a huge, coal-black pig having a coat of long black hair. On the face of the old boars are a pair of huge flattened warty growths below the eyes that look just like the large fungi that grow on decaying tree-trunks. It is the largest member of this ugly family and ranges between the dark depths of the Ituri forest and the Cameroons.

THE HIDEOUS WART HOG

Hardly less hideous are those rather terrifying-looking creatures, the wart hogs, unique in the most extraordinary shape of their heads and their violently curved tusks. The huge head looks almost too big for the body, with its ungainly muzzle and the unsightly warts below the eyes, together with smaller ones just above the great curved tusks. These tusks curve both upwards and inwards, and can grow to a length of over two feet. Unlike the

This ugly animal is the river hog. Note the long tufts of hair growing from the tips of the ears and the high ridge on the forehead.

tusks of ordinary wild swine, the upper ones are much longer than the lower pair.

The animal is found south of the Zambezi. Its black hide is bare but for a growth of reddish hair surmounting the head between the ears and extending along the nape of the neck. Like most swine, they lurk in thickets and ravines during the day, coming into the open at dusk to feed. They associate in herds of from eight to ten in number, the old males living alone. Their tusks are used for digging up roots of which they are very fond, and also for defence. They are excitable but not usually courageous. If really hard-pressed they will, however, turn with tail erect and inflict severe wounds on their attackers with their terrible tusks.

They generally occupy the deserted borrows of ant-bears or other animals, and will bound out in a kind of somersault, frequently surprising the hunter in doing so and knocking him over.

THE RIVER HORSE

Hippopotamus is the ancient Greek word for river horse, but why the ancient Greeks should have so named it is puzzling. It is a very swift swimmer and much faster on land than its appearance in a zoo would suggest. Possibly this is the reason, but it is quite unlike a horse.

Ugly and unwieldy though the river horse is,

Wart hogs coming down to drink at an African stream. These ungainly animals with their huge, in-curving tusks generally lie low during the day and feed in the evening. Though not brave, they can inflict terrible wounds with their tusks.

it is one of the most remarkable of hoofed animals and the largest after the elephant and rhinoceros.

It is actually more nearly related to the pig than to any other existing animal and, as its uncouth appearance would suggest, comes of a very ancient family. In those far-off prehistoric days its distribution was very wide indeed, fossil specimens having been found as far north as our own island.

Gorgops, as these prehistoric hippopotami are known to science, had the bony sockets for their eyes high above the top of the skull —in fact, periscopic eyes. Such eyes with the fleshy extension of their nostrils would have enabled them to come to the surface of the water, showing only four minute points—the tips of the nostrils and their eyes alone being visible.

Our modern hippo often shows little more and can submerge for quite considerable periods, so that these huge animals can remain almost invisible when there is danger about.

About twelve feet long in the case of the males, with a height of six feet at the shoulder, the hippopotamus weighs on an average about four tons. The lower tusks will weigh as much as fifteen pounds. The male expresses satisfaction with a grunt and anger with a sharp bark, or bellow, like a bull—at a distance this bellow can be confused with the roar of a lion.

Though the animal haunts rivers and lakes, it can travel overland as far as twenty or thirty miles to reach the food of its choice. It has been known also to swim out to sea from one river mouth to another, and this would probably account for its one-time appearance in the island of Madagascar.

It is naturally timid of man, but can on occasion be savage—especially in defence of its young. The babies take five years to grow up, and their favourite method of travelling is on mother's back. There is generally only one baby at a time and the mother displays great affection for her offspring.

It is only because previous to the coming of the white man, the African's weapons were primitive, that the hippopotamus has survived at all. For its flesh is good to eat; its abundant fat was of the greatest value to the natives both for cooking and embrocation; the hide, which is fully an inch thick, provides the sjamboks or hide whips notorious in the history of Africa, shields and even walking sticks that have the strength and flexibility of a cane; while their tusks are almost as good as ivory for ornamental and other purposes.

Dr. Livingstone described the regular channel ploughed through the dense vegetation on river banks by the hippopotamus in its passage to favourite grazing grounds; and also how it travelled purely by scent so that if rain came on, the great creature would be unable to find its way back and would stand helplessly lost.

In his day the rivers of Central Africa were literally crowded with the hippopotami, and crossing these rivers in native canoes was indeed a passage perilous, as these animals frequently rose under the boats, tipping the travellers into the water and, in some cases, even crunching the frail dugouts in their massive jaws.

Although the hippopotamus was well known in the circus to the Romans, it was unknown in Europe after the fall of their empire; and indeed one was not seen in any zoo until one was brought to Regent's Park about seventy-five years ago. The hippopotamus is the " behemoth " of the Bible and was probably the original of the so-called " water elephant " that appears on ancient Indian sculptures.

THE PYGMY HIPPO

There is only one other living species of the hippopotamus and that is the pygmy animal of Western Africa. This creature is about the size of a large pig, and similar in general appearance to the big type, excepting that its muzzle is not so large. Its colouring is quite different, being of a green tint shading to yellow below. Its actual size is about six feet in length and thirty inches at the shoulder, its legs being longer and more slender and its eyes do not protrude like those of its large cousin. Moreover, it has quite a long tail.

The pygmy hippopotamus is a solitary wanderer, only meeting its fellows at night at some favourite mud-hole. It delves out for itself a perfect labyrinth of tunnels in the banks of streams and runs through the dense bush, sleeping through the heat of the day in some hollow that it enlarges for itself under the overhanging bank of a stream.

HOW THE CROCODILE CATCHES ITS PREY

The so-called Nile crocodile is no longer found northward of Thebes, but it is also an inhabitant of the rivers of East and South Africa and Madagascar. In Western Africa, wherever there is a river, and in the rain forests, wherever there is a swamp, will be found these great aquatic reptiles. Travellers along such rivers as the Zambezi can see them lying like so many logs of wood on mud-flats and under the shelter of the jungle-clad banks.

It is generally supposed that crocodiles are awkward on land, but like the hippopotamus they can move easily overland, and their movements are like those of a lizard. Also, cumbersome as they may appear in captivity, they can, when necessary, move with surprising agility. It is true that they can remain completely still for hours and feign the appearance of a lifeless object, but directly their prey appears they rouse in a second and can act with amazing rapidity. Many will lie together on the mud-flats attended by a crowd of plover-like birds which hop over the monsters quite fearlessly, picking leeches from their armoured backs.

Under the water the crocodile will also lie motionless, with only the tip of its snout showing, but all the time it is watching for its prey. An antelope trots delicately from the edge of the jungle to the water's edge to drink. The crocodile's snout looks like a stone or a lump of mud, so the antelope stoops to drink. Noiselessly the crocodile edges nearer under water, then with a sudden rush and a sweep of its mighty tail the luckless antelope is knocked senseless into the water and seized in the powerful jaws.

The crocodile's diet is very varied, for it includes cattle, sheep, all kinds of wild animals,

A crocodile basking in the sunshine near its river haunt. This ferocious creature is the terror of African rivers and swamps, for its huge jaws and razor-like teeth can tear its prey to shreds.

A rare photograph of a pygmy hippopotamus. Though small, it is a fierce animal and a huge eater. It sleeps by day and hunts by night.

The shoebill stork, a giant bird of the White Nile, related to the herons and about five feet in height. Note the shape of its large bill.

Confident that there is no danger at hand to disturb them, this group of hippopotami graze
on the banks of an African river, and wallow at ease in the warm water.

birds, fish and lastly any human beings that may be caught unawares.

THE CROCODILES' NURSERIES

Crocodiles come on land, also, for making their nests in holes in the sand. The mother scoops out a fairly deep hole, and in it lays her large white eggs which are similar to those of a goose. She completely covers them with sand and keeps careful watch over them, never going far away, and spending most of her time basking there in the sun. In about three months the babies break through their shells with a special " egg tooth," making, as they do so, curious little sounds that are very like " hiccoughs." The crocodile is a good mother and shows more affection for her young than most reptiles.

The colouring of crocodiles is usually dark olive and their size averages fifteen feet in the females to about eighteen in the case of the males. Size depends to a large extent on age, for these reptiles continue to grow so long as they live. As their rather fossilised appearance would suggest, these great creatures are long-lived—forty years being quite normal with a length, say, of about twelve feet, so that those of eighteen and occasionally twenty feet may have attained to the full span of a man's life.

The ancient Egyptians worshipped the crocodile as the symbol of sunrise, though the reason is uncertain, unless it was on account of the brightness of its eye, which is the first part of its body to be seen when it emerges from the water.

The hippo has an enormous mouth with large curving tusks. He is a vegetarian, using his mouth as a scoop.

WILD LIFE OF AFRICA

Meeting the Elephants and Monkeys

LARGEST of living four-footed animals, the elephant has a most interesting history, having increased instead of diminished in size through the ages. In prehistoric days it had quite a short trunk and stood only about three feet in height—the opposite, in fact, to some reptiles that are now reduced to the size of lizards from the original giants that roamed a manless world. Even the mammoth that in our young days was thought of as a monster was, in reality, rather smaller than the hairless African elephant.

It is considered by most naturalists that the elephant has the biggest brain of all animals, not excepting the dog.

The African elephant is larger than its Asiatic cousin with far larger ears and tusks. Tusks measuring eleven feet in length are known, while the animal itself stands, on an average, eleven to twelve feet at the shoulder, with an ear measurement of six feet.

The smallest member of the modern family is the Congo dwarf species, standing only seven to eight feet in height.

The eyesight of elephants is poor but their

Part of a herd of elephants at a watering hole in a forest clearing.

The elephant is not only the largest animal, but has the biggest brain of all animals.

sense of smell is acute, and the scent of even a child is sufficient to stampede a herd.

Owing to the slaughter by hunters in the past and ivory poachers to-day, only the game reserves can save this great animal from eventual extinction.

Africa has a large and interesting monkey population, from the grim gorilla of the Equatorial regions to the attractive little vervet with its black velvety face and mischievous habits.

The gorilla is the largest member of the family—a specimen measuring seven feet in height having once been shot in the Congo area.

They live and travel in families, father making a nest for his wife and children in the fork of a tree for the night, while he himself sits at the base keeping guard against prowling leopards.

The West African mandrill is the ugliest and the fiercest member of the baboon family.

Baboons are probably the most intelligent of monkeys and they travel about in family groups.

The gorilla is the largest member of the monkey family. He likes to walk upright, but is more at home in a tree.

There is no knowing what mischief chimps will get into. The keeper has a busy time with these scamps.

They avoid human beings if possible; but will fight fiercely if cornered and can travel up in the forests from branch to branch of the trees like smaller monkeys.

Next in size come the curiously human chimpanzees so familiar in zoos and circuses.

Almost as large and far more formidable are the baboons with their massive mastiff-like jaws. They are probably the most intelligent of the animals in the bush country and also travel in families. Old man mandrill is the ugliest and fiercest of the baboon family. It is a West African monkey, which is sometimes seen in zoos, and is chiefly remarkable for its hideous bright scarlet and sky-blue ribbed face.

Guenon, guereza, green and kindred species follow. Tree-dwelling and lighter in build, they are often attractive both in colour and movement.

SOME MONKEYS
TO DRAW

Can you draw animals? The artist who drew you these monkeys is a famous animal artist.
Try to copy these delightful sketches, following the lines very carefully.

WILD LIFE OF AFRICA

Nature's Clever Camouflage

THE great plains of southern and eastern Africa were originally a paradise for antelopes, and here vast herds used to roam at will. Of these the largest was the eland that abounded in southern, eastern and central Africa, from Angola to the tributaries of the Nile. But now it is rare, except in the eastern Transvaal, Zululand, Rhodesia, Nyasaland and East Africa.

It is also a heavy animal differing from its nearest relatives, with the exception of the bongo, through the fact of both sexes bearing horns. The horns are spiral, with a few turns inclining outwards and backwards, the female's horns being the larger and more slender. Old bulls have a thick mass of hair on the forehead, which in the southern species is chocolate brown in colour.

The colouring varies with the locality, the southern species being a pale reddish-fawn or bluish-grey, the bluish tinge increasing with age as the coat grows thin. But the eland of the Zambezi district have a dark line down the back, vertical white stripes down the sides of the body and a dark garter on the inside and back of the forelegs just above the knees.

The eland is the largest of the antelopes which now roam the plains of eastern Africa.

This race was first found by Dr. Livingstone, the explorer, and is named after him.

Farther north, these striped eland develop two oblique white lines on the face below the eyes. The markings of these animals once again demonstrate Nature's camouflage; for the southern species frequent open plains, while the striped variety have a wooded or forest background, where the vivid splashes of white blend with the shafts of sunlight falling through the trees.

These fine antelopes stand about five to five and a half feet at the withers, and the length of the head and body is about ten feet. The tail being another yard. The horns average two to two and a half feet. The largest type frequents the Equatorial region and the Egyptian Sudan. Its markings are more conspicuous and its horns larger.

THE BONGO DIGS WITH ITS HORNS

Known to the natives of the west coast as the bongo, is another fine antelope, both sexes of which again bear horns. It is an animal considerably larger than a red deer and approaches the eland in bulk. The horns of the bulls are very massive and have a wider and less screw-like spiral than the eland, being distinguished also by their yellow tips. This colouring at the tip is due to the bongo rubbing its horns against tree-trunks, and using them for digging in the ground so that the outer coat wears off.

It is a strikingly beautiful animal, its somewhat silky coat being warm orange-red, traversed by a number of narrow, vertical white stripes over the neck and body, together with a chevron and other white markings on the head.

Another special feature of the bongo is the large size of the spreading ears, showing that it is a forest-dweller; for large ears are necessary to forest animals to enable them to catch the slightest sound of movements which may be otherwise interrupted by the trunks and branches of trees. Its colouring, too, serves to save it from prying eyes, as its broken nature

The kudu bull has corkscrew horns which are sometimes over five feet in length and can easily be seen at a distance.

blends perfectly with the occasional splashes of light that occur in the deeper forest.

Bongos dwelling in the mountain forests of both West and East Africa are practically nocturnal animals, and have a keen sense of hearing and of smell, so that it is extremely rare for anyone to encounter them.

They feed mainly on leaves and bark, and will rear themselves on their hind-legs against the trunks of trees to obtain the more succulent foliage higher up. Small trees are also uprooted with the aid of their horns, and the roots eaten. The red salt earth, so common in Africa, also forms a part of their diet, and also the charred ashes where trees have been burnt.

These dwellers in almost permanent darkness travel in small family parties, with their horns bent back so as to protect their bodies as much as possible from injury. Obstacles are pushed aside by sheer bodily weight, while the heavier boughs, too stout to be thrust aside, are crept under. It is astonishing how small a space they can contrive to creep through.

The kudu is certainly one of the handsomest of the largest antelopes and ranges from Cape Province, through Bechuanaland, into Angola. It is also to be found in the Transvaal, Rhodesia, Nyasaland, East Africa, Somaliland and Abyssinia.

A kudu bull can be seen at some distance,

owing to its long corkscrew horns over five feet in length. The body alone is about five feet in height and eight feet in length without the tail, which adds another twenty inches. In colour the females and young males are reddish- or greyish-brown, with eight or nine vertical white stripes. But the old males are bluish-grey.

The kudu frequents thickly wooded, hilly country and the thickets bordering the banks of rivers. They are also found in thorn jungle at the edge of the Kalahari Desert. They graze in pairs or small companies. They are not very swift and, when disturbed, still show no great rapidity of movement. The kudu of Somaliland has fewer stripes and, although in southern Africa a water-loving animal on the whole, it can exist for long periods in this and other desert country on aloes.

Another handsome group of antelopes comprises the bushbucks, together with their larger relatives, the nyala, mountain nyala and situtunga.

ANIMALS WHICH SEEM TO BE IN HARNESS

These larger species are often known as harness antelopes. The colourings in the two sexes are frequently different. The males are often dull grey-brown, while the females are extremely brilliant, having on a dark ground, pale stripes and spots so arranged that these peculiar markings suggest the animals are in harness.

One of the three larger members of the group is the inyala ranging from Zululand northwards of the Zambezi as far as the Shiré. Standing about three feet high, the bucks have straight horns two feet in length. The long coat of the males is greyish-brown in colour, marked with a few faint white lines, while that of the does is mahogany-red, with numerous and distinct stripes.

The situtunga differs from the preceding species by the great elongation of the hoofs, adapting it to a half-aquatic life among the papyrus-swamps on the borders of the great lakes and rivers of the Equatorial districts.

Situtungas stand three and a half feet at the shoulder, and the spiral horns of the males measure about thirty inches. These animals pass nearly all their lives in the water of papyrus-swamps and reed-brakes. They swim

Nature sometimes plays some odd and amusing tricks. Here is the harness antelope, so called because its spots and stripes are arranged in such a way that the animal appears to be in harness.

and dive with great ease, and when hunted can keep under water, showing only their muzzles, using, in fact, the principle of the " snort."

Bushbucks only move about at night and keep to woodland areas. They are small, averaging the size of a goat and have a wide distribution from the Cape to Ethiopia. The colour varies according to locality from bright red with numerous white spots to uniform brown.

The oryx is a medium-sized desert antelope. Both male and female carry long, straight or scimitar-shaped horns; their long tails tend to be bushy in the lower half and their necks are maned. Generally the body colour is some shade of fawn with blackish markings, but in the case of the North African oryx the ground colour is whitish with chestnut patches.

In South Africa the group is called the gemsbuck and is fairly numerous in the Kalahari and especially in Damaraland, ranging northwards in desert country as far as Angola.

The long straight horns are ringed about half up their length, and the white face has three black streaks, two of which pass through

These gemsbuck, hardy dwellers in the desert, have long straight horns, and dig out their food with their hoofs. They get their liquid refreshment mainly from water-melons and bulbs.

the eyes, all three stopping short above the muzzle, where they are connected by a transverse band that results in the appearance of a headstall. Another dark stripe runs down the middle of the throat, and develops into a tuft on the chest, thence dividing and continuing on each flank, so that it separates the fawn of the back from the white of the under-parts.

A male gemsbuck stands about four feet at the shoulder, with an overall length, including the tail, of some twelve feet. Their horns are about a yard in length and sometimes reach four feet.

This branch of the family is essentially desert-dwelling and appears to be mainly independent of water, obtaining such liquid as they need in the Kalahari from water-melons and bulbs, the latter of which they dig out with their hoofs.

A RELATIVE OF THE UNICORN?

The proportions of the oryx being somewhat like those of a horse, it has been suggested that the legendary unicorn originated from this animal.

Probably as a protection against the long, sharp horns, Nature has provided the male with a very thick hide on its shoulders. The Somalis use this hide for making their war-shields, as the Zulu used to make his from the Cape buffalo. The pointed triangular shape of the hoof in this antelope is typical of desert-haunting species, in contrast to the rounder feet of forest animals.

The chief foes of the oryx are man and the lion. But even the lion is frequently worsted by this intrepid fighter.

Although it belongs to the same group of antelope as the oryx, the sable is a type by itself and is generally considered more handsome. It is of an imposing size, being as big as the average full-grown pony, and it has a gallant and showy carriage. Altogether it is a very striking animal.

The female is almost as big as the buck, but she tends to brown rather than black in her colouring. Her horns, too, are more slender and not so long, the males' horns being usually quite a yard in length. The young sable is light brown in colour.

This graceful creature, with its strange, pointed horns is an impala buck (rooibok).

The bongo, a rare and very shy antelope, has long ears which detect the slightest sound. Its markings blend perfectly with the trees.

Above, locusts and larvæ of North Africa. *Below*, a fat-tailed sheep of South Africa.

The sable is as courageous as it is handsome and is very quick with its horns, though its speed is not as great as many less showy and slighter antelopes.

The only existing near relative of the sable is the roan antelope. Although larger, it is by no means as handsome as the sable; for its horns, though massive, are shorter, and the colour of its coat is not so attractive as its relative's rich purply-brown, with its noble head picked out with the striking black-and-white markings. For courage, however, it is second to none among antelopes, and it will turn and charge when wounded or chased too closely.

A MINIATURE GIRAFFE

A remarkable species from north-eastern Africa is the gerenuk, which is to be found—though not frequently—from Somaliland to Portuguese East Africa. It is a gazelle-like antelope, with a neck so long that it is likened to a miniature giraffe.

It has also curious horns in the shape of a long reversed " S." These horns curve forwards, upwards, backwards and then forwards again rather like a hook. The female has no horns. The general colouring is a rufous cinnamon, with a broad band of darker red along the middle of the back.

The leaves of trees and bushes form the gerenuk's principal food, and when browsing on trees it will stand on its hind-legs with its forefeet against the trunk; then the giraffe-like neck enables it to reach the foliage. These quaint animals were apparently known to the ancient Egyptians, as incised drawings of them have been found on slabs in the Nile valley.

Characteristic of the open plains of southern and eastern Africa is the medium-sized antelope, fox-red in colour, called the impala. This species is found in Bechuanaland, the Transvaal, Zululand, Rhodesia, Nyasaland and British East Africa as far as the Nile.

They are always found close to water, generally on river banks. Females and young form separate herds of their own. When alarmed these animals whistle, but in the mating season utter as well a hoarse guttural bark. Their leaping powers are remarkable, as they can clear as much as seventy feet in three bounds.

Nature has the power of providing an infinity of varied markings among her wild creatures. Here is a herd of Thompson's gazelles, with their long horns and distinctive colourings.

WILD LIFE OF AFRICA

Speed, Grace and Beauty—the Antelopes

THE most graceful form of the antelope race is generally considered to be the gazelle. Of these undoubtedly the most notable is the springbok of South Africa. Rich in its colouring and peculiar in its habits, it is familiar to all as the commonest of South African antelopes, and has become a household word especially in this country, so that the well-known South African touring football team has adopted its name.

A most noticeable point about the springbok is the peculiar fold of skin along the rear part of the back, which is lined with white hairs five or six inches long. When excited, the animal expands this fold, making a striking display of a great white fan of fur, as it does so springing perpendicularly into the air as high as three or four yards and repeating the action over and over again. This is known by Africaners as " pronking " and, of course, has always drawn special attention to this attractive animal.

As in the case of most gazelles, the springbok is a dainty creature about the size of a goat. The buck's curved horns are about fifteen inches in length; the doe's are not so large. The young are at first yellowish-grey with indistinct stripes on their sides.

The springbok ranges all over Africa south of the Zambezi, and so naturally became the symbol of the Union. It still treks at times in large herds, but the countless thousands which were the wonder of travellers little more than half a century ago cannot be seen to-day.

The vast treks of the past were due to the springbok being forced to desert those tracts of country where they had already devoured all subsistence. As they advanced to fresh pastures, these enormous herds would devour the vegetation like a swarm of locusts, and so countless were their numbers that those in the rear always remained in a famished condition.

WHEN LIONS WERE TRAMPLED TO DEATH

It is even said that lions would be carried away in these great movements, being unable to stem the flood of creatures that surrounded them. Sometimes when caught in narrow passes by one of these great " trek-bokken," there was no escape and they would be trampled to death. Probably no animal of its size has ever been so abundant; but what was once so over-plentiful that it was a pest is now protected by law lest it should be completely destroyed. For swiftness it beats the greyhound and will fight the hounds if it is overtaken in the chase.

To return to the antelopes, we come to the reedbuck, ranging eastwards from Rhodesia to Portuguese East Africa and southwards through Rhodesia, the Transvaal and Natal to the south-east of Cape Colony.

Reddish in colour, the reedbuck stands about three feet at the shoulder with horns about a foot in length. As their name would suggest, they are found in grassy or reedy valleys generally in pairs or small parties.

The graceful springbok is well known as the symbol of the Union of South Africa.

A group of waterbuck drinking. One of the largest and probably the handsomest of the antelope family, it lives on steep hillsides always near to water, and stands about four feet high at the shoulder. The males use their long horns as weapons of defence and attack.

Hornless female waterbucks, ears pricked ready for hasty retreat at the slightest alarm. In the herd it is the females who keep watch, but the males tackle intruders with their horns.

A much smaller species is the mountain reed-buck of eastern Africa south of the Zambezi. and a third is the Bohor reedbuck, distinguished by a forward curve of the horns rendering them hook-shaped.

THE FEMALES GUARD THE HERD

One of the largest and most handsome species is the waterbuck. Carrying heavily-ringed horns slightly lyre-shaped and some three feet in length, it stands over four feet at the shoulder. This handsome animal extends across the continent from South-West to East Africa and northwards to Somaliland, and southwards on the same coast as far as Zululand and the eastern Transvaal.

As its name implies, it is seldom found far from water and generally haunts steep, stony hillsides in small herds with the females keeping watch, their ears in constant movement and their eyes always on the alert. When wounded, the waterbuck charges with its horns at the ready, being no mean adversary. The females are, however, hornless.

There are a number of antelopes of this family known generally as kobs, but one may be singled out for particular notice, as the habits of the remainder are similar to those of the waterbuck. This antelope is known as the lechwi, and is a swamp-dwelling antelope. Inhabiting Zambezia and Basutoland, it may be recognised by its long and slender horns and black-fronted legs. These animals spend long hours standing up to their necks in water. However deeply they have waded in, they will always move through the water by leaps, accompanied by great splashing, instead of swimming.

Undoubtedly one of the most attractive of the smaller antelopes is the mountain-dwelling animal called by the early Boer settlers the klipspringer or rock-jumper. It is a little gold-spangled creature that springs from rock to rock and crag to crag as though it had joints made of wire and hoofs of india-rubber. It ranges from the Cape to Abyssinia, and stands less than two feet in height, its horns being only three to five inches in length. Its ears are very large for its size. The gold-spangled coat is of short, stiff hair and it has short, blunt hoofs, upon the tips of which it stands.

Klipspringers can climb very steep cliffs, and are always found on rocky ground, mostly in hilly or mountainous areas, but occasionally in river valleys. They move in small parties, feed on grasses and mountain plants and only leave their rocky haunts at night to drink.

AN ANTELOPE AS SMALL AS A HARE

Another tiny antelope is the dikdik, a little creature widely distributed over East and North-East Africa. It is about the size of a hare, with a long nose almost like the trunk of a tapir in form, and has a tuft of hair on the crown of its head and a very short tail. They are only rarely seen in captivity.

The duikerboks were first named by the Boers on account of their habit when surprised of " diving " for cover, for duiker means diver in the Dutch language. They have small straight horns usually in both sexes. Ranging from Cape Colony to Angola on the west, and Somaliland and Abyssinia on the east, they are a little under two feet in height, having straight, slender horns about five inches in length. They are more frequently met with near the coast than inland, and, when pursued, leap high as if to see above the bushes in which they are accustomed to shelter. They scarcely ever drink.

The red duiker has even shorter horns of about three inches in length, and is about seventeen inches high. It haunts forests, living in the vicinity of water, and only comes into the open in wet weather or at the close of day. Its cry is like a whistle, and it sniffs as it runs. This little animal's range is through Zululand, Natal, the Transvaal, Swaziland and along the east coast as far as Zanzibar.

The smallest of South African antelopes is the blue duiker, which is only fourteen inches in height. Its two-inch horns hardly show above the tuft of hair on its head. It is met with in the woods of the east coast of Cape Colony and in Natal and Zululand.

The last group of antelopes includes the weird wildebeest and hartebeest. The term antelope pictures for us a dainty, attractive animal; but there is nothing dainty or attractive about the gnus, or wildebeests, as they are called in Africa. The wildebeest at first sight appears to be a cross between a bull and a pony and is about the size of a large specimen of the latter. The white-tailed gnu or black wildebeest once extended from the Vaal river

The duiker is one of the smallest antelopes to be found in Africa. They were named duikers, because they duck or dive for shelter when alarmed.

to the south of Cape Province, but, with the exception of a few possible survivors in the Kalahari Desert, is now practically extinct.

It had a broad, ugly head and down-curving horns, the body sloped from the shoulders to the hindquarters, the mane was upright and the white tail was horse-like in appearance.

THE ANIMAL WHICH KNEELS TO FEED

Both sexes carried horns which had broad, thick bases, curving downwards and forwards and then upwards. These antelopes kept to the open plains near water, and had a habit of kneeling while they fed. When excited all wildebeests prance and leap in a curious manner, chasing one another round and indulging in other strange caperings as if they were mad.

Their name of gnu is a Hottentot one derived from the animal's call, which is a snort sounding very like " gnu."

The second member of the family is the brindled gnu or blue wildebeest. This is a larger animal and has a range extending from the Orange Free State into South-East Africa, Portuguese East Africa, and through Rhodesia. It is heavier in build and clumsier in its movements than the white-tailed species, but its habits are much the same. The horse-like tail is frequently over three feet long, and it stands four feet at the shoulder, and the horns in the case of the bulls are nearly three feet along the curve. The colouring of the blue wildebeest is dark bluish-grey with vertical dark stripes. The horns are curved rather like those of a buffalo and the tail is dark.

AN ANIMAL RECENTLY DISCOVERED

A unique animal of comparatively recent discovery is the okapi. First found by Sir Harry Johnstone, when Governor of Uganda, in the early part of this century, few specimens have been seen in their wild state, except by

The Buffon's kob is another type of antelope.
It takes its name from the great natural history
expert Buffon.

those curious little people, the pygmies of the
Ituri Forest, and their habits are still something of a mystery. Its general form gives us
a good idea of what the giraffe's ancestors
were probably like, and it is the only other
living member of the giraffe family.

The teeth and cloven hoofs of the okapi

are similar to those of the giraffe. Its horns
are, however, different. For one thing, only
the male has them, while both male and female
giraffes carry horns. The okapi's horns are
short, covered with hair and tipped with bone,
rather like the beginning of a deer's antlers. In
the colouring of its coat, so gay and strikingly
marked, the okapi is completely different
from its relative the giraffe and, indeed, from
any other animal.

The markings at the bottom of the limbs
and on the hind-quarters bear a striking
resemblance to those of the zebra, and, as
portions of the hide from this part of the
animal were the first to be brought to white
men by the pygmies, naturalists at first classed
it as a new kind of zebra. In size the okapi
is about the build of a large donkey.

Happening upon some pygmies from the
Ituri Forest, Sir Harry questioned them about
the strange beast that apparently lived in their
dense jungle homeland, and was told by them
that it was like a mule with zebra's stripes. It
seems to be confined to the Semliki Forest in
the Belgian Congo and appears to be purely
a forest animal, though larger than most
forest-haunting creatures. Like other forest
animals, it has large ears and is very wary and
quick of hearing.

Only a pair with young are found together,

A herd of brindled gnus come down for an evening drink in an African stream. This type is
the largest of the gnus, and is also known as the blue wildebeest. It has an ox-like head and
horns and a tail like that of a horse. The gnu leaps about in a queer manner when excited.

The strange okapi is the only other living
member of the giraffe family.

A baby camel from the desert lands in the
northern part of Africa.

Father takes charge. The male ostrich is
taking his turn to sit on the eggs.

A marabou stork. These ungainly birds have
long fierce beaks and vulture-like heads.

A flock of flamingos in Egypt. The flamingo has a beak that curves downwards; thus when
thrusting his head along the bottom of the river bed he can pick up his food.

A herd of lechwi antelopes are seen here in full flight across a jungle swamp. They always go by leaps and bounds, even when in deep water.

and they travel as most jungle animals in single file, the female leading the way. But it is the male that keeps watch when the family is feeding. The prevailing colour of the forehead, ears, neck and the whole of the body, except a part of the hind-quarters, is purplish-brown. The sides of the face are pale pink or fawn and the forehead and ears dark rufous, while the muzzle is black. The hind-quarters and the limbs as far down as the knees and hocks are barred with broad black and narrow white stripes of irregular pattern. Below the knees and hocks the limbs, with the exception of a black banded ring round each pastern and a black stripe down the front of each foreleg, are white, giving the effect at a distance of black bangles. It is a shy and harmless creature that lows like a cow.

So shy is it and so secluded in the dense Congo jungles that, as before stated, it has been very seldom seen by Europeans in its wild state. It has been established, however, largely through the reports of native hunters, that small streams with some swampy ground are necessary to the okapi. In these swampy areas a certain large leaf grows on a single stalk to a height of ten feet, and it is the young leaves of this plant that are the favourite food of the animal. Indeed, it has been said that this plant is essential to the well-being of the okapi.

During the night it wanders along in the mud and water in search of this plant. With its peculiar colouring, this strange animal mingles with the shadows, and is hardly to be seen among the vegetation.

WILD LIFE OF AFRICA

Some Queer Creatures of the Wilds

ONE of the enemies of the crocodile is the big North African lizard generally known as the iguana, but called by naturalists the Egyptian monitor. They average five to seven feet in length, and have a sharp keel along the upper side of the tail, being dark brown in colour with mottled, light olive green or yellowish spots.

When walking, these giant lizards straddle their legs and turn their long necks and heads from side to side, frequently darting out their long forked tongues with great rapidity. They are fast on land but still faster in the water, being able to remain submerged for long periods without breathing.

They feed on fish and their spawn, frogs, water beetles, dragon-flies and other insects, as well as birds and small mammals; but they have an especial liking for the eggs and young of crocodiles.

The lizard's method of eating eggs is to take them in its mouth, raise its head and, cracking the shell with its teeth, allow the contents to run down its throat. Their own eggs are soft-shelled and often laid in the nests of white ants.

A quaint little climbing lizard that, at the other end of the scale, only attains a length of six inches is the wall-gecko. It is grey or brownish-black in colour, marked with obscure dark spots, and is also found in southern Europe. It is usually seen at night looking for its food on walls and ceilings, to which it sticks by the sucker-like discs at the tips of its toes.

There is a remarkable group of lizards that live in trees and are known as chameleons. Several of these quaint little creatures are miniature copies of giant prehistoric reptiles —the horned chameleon of Central Africa in particular. On a giant scale it would have a terrifying appearance, and with a little imagination one can appreciate how sinister the man-less world of prehistoric days must have been. A curious fact is that these formidable-looking horns do not seem to have any offensive or defensive purpose, and naturalists are still puzzled as to their use.

A CREATURE WHO CHANGES COLOUR

The common chameleon may change colour half a dozen times in twenty-four hours. In the night cream-coloured with yellow patches, it becomes in the daylight grey-green with some pale brown patches. If it is excited, it develops maroon brown patches and golden spots, and when very angry the yellow spots become a very dark green. Further colour changes take place in accordance with their surroundings.

They are definitely uncanny creatures with their basilisk eyes and tail coiled like a Catherine-wheel cracker. The curious grasping of boughs with two toes on one side and two on the other, together with their static poses as if cut out of bronze or stone, provide a strange contrast to the lightning-like movement of their tongues as they are shot out like a spring to catch the insects on which these reptiles feed. Their tongues can extend to seven or eight inches and strike in a second of time.

The chameleon is a quaint species of lizard which has the power of changing its colour to suit its surroundings.

Another family of lizards which, although remaining so static that it is easy to pass them by without noticing them, and which can also move with lightning rapidity, is that of the agamas. One in particular can be selected for notice because of its brilliant colouring. This is the spinose agama of West Africa, rather larger than most lizards, being just over a foot in length, and said to be the most common reptile on the Gold Coast.

Its head is flame-red, the throat spotted with yellow and the body and limbs a deep steel-blue with a white line along the middle of its back. In the brilliant African sunlight it sparkles like some gorgeous insect of giant size. Following death, this brilliant colouring rapidly fades, while the female lacks this vivid colouring altogether.

As quaint as their colouring is their peculiar habit, when approached by a human being, of raising and lowering their heads in a series of nods. As you draw near, this nodding increases in speed until the lizard loses courage and darts away from you into some cranny.

The South African girdle-tailed lizard, so called because its slightly raised scales form a series of girdles down the length of its tail, is a small reptile of about six inches in length. Its back and tail are of a sandy orange colour, the head and feet light yellow and the underparts white.

They abound in rocky areas such as the summit of Table Mountain, where they will bask in the brilliant sunlight, suddenly and silently darting after insects in this place of perpetual silence. This little lizard is usually too nimble to catch, but should you succeed in seizing its tail it will be left in your hand while the creature itself escapes.

There are two species of rhinoceros in Africa —the black and the white. The terms are misleading, as both kinds are variations of grey:

The rhinoceros has a reputation for bad temper which he does not altogether deserve. Being short-sighted and of an inquisitive nature, he often lumbers into trouble unintentionally and charges from fear rather than anger. His speed when charging is considerable.

A close-up view of black rhinoceroses, taken while the beasts are foraging for food in the darkness. They are largely animals of the night.

but to the Boers, who first named them, it is probable that the black, which lives more in woodland and scrub, might have at first sight appeared black in the shadows; while the second, being in those days a dweller on the plains, would appear in the fuller light of such open country a much lighter colour— almost white, in fact, by comparison.

Needless slaughter by the early hunters brought the white rhinoceros to the verge of extinction, and the preservation of the remaining few in the Hluhluwe game reserve in Zululand was only just in time to avert this disaster to natural history. For next to the elephant it is the largest land animal and a direct link with the prehistoric past. The so-called " black rhinoceros " often has a mottled flesh colouring mingling with the darker grey of its hide.

GIVE A RHINOCEROS A BAD NAME!

All types of the rhinoceros have an unfortunate reputation for ill-temper. As a matter of fact, it is the limitations imposed on them by Nature which are largely responsible for this so-called evil temperament. Being very short-sighted and naturally inquisitive, the great animal often lumbers into trouble

quite unintentionally and, being worried by what it can't see, often charges blindly, more in exasperation than real anger. Moreover, sometimes meaning to escape, it will blunder into the very object it is trying to avoid.

The tales of hunters confirm this, because they have told of the rhinoceros rushing away and then returning to charge them from behind. Actually the beast has, with its limited sight and in sudden panic, rushed in a circle without realising the fact. Largely an animal of the night, it is also at a disadvantage in the vivid light of the African day.

The black rhinoceros, being mainly forest-dwelling, is more liable to be met unawares and consequently to panic. It has longer and more tapering horns than the white, though the latter is the larger animal. The black is naturally a browser, while the white prefers grazing, though it is now taking more and more to the bush. Its food on the plains being small thorn bushes, and grass is replaced by leaves and twigs in the jungle.

The upper lip of the black rhinoceros is pointed and used rather in the manner of the tip of an elephant's trunk; while that of the white rhinoceros is square. Both prefer to sleep by day under a tree or in the heart of a thicket. Often they will choose a high ledge, for despite their weight and short legs, they can climb like goats.

They will stretch out on their sides in the manner of pigs drowsing away the day while the tick birds search their tough hides for food. Their sleeping places are usually some distance from any water on high and dry ground.

As in the case of other large African animals, the rhinoceros's attendant birds are its sentinels, warning their host by their flight of impending danger and by their return that the danger is past.

Rhinos wear regular trails through the grass and tunnel through the bush to their favourite water-holes. They are conservative, too, and will use the same track for quite a long time. The shrewd traveller will, therefore, avoid these runways for camping or resting in.

THE RHINOCEROS AT PLAY

Though usually solitary or in small family parties, these great creatures, when they meet at mutual watering-places and have quenched their thirst, will romp together like a lot of overgrown pigs and they squeal and grunt in much the same way.

Tired after their " rough and tumble," the great creatures return to wallow in the water, and then scratch their wrinkled hides against convenient trees.

Seasonal wanderings take place during the driest months for then their particular water-hole may have dried up, and they are obliged to set out in search of other, deeper pools.

They have a remarkably keen scent where water is concerned and will actually dig for water, using their apparently clumsy forefeet and throwing up the earth between their hind-legs just as a dog will do.

Other animals will make use of such holes, but very few will start them as the rhinoceros will do.

The black rhinoceros is well known in zoos so that a detailed description of it is not necessary. But it may be noted that both white and black possess two horns, the front one of each being considerably longer than the back as a general rule, though, on occasions, they may be almost equal and, more rarely, the back may be longer than the front. Both sexes carry horns and the males' frontal horn can grow to over three feet.

Old bulls will stand five feet at the shoulder, with an overall length of ten feet. The white rhinoceros, on the other hand, will stand as high as six and a half feet and be as long as twelve feet—a formidable giant to meet at close quarters.

Both species are creatures of the night, and are usually only abroad in the day during cloudy weather. When a mother and baby of the black species are on the move the calf generally follows mother, but with the white the calves go in front. The calves will remain with the parent until they are quite large, and if the mother should be killed the calf will continue to stand by the body, being with difficulty driven away.

The range of the black species extends from Zululand through Central and East Africa to Somaliland and Abyssinia. Up to the beginning of the present century it was also found as far south as Cape Province. The antiquity of the family is at any rate certain, for the woolly rhinoceros flourished in Europe with the mammoth at the dawn of history.

THE " TIGER HORSE "

The striped horse-like animal familiarly known as the zebra is peculiar to Africa. There are a number of species of which the best known is Burchell's, as it is the most commonly exhibited in zoos and most widely-spread in Africa, inhabiting a great deal of open dry country south of the Sahara. In

There are many species of zebra. This Grévy's zebra lives in Somaliland and Abyssinia.

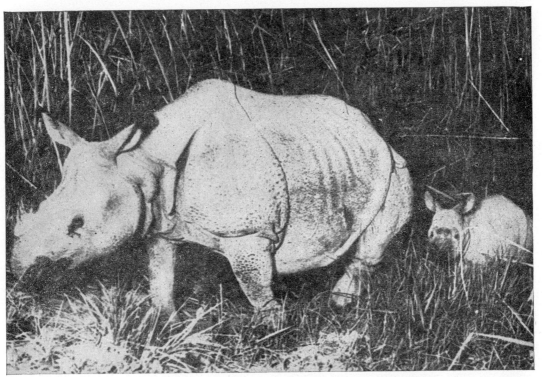

A white rhinoceros with its calf in the bush. The calf remains with its mother until it is quite large and fully able to defend itself from all the perils of the jungle.

This porcupine lies basking in the sun, his quills flat since no danger is at hand.

Drinking companions at a water-hole. A zebra meets a baby wart-hog.

Zebra and brindled gnu, or wildebeest, often roam together in herds across the plains of Africa.
One of their number generally acts as lookout and gives the alarm on the approach of danger.

appearance and size it is a cross between the horse and the ass.

It is certainly startling to see the difference between its vivid markings in captivity and the manner in which these stripes blur and blend with the animal's background under the brilliant African sun. These stripes vary not only between the species but also between local races and individuals.

All zebras are lively animals living in herds under the control of the master stallion; they feed on grass and avoid bushy localities as far as possible. Their principal enemy is the lion, who prefers zebra even to antelope as food. They are, however, very fast, and unless ambushed can usually show a clean pair of heels to most foes—the lion included. The foals have the same handsome markings as their parents and very soon grow swift enough to keep up with the herd.

The mountain zebra is nearest in appearance to the wild ass on account of its large ears and general shape. It is very boldly striped right down to the hoofs, and the markings stand out the more readily as there are no shadow markings in the white intervals. This animal stands about four feet at the shoulder, and being bred a mountain animal, can surmount the roughest and most precipitous ground. Formerly found on all the mountain ranges of

Cape Province, its diminishing numbers have been fortunately preserved in government reserves at such places as Cape Point.

Zebras, as one might suppose from their similarity to the horse, are intelligent, mettlesome and capable of affection, especially for one another, as hunters have remarked when finding a number of them lingering by a wounded comrade at the risk of their own lives. Of the many variations and local races throughout the African continent possibly one of the most interesting and certainly one of the finest is the one known as Grévy's zebra of Somaliland and Abyssinia.

This beautiful animal, acknowledged to be the largest and finest of all wild species of the horse family, was only discovered to modern science in 1882, though its background is that of the most ancient civilisation, having been apparently familiar to the Greeks of classical times under the name of hippotigris, or tiger horse, and was almost certainly the species shown in the Roman amphitheatres.

In size it equals a rather small horse with a large and beautifully formed head and ears. Its stripes are narrow, very numerous and close together, being black on a pure white ground. This fine animal has of recent years been seen in the London zoological gardens and fortunately breeds in captivity.

Polar bears seldom survive long when born in captivity. The first to do so in London Zoo was Brumas, shown here with her mother, Ivy. Brumas is now fully grown.

WILD LIFE OF ASIA

Some of the Animals of a Vast Continent

THE vast continent of Asia stretches from the eternal ice of the Arctic tundra to the tropics, split across by great mountain ranges from northern India to the Sea of Japan. The wild life of this continent is, therefore, extremely varied, and only typical examples can be mentioned here.

The Russian coastline is the Arctic frontier of Asia, and here dwell the fur-bearing animals, adapted to stand up to the incalculable cold of the region.

THE POLAR BEAR AND BROWN BEAR

The great hunter of the Arctic wastes is the polar bear, who spends as much time on the ice-floes as he does on land, stalking and killing seals or young walruses. Though huge, the polar bear is a stealthy hunter, and

is swift and agile despite his great weight—up to 15 cwt.! A fully-grown male will reach 9 feet in length. This species does not hibernate. The females have two young at a birth.

In Siberia there is also the brown bear, which measures up to 7 feet in length. It is much lighter than the polar bear, reaching barely half the latter's weight in the top sizes. The brown bear hibernates, and gives birth to two or three cubs. Except in the breeding season, this species is solitary, and though a powerful animal it is shy. The cubs sometimes follow their mother for two or three years. The brown bear is found in Kamchatka, the western Himalayas and northern Japan.

THE USEFUL REINDEER

The reindeer, which lives on a special kind of lichen, is found throughout the Arctic

Circle. In Scandinavia it has been long domesticated. Great herds are now maintained in Russia, for transport, meat, hides and milk. The wild reindeer of Canada is called the caribou.

THE ARCTIC FOX, ERMINE AND MARTEN

Small fur bearers of these cold regions are the Arctic fox, the ermine and the marten.

The Arctic fox turns white in winter, as a rule, but some specimens turn pale blue, like ice reflecting the sky. The ermine is, of course, the stoat, but the Russian furs are much more valuable than any from more temperate regions, like our own. The marten is also a weasel, and is the sable of commerce.

BIRDS OF NORTHERN ASIA

The whole area is rich in bird life, especially geese, ducks and waders, many of which we see in Britain as winter visitors.

The greylag goose, the snow goose and the white front, all nest in these desolate regions. After the breeding season they disperse and some of them find their way to British estuaries, marshes and stubble fields.

The grey plover nests in Siberia. So does the beautiful harlequin duck, which is such a

Searching for food amidst the snow, reindeer (in Canada called caribou) feed largely on a lichen known as reindeer moss.

common sight here on ornamental waters. And, of course, there are the swans.

The whooper swan is an Arctic bird, distinguished from the common mute swan, which also nests in the Arctic, by the yellow on its beak. The whooper has a wonderful voice, from which it gets its name, and it tends to swim with its neck straight, instead of

Brown bear cubs sometimes run with their mother until they are three years old.

Wolves are common in Russia, and are still to be found in France.

curved, as is the way with the swan with which you are familiar—the mute.

WOLVES

It would be impossible to leave the wild places of Russia without considering the wolf. Wolves are still common right across Asiatic Russia, where they hunt the forests and the steppes. They live mainly on mammals and birds, and often hunt in packs, when they can pull down deer. In hard winters, they have been known to raid domestic stock.

THE REMARKABLE LEMMING

One of the most remarkable animals is the lemming. There are many species, and they are related to the voles, which are plentiful in this country. And, like the voles, they are subject to great fluctuation in numbers.

When their food supply fails they migrate in search of new pastures, falling in ditches, lakes, rivers and wells, and dying in vast numbers till the waters are polluted. In Siberia there is another species of lemming the banded lemming.

ELK AND WAPITI

The most imposing of Siberian land mammals is the elk, which is the Old World cousin of the Canadian moose. The antlers of the bull elk are palmated. The elk roams the vast, primeval forests of north Russia and northern Asia, although its real strongholds are in Scandinavia.

Cow elks give birth to one or two calves each May or June. At first, the calves live entirely on their mother's milk, but they soon start browsing like adult elk on twigs, buds and leaves. All elk like marshy forest.

An adult bull elk will stand well over 6 feet high at the shoulders and weigh over 1,000 lb. The legs are very long and gangling, the gait is shambling, and the hooves large. The muzzle of the elk is broad, pendulous and hairy, and under the throat is a bell-like dewlap.

Young elks. In America elk is another name for the wapiti. The true elk, the largest of all living deer, is known as the moose.

Another imposing member of the deer family found in Asia is the wapiti, of which there are many races in the Old and New Worlds.

The wapiti stag is an imposing animal, smaller than the elk, with antlers of the red deer type, usually with five points on each

shaft. Both wapiti and elk will fight with their hooves as well as their antlers.

THE FORMIDABLE WOLVERINE OR GLUTTON

One of the most formidable and notorious animals of the north is the wolverine, or glutton, sometimes called " Injun devil " in Canada. This great weasel is found right across northern Asia to Kamchatka.

The wolverine weighs about 25 to 30 lb., stands nearly 18 inches high at the shoulder, and measures over 3 feet from nose to tail. It is one of the most powerful animals in the world for its size.

Though it feeds mainly on small mammals and birds, it will attack deer and even cattle in the extremity of hunger, and is an expert at discovering traps. A wolverine can often ruin a season's work for a trapper by finding and ripping his pelts.

ANIMALS OF THE STEPPE LANDS

Farther south, as the country becomes kinder and sunnier, the wild life changes. Over the great steppe lands roam the wild ass

The wolverine, or glutton, lives in the forested districts of the Northern Hemisphere, digging its prey out of burrows, stealing trapped animals or raiding cabins.

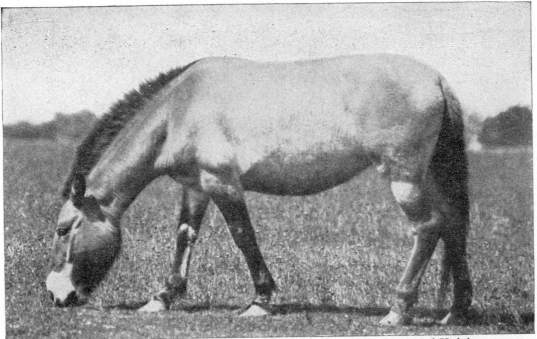

The Mongolian wild horse, now restricted to the Dzungaria desert and Kobdo.

and the wild horse, the camel and the great argali. Here we will meet the quaint jerboa, gazelles, deer, marmots, and the first tigers.

The Mongolian wild horse was once widely distributed in Asia but is now found only in the Dzungaria desert and Kobdo. It stands 4½ feet high at the withers and is dark brown in colour.

The onager, which is the wild ass of the Bible, is a gregarious animal of the steppes, with long ears and tufted tail. It runs in small herds, which are usually led by an old stallion, and is hunted for meat.

The Tibetan kiang is another ass-like beast which lives on the high plateaux of Tibet. It has a black mane and a black tuft on the end of its tail.

It is doubtful if there is now such a thing as a truly wild camel. Two kinds are used as beasts of burden, the Bactrian with two humps and the dromedary with one.

The argali is the biggest of all sheep, standing nearly 4 feet high at the shoulder. It is found from Bukhara to Tibet and Kamchatka. Both ram and ewe wear horns. Ewes with lambs run in large flocks, but rams usually move in small companies of about ten. The horns of the ram are very large.

The jerboa is a rodent, which lives on steppe and desert. It has long hind legs, so that it can jump like a kangaroo, and a long tufted tail. It is found in west and central Asia.

The five-toed jerboa is smaller than a squirrel, with white belly, reddish-yellow upper parts, and black and white tail. It lives in Russia and Mongolia.

THE TIGER

One of the most imposing and formidable of Asiatic mammals is the tiger, which is found from the Caucasus to India, China, Korea and Amur. It is found in the Himalayas up to a height of 7,000 feet. There are many races of tigers, some very large, some small and hairy. The Bengal tiger reaches a length of 10 feet, 3 feet of which is tail. The Siberian tiger reaches a length of 13 feet. The Caucasian tigers are usually small, with shaggy hair.

The Siberian tiger is rare, and is now heavily protected by the Russian Government. It is a pale tiger, and a hunter of the snowline.

All tiger skins are highly prized as rugs, but the Siberian race is particularly valuable because the skin is densely furred.

The Bengal tiger is the real tiger type, and is the one we hear most about.

A Bengal tiger photographed by flashlight on an Indian jungle path.

Tigers are night hunters, and are so powerful that they will attack young elephants. But the usual prey is deer and similar mammals. Like all the cat family, the tiger is not endowed with great stamina. Its hunting method therefore is the careful stalk, followed by a lightning rush. Tigers do not run their quarry for any great distance.

By day they lie up in some cave or deep thicket. With the coming of darkness they leave their den to hunt. Their hunting ground is usually well defined, but may cover a wide area. This habit of sticking to a defined territory makes it possible for the hunter to track his tiger.

MAN-EATING TIGERS

Much has been written about man-eating tigers. But the man-eating tiger is rare. There may be a number operating at the same time, but still the man-eater is rare among the grand total of tigers.

A tiger which starts hunting man usually does so because it has been wounded, and so is incapable of hunting its usual prey. Old tigers, because of infirmity, sometimes become man-eaters, but the opinion among knowledgeable tiger hunters is that old wounds are the main cause.

Once a tiger becomes a man-eater it loses its fear of man completely, so that it does not hesitate to come right into villages in search of prey. Such an animal can kill a large number of people before it is finally killed.

Tigers are enormously powerful, and a big beast can run off with a cattle beast weighing over 400 lb., as easily as a fox can run with a hare.

THE LION OF INDIA

It is customary to say that tigers are found in India and lions in Africa, and that it doesn't apply the other way round. But while it is true that there are no tigers in Africa, there is still, in India, a species of lion that has no mane. This maneless lion used to be quite common in India, but it is now extremely rare, and fast nearing extinction.

THE COURAGEOUS LEOPARD

The leopard of India is another powerful cat, which reaches a length of 8 feet—body up to 5 feet, with up to 3 feet of tail. In India, and the Dutch East Indies, dark forms of the leopard become more and more common, until they are almost quite black.

Black leopards are " melanistic " forms of the ordinary leopard, and in the blackest of them the spots can be detected in certain kinds of lighting. These dark specimens are often called black panthers, but as a matter of fact the panther is another kind of beast altogether,

The hairy-footed or lesser jerboa. Its long tail serves as a balancing pole when travelling at speed, and as a shooting stool when at rest. Jackals and hawks are its foes.

namely the puma, which is not found in Asia.

Leopards are extremely adaptable animals, fit to make a living in almost any kind of country. They climb well, and often make their kill from a tree. They kill all the kinds of prey that the tiger kills, but of course they are not powerful enough to tackle young elephants.

Besides being powerful, the leopard is extremely courageous, and shows more courage in the face of men than either the lion or the tiger.

An expert at taking cover, even in the barest country, the leopard is difficult to hunt. Near villages it is a great trial to the Indians, for it will kill all kinds of livestock.

When a leopard becomes a man-eater it strikes terror into the neighbourhood, for it is difficult to track down. In recent years there have been full accounts by hunters of man-eating leopards, and there are authentic stories of beasts that have killed up to 200 human beings before they were finally shot.

HUNTING " DOG " OF PRINCES

The hunting leopard of India is the chita, called cheetah in Africa. This species is trained for the chase, usually for hunting gazelle, and is the fastest animal on four legs in the world.

As with the falcons of old, the chita is normally hooded till it is ready to be hunted. Then the hood is removed, and the beast is slipped after its quarry.

Chitas have round closed spots, gentle eyes, cropped ears and a docile disposition. You will hear stories that the chita is not a true cat, that it can't retract its claws, that indeed it is more of a dog than a cat. But this is not true. The claws are retractile as in other cats, but the chita does not have lobes of skin to hide them as other cats have.

Chitas, of course, are found wild in India, but all kits are easily tamed. In the wild state the chita lives on antelope, deer, calves, sheep and goats.

THE ELEPHANT

The elephants of India are known throughout the world. They are used as beasts of burden, and the working stock is regularly made up by wild animals which are caught and tamed.

The Indian elephant has very small ears

compared with the African. Males reach a height of 10 feet at the shoulder; females rarely exceed 8 feet.

These elephants live in herds in the forests of India, Ceylon, Burma, Siam, Malaya and Borneo. In Siam, albinos occur quite frequently, so there is really such a thing as a white elephant.

Female elephants usually have one young at a birth, but occasionally there are two.

(*See also page 295.*)

THE ASIAN RHINOCEROSES

In India there are three kinds of rhinoceros and three kinds of bear.

The rhinoceros is one of the largest and heaviest land mammals living. All Indian rhinoceroses differ from the African kinds by having folded skin studded with tubercles that look like rivets.

The great Indian rhinoceros has a single horn about a foot in length. The horn is solid, but does not grow from the skull, so that it can actually be knocked off with powerful blows.

This species is almost black. It is ten feet long and six feet high. It lives among tall grass, usually near water, and is quite inoffensive. Owing to excessive hunting to supply medicine horn to China, this species is now found only along the foothills of the Himalayas from Nepal to Assam.

The sondiac is another species with only one horn. This type prefers hilly or wooded country, rather than the marshes favoured by the other, and is found from Bengal to Burma and Borneo.

Then there is the hairy rhinoceros, so called because its body is thinly clothed with hair. This species carries two horns, the front one of the pair growing to over two feet in length. The hairy rhinoceros is the smallest of the three.

All rhinoceroses are vegetarians, feeding on leaves, grass and twigs. They feed at night. All live in small family groups, and all have only one young at a birth.

SLOTH BEAR

The sloth bear is found in India and Ceylon. It measures about $5\frac{1}{2}$ feet in length and weighs up to 320 lb. It has a short, thickset body, short legs, big feet, and long, sharp claws, curved and white. The snout is long and narrow, and the lips can be extended to pick the smallest objects off the ground—for example, ants.

This animal likes hilly, forested regions, and lies up in some cave or dense cover by day. It hunts mainly at night, feeding on vegetable matter, small mammals, insects and honey.

Like other bears it leaves many signs of its presence—claw marks on trees where it has been climbing for honey, and holes in the ground where it has been scraping for ants. It gathers ants by sucking.

With its short body and long claws the sloth bear has a pronounced shuffling gait. When in a hurry it seems to roll along the ground, and, indeed, it will actually roll downhill for greater speed.

The beast's temper is uncertain, and it is in fact more dangerous than a tiger, for it will attack without provocation. When it does so, it can inflict terrible head wounds.

BROWN AND BLACK BEARS

Of the other two species, the brown bear is restricted to Kashmir and part of the Himalayas, while the black is found over a wide area from Persia to Formosa.

The black bear, like the Canadian species, is a vegetarian which takes flesh when opportunity offers. It feeds mainly on roots, fruits and nuts, but will take sheep, goats, and cattle at any time.

PANGOLINS

Among the quaintest of animals are the pangolins, or scaly ant-eaters, which hunt at night and feed on termites and ants.

The Indian pangolin, which is just over 4 feet long, including its tail of 20 inches, lives in hilly districts, sleeping in its burrow by day and hunting by night. It gives birth to one or two young in the spring.

The Chinese pangolin is a smaller animal, with more numerous scales, and is found from China and Formosa to Assam and Nepal.

THE WOLF, BOAR AND RAT OF INDIA

The wolves of India are smaller than the European wolf, and take heavy toll of flocks and herds. There is some reluctance about hunting down wolves as many Indians believe them to have supernatural powers. Some believe that to shed a wolf's blood on a field makes the field barren for all time.

India has its own special type of wild boar. This species has a pronounced mane. It reaches a height of nearly three feet at the shoulder and is found from the Himalayas to Ceylon. A smaller type is found in Siam.

Rats have caused terrible plagues in India and elsewhere, killing more people than all

Pangolins are scaly animals that can roll themselves into a ball. They are nocturnal and live on ants and termites. They have no teeth, but an extensible, thread-like tongue.

The langurs are leaf-monkeys from India,
Ceylon and the East Indies.

The purple-faced, or Ceylon, langur is one of
several species from Asia.

A baby hanuman langur from India where it
is regarded as sacred.

The orang-utan is the only anthropoid from
Asia. Males are $5\frac{1}{2}$ feet tall.

the wars of history. The Indian mole-rat is one of these. It is not unlike our common brown rat, but has long hairs and bristles on its back. It is now a major pest in Calcutta.

MONKEYS

The monkey family is well represented in India. The most familiar of these are probably the leaf-monkeys or langurs, found in India, Ceylon and the East Indies. The langurs are sacred, and are found about most Hindu temples. They are short-faced monkeys, with long tails and no cheek pouches. There are several species.

The lar gibbon is found in Siam, Malay, Borneo, Java and Sumatra. It is greyish-black or yellowish-white, with a black face surrounded with white whiskers. It is 3 feet long.

The macaque monkeys are a very large family, represented by many species ranging over a wide area. The best known is the lion-tailed macaque. As its name suggests its tail is tufted like a lion's. In addition the whiskers framing its face give it the appearance of having a mane.

Other species of macaque are the pig-tailed, Himalayan, hairy-eared and brown.

The bonnet monkey, with its hair tuft looking like a bonnet, is found in the south of India. Then there is the slender loris, with its great, round, shining eyes, so well adapted for seeing at night. The slender loris is no bigger than a squirrel.

The only anthropoid ape of Asia is the orang-utan, which is found in Borneo and Sumatra. This is a man-like ape, standing 5½ feet high when fully grown. Females are smaller than males.

Orang-utans are vegetarians. The colour is reddish-brown. The face is yellowish in young beasts, but becomes brown or black in the adult. Old males have a distinct beard. Outside the mating season, the males live alone, while the females live with the younger beasts and the babies.

CHEVROTAIN OR MOUSE-DEER

It is perhaps difficult to imagine a deer only eighteen inches tall, but in fact the chevrotain, or mouse-deer, is as small as that.

In Asia there are two types of mouse-deer, the Malayan and the Indian, the one being reddish-brown in colour, the other white-

Tapirs are pig-like in outer shape, and have noses elongated to a movable trunk.

spotted and striped. These little deer live in the jungles and are very shy.

TAPIR

One of the oddest looking of animals is the tapir, of which one kind is found in Asia. The Malayan tapir stands between 3 and 4½ feet high at the shoulder, and is black, or black with a white band round its middle. The general outline of the tapir is that of a pig. It has a flexible nose like short trunk. It lives in dense jungle, is harmless, solitary and a vegetarian.

THE GIANT PANDA

Nowadays everybody has heard of the giant panda, and many people have seen it at the Zoo. It lives in the lonely bamboo forests of eastern Tibet and south-west China, living on bamboo shoots and other vegetable matter. The giant panda is bear-like, about six feet long, and has a special bone in its forepaw which enables it to cling to the bamboo canes.

This animal must not be confused with the panda of Burma, China and Nepal, which is a cat-like animal about two feet long with a tail up to 18 inches. This animal has thick, soft, glossy fur, red above and black below, and its tail is lightly ringed. It is a vegetarian, but also eats birds' eggs and insects. It lives between 7,000 and 12,000 feet.

This mighty tusker was captured in a kheddah and is still resentful of his bonds.

THE INDIAN OR ASIAN ELEPHANT

ASIAN elephants are found in all the countries of Middle Asia from India to the borders of China, including the islands of Ceylon and Sumatra. They inhabit the more densely forested areas of the steamy monsoon belt, particularly about the foothills of mountain ranges. They prefer to spend their time where there are swamps and rivers to plunge into, but have been found as high as 7,000 feet up the mountain sides during the hot season of the year. They love swimming, and when undisturbed will spend hours in the rivers; sometimes standing in the shallows spraying themselves with their trunks, sometimes swimming in deep water, and often just walking about on tiptoe along the bottom completely submerged except for the tip of their trunks which they breathe through just like the snort of a submarine. Tame elephants often let themselves sink to the bottom in fun while they are being swum across rivers, in the hope that they will make the driver on their back let go. Men, however, can hold their breath as long as elephants, and the drivers are usually on the lookout for this trick.

Asian elephants differ from the African species in many important ways. They are shorter, varying from 8 ft. to 11 ft. in height, and more strongly built, and have shorter hind legs, which seem to give them greater power for pulling and pushing logs. Only the male or bull elephants grow tusks, but even they are sometimes tuskless, and they are much more easily trained than African elephants. They do not like strong sunlight, and rarely leave the protection of shady forests.

In their wild state Asian elephants usually move about in herds, often in family parties of ten or a dozen, though sometimes in large groups numbering a hundred or more. The

After being washed by their mahouts, these elephants lie basking in the water.

leaders of the herds are generally female or cow elephants, for the old bulls tend to leave the herd for most of the year and wander about on their own till the next mating season. Elephants court each other's favour for weeks or months before mating, and the young calves are born about 22 months later. Newly-born calves are about two feet high and are very hairy. They suckle with their mouths, like any other small mammal, and it is some weeks before their trunks are strong enough to use to pick things up.

"AUNTY" ELEPHANT LOOKS AFTER THE BABY

When they are very young they are usually guarded by two cow elephants—their own mother and a friend who has no calf at the time (the Burmese call these "Aunty" elephants). Wherever they go the two cows will keep the baby between them, night and day, watching for danger, particularly for attacks by tigers which, in spite of the efforts of the protectors, still kill one out of every four

This mother elephant was captured in a kheddah and is here seen undergoing training. The two calves will not wander far from the older elephants and so do not have to be roped.

The scene in a kheddah in the Kharapur forest not far from Mysore, India. These animals have been without food and water for several days, but are not yet sufficiently weakened to be tethered.

baby wild elephants. As they grow older and better able to look after themselves, the calves make friends of their own and roam about with them inseparably, often for the rest of their lives.

Wild elephants are captured in what are called kheddahs; that is, enclosures made of tall and heavy tree-trunks stuck deep in the ground and securely lashed and strengthened with buttresses. They are made with only one narrow entrance, into which a heavy trap-door can be dropped, and from this door great wings of heavy palisading are built out on either side for several hundred feet, making a sort of funnel which will force the driven elephants in through the gateway of the kheddah. These kheddahs are made near to some place known to be frequented by an elephant herd, and on the day of the operation large numbers of beaters are called in to help to drive the herd along. This must be done very carefully or they will stampede and break away through the beaters.

What usually happens is that two long lines of men, or " stops " as they are called, are placed so that they fan out in a wide V from the ends of the palisades of the kheddah. The men make no sound unless the elephants move towards them, and even then all they will do is to tap a stick against a tree to let the elephants know someone is about, which is usually sufficient to turn them back in the way they are to be driven. Meanwhile the beaters form a long line across the neck of the V and drive the elephants in towards the trap as quietly as possible.

The critical moment in the drive arrives when the leading elephants reach the palisade and begin to realise they are trapped. Then the beaters raise a tremendous hullabaloo, beating gongs and firing guns to make the elephants bolt through the gateway into the kheddah. Once in, the gate is closed behind them, and buttressed, and the animals are left to mill wildly around inside, trumpeting madly with fright.

If they charge the barricades, which they often do, men with spears stab them through the gaps between the logs and drive them off again. For days they are left without food and water, until at last weakness and frustration quieten them sufficiently for it to be safe for men mounted on tame elephants to enter. Strangely enough wild elephants take no notice of the riders on the tame elephants' backs, and allow themselves to be pushed one by one up to big trees, where in a flash a man will slip a chain round its hind legs to tether it.

When all have been tethered the long process of breaking their spirit begins. Men can now move about safely in the kheddah, but dare not yet go near the savage animals. They throw grass and shoots within their reach to keep them alive, but gradually the poor beasts shrink to skin and bone until, broken at last to the realisation that they are helpless in the hands of men, they give in and allow themselves to be handled. Once broken in, elephants soon make friends, but kheddah animals are never as reliable as those reared in captivity, and always carry the terrible scars of their breaking in.

TRAINING A YOUNG ELEPHANT

The training of a young calf born in captivity is quite different, and a much happier affair, which has been well described in Col. J. H. William's classic *Elephant Bill*. When he is about five years old, the youngster is put in a " crush," or cage of greased logs, and alternately petted and then pushed down by a log suspended above him until he has learnt to let his rider sit on his head and to sit down and get up to order. These essentials learnt, he goes for training to a school which is complete with an elephant " master " as well as human masters who teach him the elementary rules of good manners. He will carry his first light pack when he is eight, and receive continuous training until he is eighteen or nineteen, when he goes to a working camp to start his life's career.

Invaluable in timber yards, these elephants, under the direction of their drivers, lift and carry the heavy teak logs. Although in the yards machinery could perhaps be substituted for the animals, this is not likely in the jungle where their skill in handling logs cannot be surpassed.

An Indian taxi.

In spite of this, however, an elephant may travel nearly ten miles during the night in search of the right food, giving his driver a long walk to find him in the morning. This is one reason why the mahouts themselves are such excellent jungle men.

Almost every day in their lives starts with a long trail through the forest, up hill and down dale, following their charge's tracks among dozens of others, tame and wild. The search takes them into the deepest depths of the jungle, the haunt of tigers and bison and deer of all kinds, whose habits they come to know as well as if they were wild creatures themselves.

THE ELEPHANTS' BANANA FEAST

Wild herds, though still numerous in many parts of middle Asia, do not often trespass into cultivated areas. When they do they can soon create havoc because of the huge quantities of food they eat, but the firing of a few shots in the air is generally enough to drive them away for good. Tame elephants, on the other hand, can be a nuisance, and cases have been known where they have actually stuffed their neck-bells with mud so that they can creep silently into the village gardens and help themselves to the sleeping owners' bananas.

Every year during the hot season bull elephants go must, that is, they become irritable and treacherous and sometimes attack and kill other elephants as well as human beings. The sign of approaching must is the appearance of an oily discharge from glands in the face just below the eyes, and at such times the bulls are usually chained to a tree and fed there until the attack passes.

Occasionally elephants become what are called " rogues," that is outlaws, and take to killing everyone they see. Such animals become very wary and cunning, for every man's hand is against them, and they often kill dozens of people before they can be captured. They will lie in ambush by the village paths waiting to rush out and trample upon an unwary passer-by, or slip quietly up to a sleeping family in a field hut and batter them all to pieces. Sometimes they work in pairs, and then they are exceedingly dangerous, for they can drive their victims towards each other or stop their roads of escape.

The Asian elephant relies almost entirely on his trunk to feed himself, and any serious

Tame baby elephants are delightfully naughty. They hide behind trees or bushes and rush out and bowl over other elephant calves, and even human beings, when they are least expecting it. They creep up to the master's cookhouse window and make off with a bunch of bananas or other fruit, hotly pursued by an angry cook. They delight in scaring the wits out of themselves and others by stampeding about with great squeals of alarm, all for no reason at all. In general, elephants live to about the same age as men, and since young elephant calves under training are put in charge of boys only a few years older than themselves, elephants and their drivers (called mahout in India and oozi in Burma) very often grow old together.

Tame elephants are never tethered except when ill or must, as a full-grown elephant eats about six hundred pounds' weight of green fodder a day and needs a great variety of different kinds of food such as grass, bamboo shoots and leaves, in order to remain healthy.

When the day's work is over, their drivers set them free with hobbles on their forelegs which, while enabling them to move about at a walking pace with a sort of hopping movement, prevent them from wandering too far.

Here you can see the detail of the trappings of one of the many elephants which are in procession on a ceremonial occasion. The elephant's toes are painted gold or silver, whilst the forelegs, the face and ears bear ornate designs. The tusks are tipped with special metal spikes.

A prince in his howdah has an Eastern magnificence which is remote from our workaday world.
Used only on ceremonial occasions, the trappings are of silver, gold, jewels and silk.

injury to that useful member may result in starvation. That is why, when it is charging, it rolls its trunk up in a tight ball and tucks it in towards its mouth to keep it out of harm's way. Though it can use it as a bludgeon to strike men or beasts, or discipline a calf, it can also use it with extreme delicacy of touch. It will nuzzle a sweet out of a closed hand, and pick a tiny medicine pill out of the middle of the fruit which is meant to disguise and sugar it.

ELEPHANTS OR TRACTORS ?

Elephants are still used in many parts of Asia for ceremonial purposes, and there are few sights more magnificent than a gaily painted and decorated tusker with a golden howdah on his back, towering high above a city procession. In parts of India elephants are used as mounts for the guns in tiger shoots. Their real work lies, however, in teak forests and timber yards, pushing and pulling the great logs wherever their masters desire. No doubt some day the timber firms will use tractors instead of elephants, filling the quiet forests with noise and smoke and smell, and then there will be nothing left for the elephants to do but go back to the remotest jungles, there to live in Game Sanctuaries as museum pieces of a past age. It will be a sad day, for it will break one of Man's closest links with

the animal world, and take from his workaday world the wisest and friendliest of creatures. Though elephants dislike ponies and will stampede from a yapping terrier, they will fight bravely to defend each other. Cow elephants with young will face even tigers with great boldness, and many a mother and " nurse " carry the scars of such encounters.

Everyone has heard of the term " white elephant," meaning a useless article that nobody wants. It is derived from the fact that, very occasionally, albino elephants are born which are a pinkish grey in colour, much lighter than their normal fellows. In some Asian countries these albino elephants are regarded as sacred, too sacred to be allowed to do any work, and in the past were usually presented to the ruling monarch who was the only person who could afford to keep them in idle luxury. These Asian Kings sometimes used the white elephant to punish wealthy courtiers who flaunted their wealth too much. They would make a present of a white elephant to such men, who, being unable to bear the enormous expense of feeding and keeping the useless creature, were soon reduced to a proper state of poverty. That is why, even to-day, we still use the term " white elephant " to describe something we would like to get rid of but cannot.

THE GIANT PANDA

The Animal who looks like a Toy

BETWEEN South-West China and Tibet rise range upon range of lovely and stupendous mountains known as the Szechwan Mountains, mysterious and, even in these days, almost as unexplored as in the beginnings of time. Amongst these mountains lies a maze of valleys covered with huge trees and most impenetrable bamboo jungle. In these wild and secluded surroundings live the giant pandas (*ailuropoda' melano*), as mysterious as the ancient land which is their home.

As long ago as A.D. 621, during the Tang Dynasty, the Chinese had written about a curious white and black animal, so rare as to be almost a myth, so like a bear as to be called *bei' Shung*, meaning white bear. But it was not until the nineteenth century that the white man first saw the skin of one of these curious beasts. He was l'Abbé Armand David, a French missionary who, during his travels in China, was given a skin by a native hunter. This he sent to a museum in France. Many years elapsed before a foreign hunter or explorer saw a giant panda alive.

In 1929 a son of President Theodore Roosevelt shot a full-grown animal whilst on an expedition into South-West China. This specimen was brought to Chicago and mounted in the Field Natural History Museum. In spite of many other expeditions having been sent out to hunt and study these mysterious pandas, during which two or three were shot, nothing came to light about their manner of living and habits.

THE WOMAN WHO CAPTURED A PANDA

It was not until an intrepid American woman, Mrs. Ruth Harkness, aided by a young Chinese explorer, succeeded in capturing a giant panda cub. After overcoming the incredible difficulties of transport through miles of thick jungle amongst the great mountains, the cub was brought safely to America. However, it died shortly afterwards through swallowing a twig.

No animal can look more cuddly than the playful Panda. Full of high spirits, and always ready for fun, he enjoys all kinds of games, and loves playing with toys.

Since then a few other pandas have been successfully brought out from their native China, some to America and some to England. In 1939, at the Zoological Gardens in London, five of these animals arrived, of which three were retained.

So far giant pandas have not bred in captivity, and their reproductive habits are still unknown. The cubs are presumably born while the mother rests in hollow tree-trunks, or possibly in sheltered holes amongst rocks. Being partly nocturnal, these animals are fully awake and at their liveliest in a half light, and are therefore termed " crepuscular."

As far as is known, their main diet is bamboo shoots, but in captivity they have thriven on porridge, wheat, maize, hard apples and milk. But the fact that they refuse all offers of flesh food in captivity is no proof that in their wild state they do not feed on mammals, or even insects, as well as a vegetarian diet.

Examination by scientists of the jaws and teeth of giant pandas suggest that many thousands of years ago they were carnivorous animals. It may be that climatic changes or volcanic upheavals of their country, thereby altering its levels and contours, caused migrations of the animals upon which the pandas fed, forcing them to change their flesh diet to mainly vegetarian foods. This change would naturally be a slow process, taking place during an unknown number of centuries.

THE PANDA SLEEPS IN THE TREE-TOPS

The sleeping habits of giant pandas in their wild state are also unknown. In the zoos they will climb to the very highest part of their cage and sleep until twilight, bringing disappointment to the crowds of people who, from curiosity and interest, have come to see the mysterious beasts. It is therefore fairly safe to assume that, in the wilds, as soon as the young pandas are old enough to climb, they sleep high up in the tall forest trees of their native jungle.

Their rate of growth and increase of weight is very rapid. Females weigh less than males, which, it is said, reach a weight of as much as three hundred pounds.

and press the object firmly against this extra thumb pad.

THE PANDA WEARS A FUR COAT

The furry coat of giant pandas is deep and thick. In the high altitudes at which they live there is frequent rain, much snow and piercingly cold winds, but their coats are completely resistant to the worst weather that Nature can produce. In addition to this, the white and black markings (white is predominant) are a perfect camouflage against the snow and the deep shadows amongst the trees and rocks of their surroundings.

Of all the breeds of animals that have ever been kept as pets, none is so fascinating or interesting as baby giant pandas. In play their actions are so supple as to make them appear boneless. They have a great sense of humour and seem deliberately to play up to an audience. They love baths and will sit and splash in one just like a human baby. Unfortunately their gentleness and lively humour last only until they grow up. After maturity they become serious-minded and often ill-tempered and dangerous.

Giant pandas are very "handy" animals. They can hold bamboo shoots in their paws and then proceed to bite portions from both sides. In captivity they can even hold a mug of water or milk quite safely and drink from it. They are able to do this because, in addition to the five, claw-armed fingers, there is a curious formation of a large projecting bone at the base of the thumb. This, in its turn, has formed an extra pad. In order to hold anything firmly, pandas bend their five fingers

Puzzle picture. Can you solve it? There are clues to help you. Solution on page 345.

The Penguin can sometimes look very dignified and at other times equally comical. Did you know that there were several different kinds of penguin? Here are some drawn for you. *Top row:* Black-footed or Jackass; *middle row:* (*left*) Adelie, (*right*) King; *bottom:* Rockhopper.

A PAGE FOR CAT-LOVERS

Some of these cats are affectionate, some superior and some quite indifferent to your opinion of them. All of them, however, are fond of the good things of life—warmth, food and comfort. Here you have, reading from top left, a Chinchilla Persian, a short-haired Black, a Siamese, a Blue Persian and a short-haired Tabby.

The daisy, though a humble wild flower, has a simple beauty unsurpassed by many a rarer flower, studding the grass with stars in the bright sunlight.

THE LANGUAGE OF THE FLOWERS

THROUGH the centuries the most popular flowers, many of them common to a number of countries, have acquired legends and happy symbolism. It adds to our enjoyment of them if we remember their stories.

The familiar buttercup, for instance, was so named because it was thought to increase the quality of the butter. Actually, cows never eat the flower, but like all legends, it had a basis of truth. Buttercups grow only in dry, rich pastures, and cows that feed there are sure to give good milk and from it is made rich butter.

The daisy has always been popular, and people in some parts of Europe tell their fortunes by counting its petals. The name is really Day's Eye, because it closes its " lashes " and goes to sleep when the sun sets. In the Cotswolds the villagers call marguerites moon-daisies.

The tulip has always been a symbol of grace, and if you are ever lucky enough to see the tulip fields of Holland, or of our own Lincolnshire, you will never forget the graceful, dignified bearing of the flowers.

In ancient times the columbine was called the thankless flower, and was supposed to show folly in its wearer.

So many poets have written about the violet and its shy modesty that everyone is familiar with the phrase " a modest violet," even applied to people.

Everyone associates orange-blossom with brides, but few nowadays know that honeysuckle, or woodbine as many country people call it, is the symbol of motherly affection.

The lily is always regarded as a symbol of purity and has many religious associations. Similarly the marigold derives its name from the Virgin Mary. In France it is called the *souci*, which means care. Some legends claim that wearers of it are enabled to understand the language of birds.

WHEN IS A ROSE NOT A ROSE?

The primrose, which, of course, is not a rose at all, but in the primula family, is called in some countries the key-flower. It is supposed to show the way to hidden treasures, and certainly if you seek it you will find the treasures of the countryside in spring. The forget-me-not is also said to guard treasures.

The pansy, with its quaint " face," is a token of thoughtfulness, just as the passion flower is a symbol of faith.

The Turks say that the geranium was just a common mallow, until it was touched by the hem of Mohammed's robe. Clover is a lucky flower and the expression " he's in clover " refers to cattle who, if they are among clover, are among rich feeding. It can be too rich, however, and farmers have to watch cattle to see that they do not eat too much clover, as it is very dangerous to them when it is wet.

In Greek mythology Iris was the goddess of the rainbow, or the rainbow itself. There does not seem any particular reason why the name should be given to the flower, or to the circle surrounding the pupil of the eye, except that both are veined in many colours.

Shamrock, the national emblem of Ireland, was known as the symbol of light-heartedness and gaiety. In ancient days they said no serpent would touch it.

THE LENT LILY

Wales claims the leek and the daffodil as national emblems. The former is said to have been used by St. David, the patron saint of Wales, to distinguish his countrymen from their Saxon enemies. They wore the emblem in their caps. The daffodil was originally known as the Lent lily. It was once white, but legend says that when Persephone was captured by Pluto these flowers, with which she had wreathed her head, turned to gold. In hollyhock, the word, as in holly itself, is derived from " holy." The hollyhock is the holy mallow.

It is easy to see where the " glove " comes from in foxglove, for the flowers are just like a finger-stall, but how it came to be associated with the animal, no one knows. The Welsh often call it the Fairy's Glove. The ancients said it induced sleep, and in fact a drug is still extracted from the plant.

The fuchsia, named after a Dr. Fuchs, is regarded as a symbol of good taste. To present this flower is to compliment the recipient upon his or her discrimination.

The lily of the valley was used in earlier times as an indication of returning happiness. It was given often to people who were recovering from illness or misfortune. And though, to-day, lilies of the valley can be frozen or encouraged by heat, so that they can be brought to flower at any month of the year, they are still in their delicate purity and elegance a symbol of the encouragement and hope of spring.

Golden rod, which brings a blaze into the shadows of autumn, is a symbol of maturity.

BEWARE OF THE " BEAUTIFUL LADY "

The one flower to avoid is the deadly nightshade, whose other name is belladonna. That is the Italian for " beautiful lady," and the flower is attractive, but its berries are poisonous.

In some countries the sweet pea is offered by romantic maidens as a warning that the recipient shall be cautious, but " say it with flowers " nowadays has an unfailingly happy significance. Any flowers, even the humblest of wild flowers, are likely to give more pleasure than the dull laurel leaves which were once the victor's crown and supposed to bestow the gifts of prophecy and divination. Some ancient writers even put laurel leaves under the pillow, to give them inspiration. If any effects were felt, they were probably due to a sound sleep.

The deadly nightshade has poisonous berries.

The toothless Echidna or spiny ant-eater, one of the only two egg-laying mammals in the world. In appearance it resembles the porcupine but it is in fact no relation.

FLORA AND FAUNA OF AUSTRALIA

The Land of unique and gentle animals

Australia is the land of the most unique and gentle animals ever known. Except for the opossum of North and South America, it is the only land to have marsupials. These are creatures whose young are born immature and are then transferred to a pouch where they are nourished for varying periods. Most people think that all the Australian animals except the wild dog, or dingo, are marsupials; but this is not so. There are about 107 species of marsupials, and 106 of mammals. These mammals are all rodents except for the bats.

There are two creatures even more primitive than the mammals—platypus and echidna, which belong to the genus monotremata. These are believed to be the last living link between the dinosaurs—the " terrible lizards " which roamed the world seventy million years ago—and the mammals.

Echidna, the spiny ant-eater, looks rather like a porcupine, but actually it is no relation. It lays leathery eggs, has a pouch, and suckles its young. It eats ants, catching them on its foot-long string of a tongue, which it flashes out from a kind of beak. Platypus, the other monotreme, was called " water mole " by early settlers. This rare creature has a rubbery bill somewhat like a duck's, a fur-covered body

The Platypus is aquatic and lives in a burrow in the bank of a stream.

and a tail like a beaver; it lives in and on the banks of streams.

At Healesville, an animal sanctuary in Victoria, platypuses live in a glass tank in which you can watch them feeding. They hunt with eyes closed, guided by scent and the vibrations in the water caused by worms, 800 of which they eat daily. They spread their four tiny webbed paws like fans, turning their supple wrists like fan-dancers as they swim. When they tire of hunting food they journey to their nest through a straw-filled pipe which sleeks their wet fur.

ANIMAL MIGRATION

Land bridges, connecting Australia and the East millions of years ago, brought many animals from New Guinea and Malaya into the north of Australia. Scientists have suggested that marsupials entered the continent from the

The Dingo is an enemy of the farmer and incessant warfare is waged against it.

south, via Antarctica and the now sunken land of Gondwana, at a time when the climate was tropical. Proof of this, they say, is a fossil tiger found in Patagonia which is identical with a Tasmanian fossil. South American opossums also are similar to the Tasmanian dasyure.

Western Australia had an ocean dividing it from the East, and many of its flora and fauna differ from those in the rest of the continent, for when the ocean subsided the desert it exposed was uncrossable.

ALL SHAPES AND SIZES

Standing proudly to the left of the national coat-of-arms is the kangaroo, probably the best known Australian animal. Kangaroos come in all sizes, from the big red " boomer," stand-

The Wombats coat is long and coarse, the colour ranging from buff to almost black.

ing over seven feet, to the tiny marsupial mouse. Koalas too are famous, though rightly confined to their own land as they can live only on two species of eucalyptus. They are gentle grey teddy-bears that carry their single baby clinging to their backs. Their name means " nothing to drink."

There are four species of wombats—the soft-haired and hairy-nosed; the harsh-haired and naked-nosed—and they come in two sizes. The Flinders Island wombats grow to thirty pounds or so, the big ones to about a hundred-weight. The small ones make delightful pets and are very funny and affectionate. These nice animals have no defence against enemies except the crushing power of the last third of their backs, which is fused solid. They trot

This joey (young Kangaroo) will soon leave the pouch to fend for itself.

hunted they have acquired great cunning. Their instinct to kill cannot be subdued.

REPTILES

Australia's largest reptile is the crocodile, found only in the north. The small kind, called Johnsoni, is harmless and lives in inland rivers and waterholes. The fierce man-eater of the estuaries is said to grow to thirty feet and it is shot for its skin.

Perentie lizards also live in the north, growing to seven or eight feet, and are like the goanna or monitor of the south. Perenties run very fast and when fighting they bite, and slash with their tails. None of Australia's lizards are venomous. *Moloch horridus* is a horrid name given to a charming lizard. It is about nine inches long and appears to be covered with thorns. It never drinks, but absorbs water through its body, and must have a daily dunking. The " bearded dragon " looks fierce, spreading his beard fan-wise beneath his chin. When this is folded it provides him with a useful larder, for he keeps flies and other insects in the wrinkles! The " frill lizard " spreads his frill at the *back* of the head. When it is folded the lizard appears to be wearing a smart Egyptian headdress of the time of the Pharaohs.

after their owners like small bears and are individual and delightful.

In the north-east there is a small marsupial not unlike a kinkajou. This is the cuscus, a climber with a prehensile tail, that looks like a cross between a bear and a fat cat. Its creamy, sometimes spotted body, seen in trees, has given rise to the rumour that there are monkeys in Queensland. It is slothful, greedy, and quite charming.

THE DINGO

Dingoes, the only carnivores and most important non-marsupials, vary from terrier-size to that, say, of an Alsatian. They are usually yellow, with white markings, and every pup has a white chest. They are much persecuted because they are inveterate sheep-killers. They run in small packs of about six, though bushmen from the Territory claim that some packs there number a hundred. They never attack man. Their cry is a strange double sound, unlike the howl of wolf or dog. They usually have four or five pups and are hard to tame. To survive in a hard and hungry land they had to become killers; now from being continually

Mother Koala also carries her baby in her pouch until old enough to climb on her back.

Symbolical of most things Australian, is this " Old Man of the Bush "—proud example of Eucalyptus camaldulens syn. E. Rostrata, commonly known as River Red Gum. It follows the inland watercourses of the continent and is probably the only species of the genus that grows in every mainland State. It lives to a great age, its timber is tough and useful.

This little fellow looks friendly enough, but in actual fact it is the savage Tasmanian Devil, found only in Australia.

There are about 106 species of snakes, but few of them are venomous. Ancestors of the pythons came to the north from the steamy jungles of Malaya and are known to grow to twenty-eight feet, though most of them seldom exceed sixteen feet. They are beautifully patterned. The largest, the scrub python, has scales unsuited to the manufacture of goods, and as pythons eat rats and other pests, sensible people leave them alone. The taipan, a large and deadly snake of the north, is not so pleasant and is said to be working its way southwards. The most venomous is the tiger snake; then the deathadder, black snake and others; but the harmless and beautiful varieties far outnumber the venomous ones.

THE WATER-FILLED FROG

An interesting little creature wonderfully adapted to its environment is the " quart-pot frog." When a drought is coming this frog fills itself with water, digs into the mud and hibernates; nature seals its mouth and eyelids.

There it stays, looking like a rubber ball, until rain comes—or until something, animal or man, digs it up and squeezes the water from it.

FLIGHTLESS BIRDS

There are about 700 species of birds. Emu, sharing with kangaroo the coat-of-arms, is a flightless bird rather like an undersized ostrich without the plumes. The males brood the eggs and mind the chicks. Male emus make a deep drumming sound that terrifies horses.

A heavier flightless bird than the emu, though not so tall, is the cassowary of north-east Australia. It lives deep in the jungle, shunning sunlight, and has a horny helmet on its head. The eggs are pea-green, and both male and female brood them on a nest of rough sticks.

EAGLES

Grandest of hunting birds, the wedgetailed eagle, *uroeatus aquila*, is the fourth largest of all eagles. Graziers persecute wedgetails because they take occasional lambs, forgetting how they help to control the grass-eating pests and to dispose of carrion which breeds blowflies deadly to sheep. Wedgetails also prey on dingo pups and fox cubs, as well as on many other killers.

UNIQUE AUSTRALIAN BIRDS

Cockatoos and parrots are everywhere, from the big white cockatoo to the emerald green budgerigar. From these small parrots have been bred the many-coloured pets, of which there are ten million in England alone. Brolgas—tall, grey, crane-like birds with red faces—do stately mating dances on the plains. The kookaburra is a most delightful bird, it is the jester of the bush and a formidable snake-killer. Lyre-birds, so-called because of their beautiful tails, have wonderful powers of mimicry. The brush turkey is one of the three " incubator " birds of the genus megapodes which lay their eggs in huge mounds built by the male. There the eggs are left to hatch by the heat of decaying vegetation. The male uses his head as a thermometer, popping it into the mound to test the heat and scratching some of the mound away if it is too hot. Bower birds make and decorate their own playgrounds with coloured bits of glass and small gleaming

bones. All these birds are uniquely Australian.

TASMANIAN CURIOSITIES

Tasmania is the home of the rarest marsupial, a heraldic version of it supports the coat-of-arms. No one knows if this creature, the thylacine or marsupial tiger, is extinct, or if it still lives in remote parts of the west. Expeditions have searched in vain, and another is planned shortly. Thylacine is a big yellowish creature, perhaps seven feet long, its hinder parts striped like a tiger's, its head like a wolf's. It has a hoarse bark and hunts by night; unfortunately, it is a savage sheep-killer. It usually has two young, and its pouch opens backwards. The last tiger was seen in 1954. Some people are confident it survives and remains untrapped because " when you are tracking it, it is tracking you."

Less rare, is the Tasmanian Devil, a sturdy little fellow, rather like a bear, and with a dreadful temper! It is about twenty-eight inches long, with a mark like a white horseshoe on its black chest. It has very powerful jaws and big teeth, lives on rats, frogs and so on and is not always tameable. Owners of tamed ones find them delightful pets. Devils usually have four babies which stay in the pouch for several months. They swim long distances

Grass trees or the " blackboy " which grows only twelve inches in a hundred years.

A ghost gum standing in the dry river bed of the Finke River.

underwater, and are as fastidiously clean as any cat. There are ten marsupials, fourteen species of birds, three varieties of poisonous snakes, and two lizards unknown elsewhere.

FLORA

Variations of temperature and rainfall decide the natural growths of Australia. North Queensland has a tropical belt of lush greenery, vines and brilliant flowers. A broad stretch of limited rainfall extends northwards from Victoria, curves up the east coast, then goes across the north as far as Broome in the west. This broad swathe has a thick growth of eucalypts, which are indigenous only to Australia where there are some six hundred varieties. Their common name is gum-trees, and they shed their bark but not their sickle-shaped leaves, which some trees turn sideways to the sun to conserve moisture.

Wattle trees are one of the thousand varieties of acacias. Flowering over acres of country, the tops of the trees make a fluffy, honey-scented blanket of blossoms, a living " Field of the Cloth of Gold."

BEYOND THE TREE LINE

Farther inland there is less rain and the big trees dwindle into mallee scrub. In the centre of the continent, saltbush, a good fodder for stock, grows along with patches of scrub of mulga. Nullabor Plain, south of the desert lands, stretches along the Great Australian Bight, bearing out its name of " no trees." After rain in the semi-desert, acres of Sturt Pea flowers with heads like red parrots, turn the land into a magic carpet of crimson.

INTERESTING AUSTRALIAN VEGETATION

In Western Australia there are the oldest of all trees, the " blackboy," which grows only twelve inches in a hundred years. Its stumpy black trunk is crowned with bunches of grassy leaves. The flowers, are the tops of long,

The Sturt Desert Pea grows prolifically in Northern, Western, Southern Australia and Queensland. Its flowers resemble the heads of parrots.

The black and red " kangaroo paw," one of Western Australia's 4,000 species of wild flowers.
When in bloom this bush gives the impression of red flames covering the ground.

straight stems which look like spears thrust in a woolly head.

One of Western Australia's most delightful wild flowers is the red and green " kangaroo paw." This small bush when in bloom gives the impression of red flames covering the ground. Like something from another world are the pitcher plants that trap and feed on insects. Cyprus pine grows over much of the land and is valuable for building, as white ants will not eat it.

In the tropical north the thick undergrowth gives way to liana-twisted trees decorated by orchids. Eucalypts do not grow in tropical forests, but cedar, beech and native ash, do. This is the land of sugar-cane, bananas, pine-apples, custard apples and monsteria deliciosa, which is like a reptilian cucumber and has the flavour of a dozen fruits.

Along the flat, muddy shores in the north, mangrove swamps flourish. These smell of sulphur and long black mangrove roots rise like bunches of snakes from the mud. There, too, are frangipanni trees with their flowers of scented ivory filling the air with richness.

Lower down, perhaps an hour by air from Brisbane, is central Queensland where huge bottle trees and beautiful flowering Bauhinias, and rivers with palm-fringed banks, give the illusion of being in another world.

Tasmanian forests can be divided into two kinds; the drier forests have ironbarks, alpine ash, mountain ash and blue gum, while the rain forests on the fiercely mountainous west side are covered in myrtle, beech, blackwood, celery-top pine, leatherwood and sassafras. King William and Huon pine are valuable, but less plentiful now. The flowers and fruits of cool climates grow abundantly—not only apples but pears, apricots, quinces, raspberries, and many beautiful flowers such as clematis, anemonies, and ranunculus.

On the mysterious west coast parts of the earth are overgrown by the almost-impassable bauera scrub, known as the " horizontal." Its small branches spread horizontally a couple of feet from the ground, forming a roof that can be walked on, but is a menace if the traveller falls through it.

These specimens of New Zealand's unique reptile, the tuatara, were subsequently flown overseas to London, San Francisco and New York. They were caught on Stephens Island in Cook Strait.

FLORA AND FAUNA OF
NEW ZEALAND

NEW ZEALAND, in contrast to Australia, was a land quite without mammals, except for two varieties of bats, and one other " doubtful "; a kind of rat believed to have been brought to New Zealand by the first Maoris. The only marsupial is an opossum introduced by the white men, which is a pest because it eats the native trees.

But if these strange islands—ranging from volcanic, semi-tropical regions in the north, to the South Island's snow-topped and rugged mountains—have no native mammals and no snakes, they still have one reptile and a host of flightless birds, all of which are intensely interesting. The reptile is a thirty-inch lizard called tuatara; its ancestors were the dinosaurs that once walked the world.

EFFORTS TO PRESERVE RARE SPECIES

Before colonisation tuataras were plentiful in New Zealand. When the Maoris brought dogs, and later when white men brought cats and pigs, tuataras were drastically reduced. To-day they are not found on the mainland at all, but only on several small islands off the coast. It is forbidden to kill tuataras or to keep them as pets. Their numbers have now increased so that a few zoos have been allowed to import them. The special feature of this small reptile is a transparent scale on the top of its head which is its third eye. This eye has an optic nerve which may enable it to distinguish between light and darkness. Æons ago, numbers of animals, including man,

316

probably had a third eye, but only the tuatara has retained a trace of sight in it. Tuataras share their burrows with the petrel bird, and are said to eat the young birds, which seems most ungrateful. They are silent creatures, except at mating time when they croak like frogs. Their eggs take a year to hatch. Tuataras are an even older link with the past than are Australia's monotremes.

Emus, ostriches, cassowaries and rheas, all flightless birds, are still to be found in several parts of the world; the moa, a native of New Zealand, and now extinct, was the biggest of them all, growing to a height of twelve feet. There were two dozen known species of moas. Though all these were said to have become extinct at the end of the eighteenth century, some scientists believe that one of the smaller moas may yet be discovered alive in some heavily-wooded area. In 1952, moa footprints were believed to have been seen near the Teremakau River in the South Island.

These claims are considered possible, as the footprints of the takahe, another flightless bird, believed to have been extinct for fifty years, were found in wild country near Lake Te Anau, South Island. An expedition penetrated the dense forest to the snow line, and there they netted two takahes. These were photographed and released. The takahes were eighteen inches tall, with bronze breasts and rudimentary wings.

Men argued that if such a large bird as this could conceal itself for half a century, then why might not one of the smaller species of moas have done the same? Takahes were eaten by the Maoris, but only four were ever caught by white men. When a dog dragged one from the undergrowth in 1898, the New Zealand government bought the bird for over £200.

Still living, but fast dying out, are the kiwis, which are wingless. They are the size of hens, and the three species differ in colour. The brown bird of the North Island is smaller than the grey variety of the South Island. Kiwis have hair-like feathers and shun sun-

A Kiwi with its large single egg. This flightless bird is native to New Zealand and differs from other birds in having no tail, and no wings.

shine. Their sight is poor, but their hearing and sense of smell are acute. They feed at night, mostly on earthworms and grubs. By torchlight, the tailless, gnome-like figure of a feeding kiwi, looks like a little man bending over with his feathered cloak folded about him. During the day kiwis sleep in holes in trees. They can run swiftly on their sturdy feet, and defend themselves by using their sharp claws. A kiwi egg weighs a pound, which makes it the biggest egg of any bird, relative to its size. It lays one or two greenish-white eggs on the earth, never on grass, between June and October. The male broods them.

INTRODUCTION OF CARNIVORES

New Zealand's lack of mammals proved to be a delayed sentence of death for many species of flightless birds. When man introduced carnivorous animals the poor birds had no instinctive knowledge of mammal-ways, as they would have had if, early in their evolution, they had spent their lives in more mixed company. Even the giant moa had only its size and its super-ostrich kick with which to defend itself. It had no chance against alien enemies. The story of New Zealand's wonderful bird life seems to be drawing to a close.

THE ROYAL ALBATROSS

A splendid winged bird nests on a stony headland at the entrance to Dunedin's harbour, which is its sanctuary. This is the royal albatross, not the largest but the rarest of these lovely birds. Elsewhere, Royals nest far from man, and the Dunedin sanctuary is the only one where they can see the activities of man as they soar in from the ocean on wide wings. Their wing-span is ten feet six inches. Royals look like enormous gulls, and are larger than geese. Both males and females brood, and the large bald chick is hatched on rocky ground.

These birds are eight years old before they begin to breed, perhaps because parent birds must be strong in flight, flying hundreds of miles across the Pacific, sometimes staying away for a week hunting their favourite food —small squids. The sitting albatross waits, nibbling its snowy breast with its hooked beak which is an almost translucent pinkish-yellow. The chick cannot fly until it is a year old, during which time the parents feed it pre-digested

The Kea has a reputation for savagery, but in captivity is a gentle and clown-like bird.

food which they regurgitate with great effort. The Maoris made a small tattooing instrument and a tiny flute from albatross wingbones.

A SONGSTER

A beautifully-feathered New Zealand songster is the Tui bird which has a rippling song of five notes, akin to the bellbird's song, perfectly described by the poet, Kendall, in the line—"the notes of the bellbird are running and ringing."

THE KEA

The kea, from the cold, mountainous regions of the South Island is a beautiful bird with a bad reputation. But the kea was taught the ways of savagery by the carelessness of men who killed sheep and threw the kidney fat away for the keas to eat. They developed such a taste for it that they found their own cruel method of getting it.

In captivity the kea is a gentle and rather clown-like fellow. There is one in the Regent Park Zoo. This bird has a finely curved bill, and glorious plumage, olive green with scarlet-lined wings. Keas got their name from their cry " kea! kea! " They are strong flyers, nesting in crevices of rock at inaccessible heights, and coming down into the gullies during the winter. They lay pitted-shelled white eggs and usually breed in early July.

Climbing the Kauri tree to collect the resinous gum. The trunks of these trees grow to a height of sixty or seventy feet before branching out.

SEA LIFE OF THE ARCHIPELAGO

There have been reports written years ago of blind fish called koaro, born in the crater lake of Mt. Tongariro, North Island, a strange form of life. It is said that they spawn in the lake and their eyes are covered by a film. They travel underground through long channels to Lake Roto Airo where the film covering their eyes dissolves.

Dolphins, enchanting mammals of the Pacific, have been friendly and fearless to man around New Zealand shores. Many years ago a famous dolphin called Pelorus Jack, used to pilot ships in Admiralty Bay. Recently a dolphin christened Opo, from the village of Opononi, 150 miles above Auckland, swam close to the beach and played with the swimmers, giving children rides on its back. Its antics turned the sleepy little town into a prosperous tourist resort, until, to the general grief, handling may have removed the protective slime from Opo's body, and he was found washed up on the rocks, dead.

The beautiful tree-fern which gives an exotic semi-tropical appearance to the landscape.

FLORA OF NEW ZEALAND

To go into some parts of the bush on the North Island is not unlike entering a cathedral. Tall trees form a roof through which the sun scarcely penetrates, so that everything is hushed and dark and there is no undergrowth. Vines twine among the trees, but there are no big bright flowers as in the tropics; the trees themselves have blackish trunks, and foliage that is dark and leathery, because the leaves are evergreen.

Many of the vines are epiphytes, which means that, unlike parasitic vines, they receive no nourishment from their host-trees, but merely use them as ladders to climb to the light. Orchids and mistletoe grow on the trees, delicate white clematis twines through branches of the dark forests.

NATIVE TREES

North of Auckland is the last of the once vast forests of beautiful kauris. They rise on trunks like grey columns to sixty or seventy feet before branching out. Kauris are slow growing, they give a resinous gum which is collected by climbers and used in the manufacture of varnish. The Maoris once used it as fuel to light their fires and torches.

Totara was once among the most useful of the North Island trees; in the damper lowlands of the South Island rimu is plentiful. A big, squat solid tree with silvery leaves, called Pohutakawa, blooms for three weeks at Christmas when the tips of its twigs show a blaze of brilliant red flowers.

Many trees are common to both islands. Miro, a big tree with blackish bark and narrow leaves, has red fruit the size of plums that ripen in the winter and taste of turpentine. Tallest of the trees is kahikatea, or white pine, towering to two hundred feet, its fruit is a red berry, eaten by the Maoris. It grows on swampy land and its wood is used to make butter-boxes because of its lack of odour.

VARIOUS PROPERTIES OF TREES

Captain Cook was more than a great sailor; he was also a practical man and his journeys were sagas of ingenuity. Scurvy was the sailors' great enemy in his day, and Cook

A Maori tohunga (holy man) drinking from a flax cup. Strips of the New Zealand flax are also used, sun-dried and bleached white, to make mats similar to the one pictured here.

tackled it with practical common sense. From the young branches of the rimu, or red pine, he had spruce beer brewed, this proved to be a specific against scurvy. The rimu has seeds not unlike acorns. The Maoris claimed that if the bark was taken from the side of the tree facing the sunrise, it had healing properties.

Early settlers lost many of their animals which ate the poisonous leaves of the tutu, but the Maoris made a drink from the juice of the berries. Another small tree is the ngaio. It has white, lilac-spotted flowers and leaves of bright green, and grows by the seashore. The Maoris believed that a ngaio tree grew on the moon.

MAORI USES FOR PLANTS

The foothills of the Southern Alps are called tussock-grass country. Near watercourses the toe-toe grows, a grass that resembles the pampas of the Argentine. A quarter of a century ago there were four million acres of ferns in New Zealand. The fernlands are at their best north of Lake Taupo where the bracken grows to a height of ten feet, forming miniature forests which, with the tree-ferns, give the islands its semi-tropical look and its name, " The Land of Ferns." The nikau palm, which grows to thirty feet, has ringed green stems and white flowers; its leaves are fourteen feet long and were used by the Maoris to thatch their huts. Such thatching is quite rain-proof.

Cattle eat the leaves of the cabbage-tree and it is also used for thatching and to make a rough cloth. Early settlers used the young heads of the palm as a substitute for real cabbage. Roots of bracken were soaked and beaten by the Maoris between two stones, the fibres were removed and in the end the roots produced a sort of flour, a little like coarse arrowroot, and this added to their rather sparse diet.

Another domestically-useful plant is New Zealand flax. It has flower stems that are twelve feet long, and leaves of half that length. Strips from the leaves are used to make an almost unbreakable string. These strips can be sun-dried until they are bleached white, and then they are used to make mats and baskets.

TRAPS FOR THE UNWARY

In the South Island part of the ground is covered by a scrub with a flattened top which can be walked over, like the " horizontal " of Tasmania. Like that too, these flat-topped bushes are very tough and if the enterprising walker happens to fall through, he has great difficulty in forcing his way on top of the bushes again, even though he may only be on the ground a few feet beneath their almost impenetrable branches.

Heaths grow abundantly, as does New Zealand bramble, and there are many flowering trees and bushes. The largest of the shrubs is possibly the southern rata, or ironwood, which is more of a tree than a shrub in size, as it grows to a height of sixty feet. Its flowers have small scarlet petals and the flowering tree simply blazes with colour.

THE CREEPERS

Rata vines, related to the shrub, twine themselves round forest trees and strangle them. Supplejack is a creeper that makes penetrating the bush almost an impossibility. It binds the trees together like ropes, and it is used in this way to bind the posts of houses. New Zealand has a plant-reminder of Western Australia, for it has that strange, carnivorous plant, the sundew, which feeds on flies and other insects.

VARIETY OF VEGETATION

In the South Island the vegetation ends at the line of perpetual snow, though a wealth of sub-Alpine plants remains: flowering shrubs, masses of white wildflowers and a great variety of leaf-forms that flourish in the spring.

Palm and pine, rata and manuka, cabbage-tree, beach and fern—New Zealand is a lavish, exotic land. Her soil produces growths that, like the supplejack, cabbage-tree, New Zealand flax and many others, contributed to the living conditions of her splendid natives, and are still desirable in this more modern world.

The great wolf-packs of legend have not stood up very well to modern research. Wolves do pack, of course, but the usual unit is a family who run together through the Winter.

WOLVES

AND WOLF-PACKS

Walt Disney has done for the wolf what the Scottish poet Robert Burns did for the Devil—made a stage villain out of him. To-day, children laugh at the antics of the big bad wolf, knowing perfectly well that half-a-dozen little piglets are going to make a fool out of him in the end. Cry " Wolf! " to-day, and toddlers titter. They know that Little Red Riding Hood always escapes. . . .

Yet the real wolf, who was really quite un-like Disney's comic-opera villain, roamed the Scottish Highlands for half a lifetime after the union of 1707, which isn't such a very long time ago. The clansmen who marched with Charles Edward Stuart in 1745 had known the wolf, or heard first-hand accounts of him from their fathers. At that time England had long since lost the wolf. It had just become extinct in Scotland. But it still lingered in Ireland.

In those days, long before the last of the Stuarts had raised his standard at Glenfinnan, special shelters were erected in the lonely Highland glens where travellers sought refuge from—wolves! There is very little in historical records to show whether wolves were, in fact, a menace to travellers, but the shelters were there anyway. The wolves to-day, as in the past, are more interested in deer and other food animals than in man.

HISTORY OF THE LAST SCOTTISH WOLF

The last Scottish wolf died, if we take note of all the records, in about a dozen different places! He died in about as many places as the Prince slept in. There can be no unassailable record of his final demise, but certainly he had disappeared by the middle of the 18th century, and the year seems to have been 1743. Equally, the distinction of killing the last wolf must have been claimed by a number of people. The best account—the one that ought to be the right one, even if it isn't—is as follows. . . .

MacQueen of Pall-a-chrocain, deer-stalker on the Findhorn (where the great gentleman St. John amused himself killing ospreys) is the man usually given credit for the death of the last wolf of Caledonia. More people should know the story of him. . . .

When the black beast, as the wolf was called, had killed two children the Laird of McIntosh called a *tainchel* to round him up, and MacQueen was appointed leader of the expedition. The men were a long time on the hill and, as the day wore on, with no sign of MacQueen's return, the Laird became angry at the delay. Tradition does not suggest that he was in any way alarmed for the safety of the men; he was merely angry at their long absence. However, his anger turned to elation when the stalker turned up at dusk—his mission successfully completed.

For MacQueen had the bloody head of the wolf hanging from his belt! And he had a wonderful story to tell—a story that is a masterpiece of understatement and restraint. For it has to be borne in mind that the man was armed only with a dirk. Said the Mac-Queen. . .

" As I came through the slochk by east the hill there, I foregathered wi' the beast. My long dog there turned him. I buckled wi' him, and dirkit him, and syne whuttled his craig, and brought awa his countenance for fear he should become alive again, for they are precarious creatures."

There, surely, is one of the shortest and

There are many species of wolf. The common wolf is like a big Alsatian dog, and the colour varies from grey, yellow, brown to near-black.

Dog and bitch wolf share the work of rearing a family, the male, providing all the food in the early stages and afterwards sharing the work with his mate.

most wonderful animal stories in all literature! Danger? Personal prowess? No! the Mac-Queen simply foregathered wi' the beast—as if he had been meeting an acquaintance for a chat—and dirkit him. It was just another job of work to the MacQueen.

OTHER LAST WOLVES

Ireland kept her wolves for longer than Scotland, as I have said, and that despite the £6 a head offered by Cromwell for every bitch wolf killed. It almost seems that the Irish refrained from killing wolves to show Cromwell that they didn't want his money. Anyway, it was 1770 before the last wolf made his final bow on the Irish stage. The wolf has gone; Cromwell has gone; but the Irish still linger. . . .

What about England? The wolf was exterminated by Royal decree, helped by the bounties offered for each scalp, and had gone at the dawn of the 16th century, nearly 250 years before it vanished from Scotland. The beast created considerable havoc in the shrinking English countryside, and the total war against it began early.

There is little in the literature about the wolves of this country that is reliable; they disappeared before the days of the great, inquiring naturalists. It would seem that the people of those far-off days were so afraid of the wolf that they thought only of avoiding, or killing, him, and made no effort to study him. Fact and legend have come down to us in inseparable mixture, and the picture we get is of an animal cruel, sinister, a menace to man and his stock, even evil, or with supernatural powers. Legend has had a long start over facts, but present-day research is slowly discovering the truth.

THE COMMON WOLF

There are many species of wolf, but the animal that once roamed over Britain was kin to those still found in Germany and Spain, Eastern Europe and Russia. The common wolf is like a big Alsatian dog, in a good specimen well over 130 pounds in weight and fully six feet in length. There are wolves bigger than that, great muscular beasts built for speed and endurance, with no fat on them. Colour varies through many shades of grey, yellow to brown; there are paler types, and some specimens are near-black.

The immense wolf-packs that howl down the long corridors of history—packs of a hundred or more ruthless, ravening beasts, organised like army formations, with commanders and lieutenants planning offensive actions—are mostly the stuff of legend. People were so afraid of wolves, as many are of any large dog, that the sight of a small pack caused panic, and the small pack became bigger and bigger with much telling until it became a regiment sweeping irresistibly across the snow.

The great wolf-packs of legend have not stood up very well to the remorseless scrutiny of modern research. Wolves do pack, of course, but the usual unit is a family—dog, bitch and puppies—who run together right through the winter. In severe winters, stragglers may join a family group, or one family may link its fortunes with another, and the pack, though still small in numbers, becomes powerful. Thus comes into being the " big " pack, but such packs are a mere handful compared with the great clans of the legends.

I have never seen a wolf-pack at any time; I have seen single wolves and a wolf with cubs. Packs of more than a family are, indeed, rarely reported, or, if reported, are usually found to have been exaggerated. Twenty wolves can easily become fifty, and wolves skirmishing at night over an area may seem to be a hundred strong.

Why should wolves pack? For increased strength one imagines. The pack can tackle far bigger game than any single wolf, or pair of wolves. The moose and the caribou become easier prey. The pack will make daring raids on domestic stock, and at night their quavering cries may give the impression of a great clan on the move.

DOUBTFUL STORIES ABOUT WOLVES

Will the wolf-pack attack man? There are plenty of stories of wolves doing so, but few indeed stand up to scrutiny or disciplined investigation. Here is a story from Ireland, told by the well known sportsman-naturalist Wentworth Day. . . .

One Jonathan Grubb wrote to the then Editor of *The Field* that " his grandmother was born in 1731 and that she remembered her uncle telling her how, in County Kildare, his brother came home on horseback pursued by a pack of wolves, which overtook him and

There are many stories of wolves following a sleigh, drawn either by dogs or horses. How much
is legend and how much is fact, careful research may one day supply the answer.

kept leaping on to the hindquarters of his horse until he reached the door."

For wolves to attack a horse would be quite in accordance with habit. But would they attack a horse carrying a rider? That would depend, I imagine, on how hungry they were and how bold hunger had made them. Or, perhaps, they were quite unaware that the horse had a rider. This account could be perfectly accurate, for there is nothing to suggest that the pack was attacking the man.

There are many similar accounts of riders being followed by wolves, or of a pack following a sleigh drawn by horses or dog-teams. But what were the wolves, in fact, following —man or his livestock? What is the evidence that wolves will attack man himself, when there is no room for doubt or conjecture? It is very slender indeed.

In the story of the stalker MacQueen, which I have told, there is the statement that the wolf had already killed two children. Now, a wolf could easily kill two children if it wished to do so. And one could imagine circumstances which would make such a thing possible. But would a wolf attack two children? All the evidence is against such a thing, but there is no valid reason why it couldn't happen. So the MacQueen story might be true.

Most of the stories of wolves attacking human beings came from Russia and the Balkans; later America and Canada contributed their share. What is the true position, at least as far as careful research can discover? In America, twenty-five years careful research by the United States Fish and Wildlife Service failed to substantiate one case of wolves attacking human beings. In Canada, however, there is one case, which seems to be authentic, of a wolf attacking a man—a single wolf attacking an unarmed man who was rescued by friends. Russian opinion is that wolves will not attack man under normal circumstances, and "normal circumstances" are the operative words.

The late Mortimer Batten, who knew the wolf well in Canada, remarked more than once on the fact that trappers and hunters, who had killed by traps and poisons a great many wolves over many years, had never seen one wolf alive and free in their lives. This indicates that, under " normal circumstances " the wolf is more likely to be heard than seen, and that it avoids man more often than not.

I could find no authentic case, in the north of Spain, of a wolf attacking a man deliberately though there, too, the majority of people dread the *lobo*. But, then, people in India fear the tiger, though only a very small minority of tigers become man-eaters, and therefore dangerous. Wolf-fear, and the accumulated legends, may be based on isolated but authentic cases of attack in unusual circumstances.

Circumstances not covered by the term " normal " might be visualised in the case of a wounded wolf driven by famine, or wolf in a trap, or a she-wolf cornered with cubs. But only the first and last would be able to do much damage. So we are left with the weight of evidence against the likelihood of free, wild wolves constituting a threat to the lives of people in normal circumstances.

" ATTACK " OF WOLVES

Domestic livestock is another matter, and wolves can do a great deal of damage. They are not, however, a menace to wild game; rather do wolves help to keep a balance by pruning down the numbers of grazing animals, like deer and wild sheep.

When we speak of a pack of wolves attacking and pulling down a deer, the word "attack" is properly used. In the case of a wolf attacking a man the proper description is more likely to be " counter-attack," and this is probably true in the majority of cases where a human being becomes involved with a large animal.

I think the following is a good illustration of what I mean. I knew a man who set his dog on a travelling otter. After the dog had chased the otter, and slashed at it several times, the otter turned against his tormentor, inflicting painful wounds. The man then ran at the otter with a hatchet and killed it. When he told me about the encounter, and I asked why he had killed the otter, he said he had done so because " it attacked the dog."

A wolf will fight back if cornered; so will a rat. So will a badger. So will a wildcat. But none of these can really be called attacks,

because they are purely defensive actions. A bull which chases a man from a field is a different matter entirely, and the bull which catches the man and tries to gore him is attacking in the true sense of the word.

What about the wolves which skulk about the camp-fires of trappers or hunters in the far north of Canada. Wolves have been known to play camp-followers in this way, and many a lonely hunter has imagined himself in danger of attack. But wolves are more likely to do this because they think there will be pickings after the man has gone, or because of curiosity. The wolf has learned the meaning of rifle fire, and its association with hunters, so it isn't surprising that he will keep in touch with a party of hunters. The raven in the Scottish Highlands does exactly the same thing during the stalking season; the birds flock into the deer forest knowing full well that there will be grallochs for them at the worst, whole carcasses at best. The stalkers know this so well that, when they have to leave a carcass on the hill overnight, they place some object beside it to scare the ravens off. Trappers in the north do the same thing to protect their caches from wolves and wolverines.

Wolves also learn quickly that domestic livestock is vulnerable at night when men are abed. So you will hear the pack close enough at hand during the darkness. Traps and poison baits are set to catch them, but many wolves become experts at avoiding traps and disdain the tempting baits. These are the beasts which become known, which develop reputations, so that they become legendary, with legends gathering thick around them.

The wolf, however, has his uses. Besides being a cog in the wheel of biological control, he is useful in improving the breed of dog teams used in the Arctic. The best dog teams are part wolf, and captive wolves are mated to sled-dogs, the offspring being carefully bred from afterwards to produce the best type of beast. If you consider that the average wolf will tip the scale at about eight stone, and that North American specimens may weigh up to half as much again, you can easily understand what the wolf gives to the sled-dog in bone, muscle and power.

THE VANISHING WOLF

Wolves are not, of course, either as plentiful

America and Canada still have their wolves. The wolves which preyed on buffalo stayed to harry domestic livestock when the white man had exterminated the buffalo.

or as widely distributed as they were even 100 years ago. They have gone from Britain, and are scarce in western Europe. The mountains of eastern Europe, and Russia, are their old-world strongholds to-day. In America they have been exterminated in many states; they have been deliberately cleared out of all America's national parks, an act about which the United States field staff are having second thoughts. Yet it is probably in America that the best work on the wolf has been done this century.

Ranchers and sheep-men raised the cry of Wolf! in the U.S.A. The wolves which preyed on the buffalo herds stayed to harry domestic livestock when the white man had exterminated the buffalo. So the wolf had to be exterminated over most of the country. But America and Canada still have their wolves (more than one species indeed) and in these countries their habits and movements have been carefully studied in recent years by skilled observers. The wolf, indeed, is an interesting member of the North American fauna, and America intends to keep him.

W.W.N.

WOLF RESERVATION

Much interesting work has been done on the wolves of America, particularly in the Mount McKinley area, and there a definite number of wolves is maintained as part of a deliberate ecological policy. In that area the wolf has a place as an ecological unit, helping to maintain at a safe level other creatures such as deer and wild sheep. Money and labour expended in killing excess deer and sheep can be saved if wolves can do the work.

KINSHIP AMONG WOLVES

Close and continuing study of the wolf in America has shown that dog and bitch wolf share the work of rearing a family, the male, like the dog fox, providing all the food in the early stages, and thereafter sharing the work with his mate. It has also been established that single, unmated wolves will sometimes put down food at a den containing cubs; in other words there seems to be some kind of kinship among the wolves of an area. Game killed by wolves is normally much bigger than that taken by foxes or coyotes—prey like

L2

The average wolf will tip the scale at about eight stone, and North American specimens may be as heavy as twelve stone.

deer and caribou being usual. They do, however, kill rabbits and hares, and will take prey much smaller than that when larger game is scarce. Contrary to popular belief wolves are not a menace to the continued existence of deer and other big game animals; they are, in fact, beneficial in reducing excess population on their range.

TAMING THE CUBS

Wolf cubs are very much like fox cubs in behaviour. They play just as much near the den mouth when they are very young, and are just as much given to hiding things they like. In the same way as young foxes, they often carry a favourite plaything about with them. Wolf cubs taken young enough can be tamed, but are likely to prove difficult as adults. Some remain manageable, but others become morose and aloof. Probably man produced his original dogs by breeding only

North American timber wolf, an interesting member of the fauna of North America, whose habits and movements have been carefully studied in recent years by skilled observers.

from those specimens which remained tame and manageable.

Wolves hunt over a vast range, but investigation has shown that they are not really nomads. They have their fixed territory, large though it is, and they work their ground by definite routes. This is not obvious at once, for a beast which kills at dusk may have travelled from thirty to forty miles by sunrise. Nevertheless, it makes its circuit by favourite routes, returning eventually to its starting point, from which it will begin its excursions over again in due course.

WOLF CUNNING

Many stories are told, and not all originating from the new world, of wolves which became notorious, not only for their depredations but for their cunning in avoiding traps and poisoned baits. Once a wolf has become trap-wary, and learns the killing power of the modern rifle, it constitutes a serious problem to stock-men. There is no reason to believe that Ernest Thompson Seton's account of the Currumpaw wolf was exaggerated; rather does it indicate how much we still have to learn about the workings of the animal mind. Professor Osmond P. Breland of the University of Texas tells the story of a wolf called Three Toes who was alleged to have destroyed stock to the value of more than twenty-five thousand, and perhaps up to fifty thousand, dollars in his life-time, and that despite the fact that every man's hand was against him.

Why is it, then, that the fox has survived in many places where the wolf has, long since, been exterminated? Is it because the fox is more cunning, more difficult to trap? Or is it, rather, that the wolf, killing large animals, had to be taken more seriously because his predations were more serious? The fact that the fox is small, and a habitual user of small burrows, must have helped him a great deal.

The first step before starting to train your dog is to win his affection and at the same time his respect. Fuss him, pet him, but be firm.

THE TRAINING OF A PUP

Lesson No. 1

Obedience is the first thing a puppy has to be taught, no matter for what purpose he has to be trained.

In the present instance I am starting off with a raw Labrador puppy, in the hope of producing eventually a no-slip retriever. But his primary schooling will consist of obedience, obedience and more obedience.

I shall want him to sit when I say so, or when I lift my hand or stamp my foot; to come when called, instantly; to walk at heel; to sit when I halt; to sit when I walk away and stay down till it pleases me to call him; to drop at any distance, (even when he is coming back at top speed) the instant I raise my hand ... Which is enough to be going on with....

FIRST SIMPLE COMMAND

By now I have won puppy Fencer's affection and respect. I have fussed him and petted him, and been firm with him. In short, I have got him where I want him. To-day I started his schooling. ...

I took him into the field a hundred yards from the house to teach him to sit. I could have started just as well in the yard or in a room of the house, but I prefer to work outside.

With the pup on a lead I put my hand on his rump, pressed him on to his seat, and said: " Sit! "

It didn't mean a thing to him and, of course, he promptly rose up the minute I took my hand away.

And he did the same thing the second time, and the third, and the fourth and the twenty-first. But each time I pressed him down again, repeating the word: " Sit! "

And there came a time when I straightened my back, and kept it straight for thirty seconds —with the pup sitting.

I walked him round once or twice before making him do it again. Twice I had to press him down, and twice he rose; but the third time he sat at the word, and stayed on his seat. HE WAS BEGINNING TO GET THE GLIMMERINGS OF AN IDEA.

I petted him and told him he was a good dog, then put him to it again. And I kept him at it till he went down at the word, without any hand work.

And now let me go from the particular to the general.

Having sold the puppy the general idea this simple lesson should be repeated for a couple of days till he goes down every time at the word of command.

And don't confuse him by varying the word. Stick to Sit!

HAND SIGNAL WITH COMMAND

On the second day you can introduce him to two other signals, without pushing them. They are the kind of signals that will grow on him by their constant use. WHEN YOU TELL HIM TO SIT RAISE ONE HAND AND DO IT EVERY TIME, FOR THAT IS THE SIGNAL THAT WILL EVENTUALLY REPLACE THE WORD ALTOGETHER.

As soon as you are ready to move on, tug the lead cord and make a clicking sound with your tongue. From then on the sound will be the puppy's instruction to rise and follow.

The reason for this is obvious. The puppy has to sit down till he is told to rise. The click tells him. But it has nothing whatever to do with walking to heel. He will have to be taught that. It gives permission to rise and follow—nothing more.

Lesson No. 2

I have described how I get a pup to sit, using that word accompanied by a lifted hand. It is so simple that a child can do it, after four days. And without a check cord!

Teaching to walk to heel is done at the same time. And, when you bring the pup home, you can teach him to go to basket or kennel at

the word. He should be proficient in all three after four or five days.

When walking the pup around between sitting lessons, keep him on a short cord at your heel. Do the same when you take him for a walk, from the moment you leave the house. Never allow him to rush off at the outset; he will run on by your permission—later.

When he is walking well, let the cord trail slack, so that he has yards to spare. He will discover it and probably go ahead. Stop dead, pull him back gently, put him in his proper place, and say, " Heel! " And do that every time he moves to the front.

Continue with the cord paid out. If he makes a bolt he will be brought up short. Again reel him in gently and tell him, " Heel! " He'll soon realise, and appreciate, that he is under control, even when the order takes the place of the cord. Never quicken pace to get in

A simple lesson should be repeated for a few days before going on to the next lesson.

Do not quicken your pace to get in front of the pup. The pup must learn to come to heel, and it is up to you to see that he does not get away with even his nose in front.

front of the pup. That is fatal. The pup must *come* to heel. Don't let him get away with even his nose in front!

Say, " Heel! " every time you put him in his place. If you do this patiently, without letting him away with a single default, he should be following naturally, free of cord and collar, by the fourth day!

ENSURE INSTRUCTIONS ARE CARRIED OUT

Kennelling, or going to basket, is simply taught, and should be done in these early days. And here, as in the other two lessons, you should not give the order unless you are in a position to see that it is obeyed.

Take the pup to his basket, remove the cord, get between him and escape, then say: " Basket! " or " Kennel! " as the case may be. The word will be so much Chinese to him at first. But put him in the desired place and repeat the word.

In the case of kennelling, he will then be shut up and you need bother no more till you are putting him in again. But in the case of a basket, he has only to step out when it pleases him. So, having put him there, tell him to sit. And, because he has learned to sit, and not to rise till he is told, he will stay there.

But don't make him stay overlong the first time. Call him out, and fuss him. Then go through the performance again, getting into an enforcing position as before. And repeat it at intervals, till he knows what basket means.

He should thereafter go there from any room in the house. But don't send him if you are going to ignore a default. If you send him see that he goes there.

Don't accept default by saying, " Och, the wee fellow's done very well till now. He's due a break." If you do, there'll be a next time. Let there be no misunderstanding.

Lesson No. 3

DON'T USE TOO MANY WORDS

The pup should now have three lessons mastered. And you should be getting along on three words and a hand signal—" Heel," " Basket " and " Sit " with a raised hand to replace the last when it suits you.

Here, let me emphasise that the fewer words you use the better. For example, use " No! " for everything that is wrong. It will save endless scolding and arguments, and will cut into his mind like a whip every time he makes a wrong move. Remember, too, there are no short-cuts; so if your pup is not coming along as you would like, you should cross-examine yourself before you rate him. Have you been impatient? Have you bossed instead of teaching? Has the pup lost confidence in you? Have you spoken so much that the pup is talk-drunk?

Never scold a slow puppy! Reserve that for wilful flouting of your wishes after he knows the time of day. A slow pup often turns out a workmanlike dog.

The pup's next lesson is designed to get an automatic reaction and is given while he is walking at heel. To begin with, tell him to sit every time you stop; and make a point of stopping frequently— every twenty or thirty yards. Presently, he should start beating you to the word. When he gets to that stage, stop using it. Simply halt and watch him.

Give him a moment or two when you stop. If he goes down on his own, good; if he doesn't tell him again. And carry on like that till he sits automatically every time you halt. You'll be surprised how quickly he'll catch on.

His signal to rise and follow at heel will be a click of the tongue; nothing more. Although he has some inkling of what this means he may not respond the first time. In this case call him up by name, then click your tongue. The two will become associated in his mind, and, presently, the click alone should lift him.

LEARNING TO STAY SEATED

And now he must learn to stay seated when you walk away and leave him. This is a supreme test for the puppy. So go easy with him.

The desire to follow you will be very strong, especially if you and he have struck up the right kind of partnership. But you must insist absolutely, without any half measures.

Take him out as usual, complete with long cord, and seat him in a place which puts you between him and the way home. Now take up the slack cord in one hand, raise the other,

He should sit when you stop.

Teaching him to stay seated by hand signals only.

Your puppy knows he has to sit until you return or you give him the signal to rise and follow you.

and back away from him slowly. Keep your hand up all the time.

The puppy may get his eyes fixed on the hand and let you go back without moving; on the other hand he may rise and try to follow as soon as he realises you are leaving him behind.

If he stays seated, walk slowly back the length of the cord, still keeping your hand raised, and fuss him. Play around with him for a few moments then seat him, and try the lesson again.

If, however, the puppy makes to follow you, go back to him, pick him up gently, and seat him on the spot from which he rose. Don't just put him down where you meet him; take him right back.

On no account speak harshly to him. After all it is the most natural thing in the world for him to want to follow you. Just keep putting him down on the spot, and back away with one hand raised, and the slack of the cord in the other.

The idea of holding on to the cord is that, if he makes a break, you can halt him. Another way is to leave the cord on the ground at full stretch, and actually back along it, so that you can put your foot on it at once if the puppy tries to run off.

If you do this properly the puppy shouldn't want to run off. He will, in most cases, get the idea that he has to stay down after a few mistakes.

Once he sits and lets you back to the distance you want, try moving to left and right, still keeping your hand raised. He will keep his eyes on you and stay down. Go to him frequently and pet him, telling him he's a good dog.

When he has passed this test try walking right round him. He should turn his head, or turn round on his seat, but he shouldn't rise.

When he has come through all these tests you should now try moving much further away from him, up to a hundred yards by degrees. By then you will have stopped raising your hand. He knows he has to sit until you return and click him up with the sound you have taught him. If it makes you feel any better you can tell him to *Stay* when you walk away, but this is quite unnecessary.

Victory is yours when you can turn your back on him and walk away briskly, knowing he will still be seated when you turn around a field's length away.

Lesson No. 4

Probably the biggest single headache experienced by dog owners is getting a dog to come at once when called. We have now reached the stage of teaching this supremely important lesson.

And it has to be taught.

Dog owners often say to me: " If my dog would come back every time I called him, I wouldn't care about anything else he couldn't, or wouldn't do. So why not begin there and get the main thing first? "

No! Main thing first may be desirable; but first things first are essential. Carts don't go before horses. Starting a puppy off with the recall is like serving up Shakespeare to a child who is still sounding vowels.

If you cannot control the dog you have on a cord, or that is scampering about your feet, how are you going to begin to control a free dog some distance away?

You can get your answer every day, if you listen to a hundred exasperated dog owners babbling a dog's name, at varying pitches, and with varying degrees of urgency and anger, without the calls touching any responsive cord in the dog's consciousness.

That kind of come-hither begets a-go-as-you-please. It is full of sound and fury, signifying nothing. And nothing is the result. . . .

The pup has to be built up to it. By now he knows certain words and responds to them in different ways; He reacts to the movement of your hand as if he was tied to it. Tied is the word. In his mind the idea has grown that he is under your control.

He knows what you mean, and responds by habit. Later, if you and he are on the right footing with each other, he will bring to the partnership the priceless asset of finding pleasure in pleasing you.

We seem to have gone a long way from the question of calling in a dog. We haven't. We have just reached the right frame of mind.

RECALLING YOUR PUP TO YOU

I must emphasise the importance of getting the puppy to stay down while you walk away for some distance. I want to stress it again. Move about, give him plenty of temptation to rise, and go back to him periodically to congratulate him on his behaviour. You have sold him the idea of control at a distance.

To call him in? Your work till now has been designed to prevent him from coming in! Here is a pup sitting 50 yards away, a pup that was desperately anxious to follow you, a pup that is only prevented from so doing because he KNOWS he must sit on. He isn't going to need any coaxing; he wants to come. He is awaiting your permission!

And that's the proper approach to the delicately adjusted canine mind. You don't have to command; you confer a privilege. You authorise him to rise and come to you. All you have to decide on is the cue!

In the first instance, take up a position between twenty and thirty yards from him, and call him by name. He may not rise, having developed a sit-fixation. Call him again, and pat your thigh encouragingly.

He'll come, gladly, at high speed, when he understands.

Next time, give some kind of beckoning signal when you call his name, or a whistle. It is as well to be able to bring the dog in without always calling his name, so in this lesson you should drop it, as soon as he rises to a whistle or signal.

My own signal to lift a seated puppy from a distance, as distinct from pulling up a ranging dog, is to make a backward and forward movement with my hand, patting my hip as the hand comes forward. I have never had any difficulty with it, and dogs recognise it at a surprising distance.

Lesson No. 5

I have suggested that, while you should call a pup from his distant seat by name in the first instance, you should drop the name in favour of whistle and hand signal as soon as he understands what is wanted.

I shall explain the everyday application of

A puppy sitting desperately anxious to follow you, should continue to stay seated until he gets the command from you to rise.

A black Labrador with a Roe fawn. If you teach your puppy to leave livestock alone, he will do so.

these, and the previous lessons, later in my article. In the meantime, drop the name at the earliest opportunity.

On the second day of this lesson, put the pup down as before and walk away some distance, keeping a sharp lookout over your shoulder in case he rises and makes to follow on. If he does, put him back on the spot with a stern command to sit there.

Having got away as far as you wish, give him the beckoning signal and the whistle simultaneously. He'll come on—at the double. And that's as it should be.

He will, in fact, usually come right up against your legs, fussing and wagging his tail. Fuss him in return, and tell him: " Good dog! "

Keep at it, walking him around at heel, and putting him through his other lessons between times, as a variation. He'll appreciate variety.

But see that he comes smartly to heel each time and call him in, indicating the side with your hand if you like. He'll generally come on that side to lick your hand. Thereafter he'll watch for it.

And now a warning. If the pup rises from his seat and, instead of sitting again when you order him, breaks away and runs in the direction of home, you SHOULD NOT RUN AFTER HIM. Never chase the puppy!

Let the pup go on home. Stop issuing orders immediately you see he is out of your control. You are not in a position to see that he obeys. Forget it!

Go home for him. Put him on a cord. Take him back to the spot from which he rose. Don't nag him, or bully him. Do not thrash him.

If a pup doesn't default you get no chance to reward good behaviour. Be firm; show him you are displeased; but never punish for a first offence. By taking him back at once you impress on him that he can't run out of your control.

Leave him sitting longer than usual this time. He'll know why you're doing it, for dogs have a sense of justice. Then start calling him in again.

You shouldn't have a repeat. Let him know your confidence is restored by removing the cord.

Now you must teach him to drop at any point after you have called him in. This is done by the hand signal that he understands, accompanied by a stamp of the foot. He is ready for it, and teaching him should cause you no headaches.

Go away thirty yards or so, then wave him in. When he is half-way, throw up your hand, stamp your foot, and snap out: " Sit! "

He'll probably stop, wondering. Keep your hand raised and your foot going, and tell him again to sit. When he goes down, you should go back back to him and make no end of a fuss over him.

If, on the other hand, he comes right on, a little confused, take him back to the point at which he should have dropped, and put him down gently but firmly. Then try again. You'll be surprised how quickly he'll catch on.

Thereafter he should drop to your signal, without the word, " Sit."

Lesson No. 6

The lessons so far learned bring you many advantages in their application to everyday life—and without additional teaching. Let me summarise. . . .

You have taught the dog to sit when required The advantages of this are obvious. You have taught him to walk to heel. The same thing applies.

You are walking on a country road where there are no pavements, and your dog is running ahead enjoying himself. A lorry suddenly appears. You call the dog to heel, walk to the verge and tell him to sit. The lorry passes on and you still have a dog.

That is just one aspect. You can think of others. Control has been established in two things that apply to hundreds of circumstances.

Your dog, walking at heel, now stops automatically when you stop, and sits down. He is not concerned with why you stop. He simply reacts by sitting down. But what are the benefits to you?

You come to a main crossing, and stop to look right and left before stepping on the road. You don't have to worry about the dog. He's seated at your heel.

You live up a stair? The dog won't rush down ahead of you, sweeping old ladies and toddlers before him. He'll sit while you lock the door and come down at your heel. If you're waiting for a bus, he'll follow you on, instead of shouldering his way through the crowd ahead of you, and perhaps taking a trip on the bus by himself if you can't get on.

He takes his cue from you. You have got him under control by instilling a habit.

The advantages of having a dog that will stay seated when you leave him are obvious. You may want to be without him for a few minutes—stepping into a friend's garden, going into a crowded shop, into a public library, up a stair, to call on someone who is nervous about dogs, and so on. He thinks nothing about it.

The dog that will drop to a hand signal is a boon under any circumstances. I once saved my dog because of his instant response.

I called him from a field, and when he was well in his stride, ready to burst on to the road, a car swung suddenly into view, travelling fast. I dropped the dog before he jumped the fence, just as the car shot past the spot. And that is only one thing. . . .

THE RECALL UNDER DIFFERING CONDITIONS

And now the recall. There shouldn't be any difficulty about this, but I think you should sort out the name, whistle and hand signal to suit the circumstances.

For instance, the hand signal alone should be used for the dog who is watching you for instructions. Whistle if it pleases you but the whistle is useful for attracting the dog's attention at exercise or when you are walking him—that is when he is not looking.

Snapping out his name should be an emergency call—for example when he's playing with other dogs, and a whistle might apply to any of them.

Having taught the dog all three things, you can please yourself how you use them. But if you stick to using the name and whistle to attract the dog's attention and then give your instructions, you'll be well repaid. After all

The picture above and the one below emphasise the point of a pet being tolerant and having a good relationship with other livestock or other pets in the family.

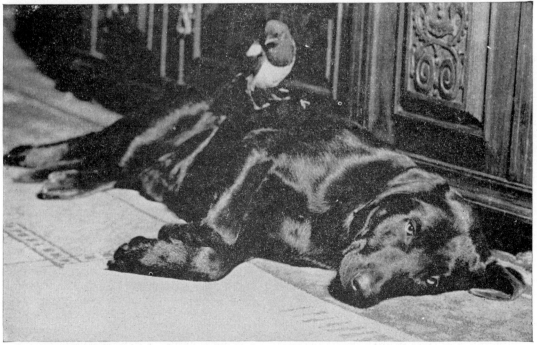

It is essential that your dog understands he has to live with other animals as well as humans.

you will often wish to attract his attention without wanting him to come back. It is worth thinking about in that light.

Lesson No. 7

RULES OF BEHAVIOUR

Now that your puppy is completely biddable, it remains for you to teach him certain forms of behaviour, and to show him right from wrong. By forms of behaviour I mean such things as knowing how to behave on trams and buses, what not to do in a butcher's shop, how to act when a child suddenly pats him in the street, on a public vehicle, at a school gate or in a crowded place.

There are a host of others, but these will give some idea of what I mean. As an owner, you should feel obliged to start your dog off on the right foot in such matters.

Behaviour on a public vehicle is a matter of practice. I always make a point of taking the pup for a number of short journeys on trams and buses at quiet times, so that I can teach him how to get upstairs and where to lie when he gets there. It pays to do it.

When he has got the idea, I try him when vehicles are busier.

A dog should never be an annoyance to other passengers. Passengers are entitled to object if your dog persists in getting on to a seat, or climbing on to somebody's knee. And people don't like a soaking long-haired dog careering all over a bus.

You will avoid all kinds of unpleasantness if you think and teach a little beforehand.

YOUR DOG'S GOOD RELATIONS WITH OTHERS

Spend some time teaching your dog the right attitude towards children. Few dogs, unless completely spoiled, crab at children as a matter of course. The crabber should never be loose where children are playing, and should be tightly under control when you take him among them.

It is no defence, and quite absurd, to argue that your dog doesn't like children. Be as firm with your dog about crabbing at children, as you would be with a child for throwing stones at your dog! And cross-examine yourself to find out what you have not done to make the dog behave as it does. . . .

One more point on behaviour. There is no greater form of nonsense than to argue that a dog at his food is justified in growling like a volcano at anyone who comes near. I would not tolerate for a single instant the slightest nicker from any of my dogs at feeding time. I have, in fact, never experienced it. Why?

Because, when I am working with puppies, I purposely arrange for children to sit beside them, to pick morsels from the dish and hand them to the pup, to stroke the pup when he is eating.

The pup grows into a dog with no sense of jealousy, or fear, in the matter of his food. This fault, like almost all the others, is man-made. Which means, in most cases, that it is the fault of the owner!

Then there is the vexed question of other people's livestock, whether it be hens, ducks, rabbits, or sheep. This is something you should get started on as soon as your pup is handling well.

Take him among hens by arrangement if you haven't any of your own. Walk him among them, telling him NO if he shows undue interest. Put him down and let the hens feed round him.

He'll soon realise hens are out. And he'll behave like that by habit, instead of by your say-so. Which is the really important thing.

Do the same with sheep. Most shepherds or farmers will be more than glad to co-operate. You'll be amazed how easily a really serious habit can be avoided.

Once the dog *knows* that he shouldn't chase livestock, you'll be justified in chastising him severely if he does. Because then he's wilfully doing wrong.

Lesson No. 8

WHIP YOUR DOG WHEN

I want to deal, in this article, with the thorny question of punishment.

Have I ever given my dogs a thorough hiding? Of course I have—mostly once. And by that I don't mean the reprimanding slap on the rump for a momentary indiscretion. I mean a real whipping, designed to be felt.

Let me summarise my attitude to dogs. I am extremely fond of dogs, and make friends with them easily. I have spent a great part of my life caring for sick and injured dogs; I think

Start with a puppy as you mean to continue. Give him care, affection, encouragement and praise. After the initial steps in his training you can go on to more advanced training.

This is a pup on a more advanced training programme. He is retrieving one dummy and ignoring a dummy of a similar kind.

nothing of sitting up at night with a dog that needs it; I have broken down unashamedly over a dog that has died. My dogs have reigned long in my affection, without running me or the house.

I start with a puppy as I mean to continue. I give him care, affection, and encouragement and praise. I spend a lot of time playing with the puppy, take him frequently on my knee, and do not hesitate to " spoil " him.

I train him with patience and kindness, firmness and petting, and work to a plan. But I am also exacting, and let the puppy know that I expect to be obeyed.

I detest the daily, meaningless nagging at dogs which is so prevalent. I have no use for the owner who thrashes, thrashes without ever teaching the puppy the facts of life. And I think the owner who whips a dog six times in six weeks should give the seventh to himself, because he obviously needs it more than the dog.

But the dog must understand that the kind, tolerant, considerate being who is his master can get tough when the occasion arises. And, having a sense of justice, he won't hold the hiding against you if he knows what it was for.

My last dog used to leap fourteen feet into water at a certain pond, because he had the idea it made me feel proud of him. He did it again and again. I didn't like it because he might have injured himself but how could I possibly tell him off for such tremendous courage, displayed during legitimate work? He was doing it to please me.

If a dog, warned against sheep, decides to harry them, he should be whipped severely on the spot—whether the shepherd is watching or not. You can take it from there.

My present puppy has never known punishment. He may never know it. I have got through to the death with others without it, and they were rock steady.

But if this pup, who bids fair to take over the niche held by a terrific predecessor, ever rushes through sheep, scatters hens, attacks the postman, growls at a child, deliberately rushes across the road, after I have expressly forbidden it or ... I shall regretfully, but unhesitatingly, walk into him with a whip ...

And I yield first place to no one in my affection and profound respect for my dogs.

ANSWERS TO PUZZLES.

Page 118   Patterns made by boats in the mud as the tide is going out.

Page 197   (a) Madam occurs 60 times.

(b) 8 (one of several methods is AD, DG, GB, BE, EH, HC, CF, FA.)

Page 228   (a) Too many cooks spoil the broth.

(b) Robin, jay, linnet, lark, kite, teal, hawk, raven.

Page 303   Towing logs across Lake Superior.

INDEX

WHITE
SNAKE HAWK.

PRONGHORN.

ROE DEER
FAWN.

INDIAN PALM-SQUIRREL.

MALAYAN TAPIR.